PELICAN BOOKS
The Last Resource

Tony Loftas has been interested in the oceans ever since specializing in marine ecology at the University of London. He puts this ever-growing interest down to the fact that his birthplace was 100 miles from the nearest sea. In his early days as a science writer he had to cover most areas of science and technology, but now he spends most of his time on marine topics. This has taken him to some interesting places, from a trawler exploring the fish resources of the South China Sea to Food and Agriculture Organization fishery projects in Latin America. Apart from experiences in the field, he also drafted the UN Secretary-General's report on marine pollution (May 1971). He acted as Special Consultant during the preparation of a UN study on the uses of the sea. He has been the marine consultant of *New Scientist* for many years and regards his work there, among active science communicators, as one of the most pleasant aspects of his career.

The Last Resource

Man's Exploitation of the Oceans

Tony Loftas

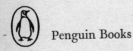 Penguin Books

Penguin Books Ltd, Harmondsworth,
Middlesex, England
Penguin Books Australia Ltd, Ringwood,
Victoria, Australia

First published in the U.S.A. by Henry Regney Co. 1970
Published in Great Britain by Hamish Hamilton 1969
Revised edition published in Pelican Books 1972
Copyright © Tony Loftas, 1970, 1972

Made and printed in Great Britain by
Richard Clay (The Chaucer Press) Ltd
Bungay, Suffolk
Set in Linotype Georgian

To my parents with love

Contents

Acknowledgements

Throughout the preparation of this book, I have been obliged to call upon friends and experts, among them Peter Bush, Bill Gunston, Joe Lucas, Dr I. H. Newson, Professor R. S. Silver and M. J. S. Smith, for help and advice. However, chief among my helpers, and a source of continual encouragement, has been John Ballinger. During the later stages of the work, I derived considerable benefits from his advice and sometimes lengthy comments. I am truly grateful for his unselfish assistance. At the same time, in fairness to all my helpers, I must make it clear that any mistakes which may remain are mine and mine alone. I should also like to thank whole-heartedly Amy Scofield and Kathleen Fletcher for their help in preparing the manuscript, and Christopher Sinclair-Stevenson of Hamish Hamilton for his advice on the book. All credit for the artwork in the book goes to Michael Bates, whose skill in design was exceeded only by the speed with which he prepared the diagrams. Finally, I must give very special praise to my wife, Marian, who has had to bear the brunt of sacrifices made in the great cause of 'The Book'.

Introduction

The Blue Planet

Resources on the land are coming under increasing pressure as the world population swells and demands for better standards of life become more clamourous and urgent. Eroded, worked-out soils, abandoned mines and irreversibly altered landscape bear witness to their exhaustion. Clearly, if the pace of this inexorable drain on the land is not to quicken dramatically, additional sources of food, water, metals and minerals as well as less tangible comforts must be found. The oceans are the last great resource available on Earth. Moreover they have at least one exceptional property when compared with the land – they are self-renewing. Terrestrial mineral supplies are being exhausted while those in the ocean increase; the agricultural yield of the land relies on intensive care involving such things as the application of fertilizers and other chemicals to restore vigour, whereas the fisheries supply food steadily, providing that catches are not greater than the reproductive capacity of the fish stocks; and any fresh water removed from the oceans by evaporation, both man-induced and solar, eventually returns again to the ocean reservoir. In other words the oceans need never become worked out and derelict like an increasing proportion of the land.

No other planet, as far as we know, has anything resembling an ocean, but the fact that more than seven tenths of the Earth's surface is covered with water has now become a traditional introduction to most articles on marine topics. The ocean reservoirs hold about 97 per cent of the planet's stock of water – some 330 million cubic miles of it spread over an area of 139,440,000 square miles. The oceans also receive minerals leached or dissolved from the land by rain and rivers, thus giving sea water its characteristic salty tang. The principle constituent is, of course, common salt; there is enough salt to cover the continents with a layer some 500 feet thick.

The average depth of the oceans is 12,500 feet (nearly 2·5 miles) compared with an average height for the land of a mere 2,500 feet. And at one of the deepest points, the Marianas Trench off the Philippines, the ocean floor lies over 36,000 feet beneath the surface, deep enough to take the world's highest mountain with some 7,000 feet to spare. At this great depth the water with its density of 64 pounds per cubic foot exerts an overall pressure of some 7 tons per square inch compared with an atmospheric pressure at the surface of only 15 pounds per square inch. However the Earth's ocean canopy is by no means uniform; there are different layers according to temperature and salinity which together with currents add up to a structure that still defies detailed description.

The continents seem to be nothing more than large islands scattered in a far larger global ocean. The Earth has three major oceans – the Pacific, the Atlantic and the Indian – all of which share similar geological features but differ markedly in size and shape. The Pacific Ocean dominates the Earth, covering nearly a third of its surface. Roughly circular, its area at 64 million square miles is just over twice that of the S-shaped Atlantic or the oval Indian Ocean – the Atlantic stretches over some 31 million square miles and the Indian covers about 29 million square miles.

In addition to the three major oceans, most maps of the world shows a further two – the Antarctic and Arctic oceans – as well as numerous seas. These distinctions are as much accidents of history as anything else although the seas can be placed in one of three groups: marginal seas – separated from the oceans by island arcs; shallow seas – lying over continental regions; and deep seas – covering true oceanic parts of the Earth's surface. As for the polar oceans, the Arctic is generally considered to be an extension of the Atlantic Ocean and the Antarctic manages to straddle all three major oceans. Therefore, although arbitrary lines extending towards the South Pole separate the Indian Ocean from the Atlantic at the Cape of Good Hope (20° East) and from the Pacific at Tasmania (147° East), and separate the Atlantic from the Pacific at Cape Horn (70° West), the major part of the Earth's surface is covered by a continuous mass of water, a truly global ocean.

What is it like to move from the edge of the land towards the ocean deeps? First comes the gentle incline of the continental shelf with a gradient of about 1 in 500 and stretching down to an average depth of 430 feet, although the accepted limit, for historical reasons, is taken as the 100-fathom (600-foot) line. The continental shelf is covered by marine sediments which may be thousands of feet thick. It varies considerably in width and occasionally is absent altogether. The end of the shelf is generally marked by an abrupt increase in gradient to 1 in 40. Dramatic though this change from shelf to continental slope may seem, the eye would hardly detect it. In places the surface of the slope is dissected by shallow valleys and by canyons some of which, like the Hudson Canyon off the New York coast, rival the Grand Canyon and stretch back to the continental shelf itself. Beyond the slope occurs the continental rise which slopes more gently down to the abyssal plain of the deep ocean. Some of the flattest areas on the Earth's surface occur here where sediment collecting over millions of years has filled in any depressions. Only sea-mounts, some with flat tops known as guyots, rise above the plain, the surface of which may be etched with wide and shallow 'canyons' thought to have been created by rapidly moving 'rivers' of sediment known as turbidity currents.

The abyssal plains with their sea-mounts, guyots and shallow canyons and valleys are not the only features in an ocean basin; one of the most dramatic pieces of oceanic scenery must be the mid-ocean ridges. These craggy chains of rock tower towards the surface. Sometimes they rise above it producing strings of islands – the Tristan da Cunha group mark one area where the mid-Atlantic Ridge clears sea level. In direct contrast to these heights are the deep trenches which generally occur along the margins of the continents. Off the west coast of South America, one such trench merges with the continental slope which, because the continental shelf is very narrow, leads almost directly to the adjacent mountains of the Andes. From the peaks of the Andes down to the depths of this trench involves a descent of about eight miles!

For the most part this is a world of darkness – a place that has remained unlit by the sun since the oceans formed. The reason for this is that water acts as a filter. First it removes the longer wavelengths of visible light, such as red and yellow, and finally the shorter ones of green and blue. This effect is apparent even in the comparatively shallow water of a small lake which usually seems to be tinged with blue particularly at its deepest part. It is more obvious still to someone swimming some feet below the surface of the sea; the sunlight coming from above appears to be blue or blue-green. Colour photographs taken underwater confirm these effects – the entire picture seems awash with blues and greens.

The depth at which all wavelengths of sunlight are finally absorbed varies according to the nature of the sea water. Obviously if mud and sand particles are being swirled around the light will soon be reflected and scattered just like ordinary daylight in a mist or fog. Animals and plants as well as their decaying remains can also exercise a considerable influence on the depth to which light penetrates the oceans. Generally speaking, sufficient light for plants to carry out photosynthesis – the process by which they use light to convert simple chemicals into food – penetrates the top few hundred feet in clear ocean waters. In more turbulent conditions, this figure is reduced considerably to less than the top 50 feet. Even in the most favourable conditions, by the time the 1,000-foot mark is reached the only colour is the deepest of blues grading imperceptibly into black. The only light in these regions is that emitted from the luminous organs of the animals which live at such depths.

Oceanography to oceanology

The extent of the world's watery mantle was gradually unfolded by adventurous voyages of exploration in the fifteenth and sixteenth centuries, when Columbus, Magellan and other navigators roamed the seas. The goals of the early explorers and their sponsors had little to do with probing the secrets of the oceans; they were more concerned with finding new trade routes and territories, and the serious study of the oceans had to wait several hundred years, until the nineteenth century. The first really ambitious deep-sea expedition came on 21 December 1872, when a small sailing ship with auxiliary steam power left Portsmouth. The *Challenger* did not return to Britain for three and a half years, by which time she had travelled over 68,890 miles of ocean. This pioneer expedition organized by Charles Wyville Thomson, professor of natural philosophy at the University of Edinburgh, is generally considered to mark the beginning of oceanography, of what the eminent Norwegian oceanographer H. U. Sverdrup defined as the 'application of all sciences to the study of the sea'.

The Royal Navy supplied both ship and crew under Captain George S. Nares; Thomson selected the scientists and other civilians needed for the expedition's investigations. First the *Challenger* had to be transformed from a warship boasting eighteen guns to a research vessel with laboratories and a different form of armament – dredges, winches, sounding ropes and nets – and only two guns. The modifications completed, *Challenger* set sail almost straight into the teeth of a storm. Far from being in the least perturbed, Thomson considered this a good test for both the ship and its occupants. As *Challenger* sailed towards Bermuda, the scientific staff set to mastering the techniques of deep-sea investigation. During the course of the expedition they were to make observations at 360 locations or stations to provide the first overall scientific view of the world's oceans.

The expedition took place at a time of controversy, particularly in the sphere of biology. Although Darwin's treatise on the origin of the species had been published slightly more than thirteen years earlier, the debate on evolution continued. Every new animal or plant found during the voyage had to be fitted somewhere into this new order of things. And the oceans teemed with life – 4,417 new species were found. To make the most of the vast amounts of data collected during the long voyage, a commission was set up at Edinburgh, first under Thomson and then, after his death in 1882, under Sir John Murray, to produce a report. The report came out in fifty volumes – two describing the voyage, two summarizing the scientific results and the remainder as monographs by leading scientists of the day including T. H. Huxley – a vigorous defender of the theory of evolution – and E. H. Haeckel, the principal exponent of Darwin's views in Germany.

Other deep-sea expeditions followed: the U.S. ships *Blake* and *Albatross* under J. E. Pillsbury and A. Agassiz (a contributor to the *Challenger* reports), the German *National* under V. Henson and *Deutschland* under W. Filchner and W. Brennecke, the Norwegian *Fram* under F. Nansen, Prince Albert of Monaco's ships *Hirondelle I* and *II* and *Princess Alice I* and *II*, *Belgica* from Belgium, *Siboga* from the Netherlands, *Ingolf* from Denmark, the *Vityaz* from Russia under Admiral S. O. Makarov, and many others. This was an era of exploration when oceanography was strictly descriptive and still very close to its geographical origin.

Not until the 1920s did more rigorous, quantitative investigations start. During the period from 1925 to 1927 the

German research vessel *Meteor* made fourteen crossings of the Atlantic Ocean on latitudes between 20°N and 64°S. These crossings were significant because of the closeness to each other of the stations and because of the standard collection of oceanographic data made at each one. The *Meteor* expedition also carried out one of the first systematic surveys of the ocean floor using an echo sounder – and the ocean bed proved far more irregular than indicated by earlier isolated soundings. These Atlantic studies prompted a whole series of investigations along similar lines by other nations – the Dutch *Willebrord Snellius* expedition in the East Indian seas, the British *Discovery* surveys in the Antarctic Ocean and the American *Atlantis* investigations of the North Atlantic are important examples. This era of intense national activity was curtailed only by the onset of the Second World War.

In spite of the prewar background of national oceanography, a truly international oceanographic expedition was slow to arrive. Not until the 1950s did a major international investigation take place, when combined studies of the Atlantic were organized as part of the International Geophysical Year (IGY) in 1957. The Soviet Union collaborated in deep-sea research for the first time, bringing in its largest vessels – *Vityaz*, *Mikhail Lomonosov* and *Ob* – to mark the occasion. World Data Centres were set up to handle the accumulating IGY results, establishing a pattern for future cooperation.

Superimposed on the national and international growth of oceanographic effort came further evolution of the science itself. Many of the instruments and techniques used in modern oceanography were unknown before the Second World War and owe their existence to the tremendous advances in electronics which have occurred in the past twenty years or so. Particularly important are those instruments which, provided they have a power supply, can operate automatically without any assistance from the scientist. They have opened up vistas of networks of buoys in the oceans transmitting information via satellite to Oceanic Data Centres where complete synoptic maps of the oceanic conditions akin to weather maps of the atmosphere can be constructed. Already some instrumented buoys exist, such as the American NOMAD buoys which can transmit both meteorological and oceanographic data over several thousand miles and are obvious forerunners of what must become commonplace devices as the age of synoptic ocean-ography progresses.

The first attempts to gain an overall view of oceanic con-ditions date back to the nineteenth century and even earlier. Their object was to improve sailing times by build-ing up a picture of ocean currents and winds. Benjamin Franklin was responsible in 1770 for producing a chart of the Gulf Stream, the current which sweeps across the North Atlantic from the east coast of the United States to western Europe. By setting a course from American ports which put them in this massive ocean river, ships could achieve good times on the crossing to England and conversely could pre-vent unnecessary slowing down on their return by avoiding the current. Major James Rennell of the British East India Company was a further contributor by making a compre-hensive study of ocean currents in various parts of the world. However, the name most commonly associated with this aspect of physical oceanography is that of Matthew Fontaine Maury. An American naval officer, Maury was among the first to recognize the value of observations of currents and winds by merchant vessels and by warships of all countries. He prevailed upon the United States govern-ment to arrange an international congress where a system of making such observations could be agreed upon. It was convened in 1835 and led directly to the first wind and cur-rent charts in 1847.

Findings from oceanography have an even wider com-mercial application in present times, as applied ocean-ography leads imperceptibly into technology and engineer-ing. For example, the design of an ocean drilling platform must take into account the conditions it is likely to face during a working lifetime, and such information comes only from oceanographic research; the study of marine geology provides a broad guide to companies interested in mining sand, gravels and other marine-mineral deposits; and a knowledge of ocean currents can help the fishing industry by indicating where good catches can be expected. As a result, more and more companies are becoming involved in ocean technology or oceanology. They cannot afford to neglect something which promises to be highly lucrative in the future both for those actively exploiting the ocean and for service industries supplying, say, oceanographic instruments.

The British Commercial Oceanology Study Group which was set up in 1965 is a case in point. Six companies joined to establish this investigation of the marine market – British Petroleum, Richard Costain, the Hawker Siddeley Group, Imperial Chemical Industries, the Rio Tinto-Zinc Corporation and Unilever. Each one already operated in one or more areas of oceanology: BP is naturally involved in the development of under-sea oil resources; Costain is concerned in marine civil engineering projects such as harbour and coastal installations; Hawker Siddeley has an interest in marine transport as well as oceanographic instruments and buoys; ICI covers a wide range from new materials to the extraction of chemicals from sea water; RTZ is a mining and mineral extraction company; and, finally, Unilever is primarily concerned with fisheries and the food aspect of the sea.

Although there has been no startling breakthrough in the field of British oceanology, this area of activity has expanded steadily. As a result, an Association of British Oceanological Industries (ABOI) has now been formed. So far, the UK's most significant efforts have been by small firms or small subsidiaries of large companies. The result, according to Mr W. Richardson, managing director of Vickers Shipbuilding Group, is that the industry is fragmented and weakly structured financially, and is thus unable to attract a suitable level of investment. As in many other cases where high-risk venture capital needs to be injected, large companies are unwilling to speculate without adequate government assurances of support. The government, for its part, is hesitant to become involved in an embryonic industry that lacks any overall view and is still often dominated by pioneering personalities rather than by a strong market demand. In 1971, the government invited leading manufacturers to submit a scheme proposing ways of developing the industry on a more organized, integrated basis with a view to securing a larger share of overseas markets for both products and services.

While British companies have 'tested the temperature', American ones have been diving straight into oceanology. The American aircraft industry closed in on the oceans with such alacrity that warnings from oceanographers about the lack of a quick pay-off from oceanology became almost *de rigueur* in the early 1960s. According to them, a rapid profit through diversification into under-sea work would not be realized until well into the 1970s. Nevertheless, oceanology remains a growth area. The large number and variety of underwater vehicles alone bear witness to American confidence in its future.

The growing interest in the oceans of countries which already have strong maritime traditions is reflected in the size of their investment in marine science and technology. In 1967–68, the total British expenditure in these areas amounted to about $31 million. This compares quite favourably with Japan's reported investment of about $8·4 million, Germany's $7·5 million, France's $19·2 million and, on a proportional basis, Canada's $38·4 million. But it is not just a question of the total government investment, the steady growth of the outlay in marine areas is, if anything, far more instructive. There is no better example of this growth than the United States where the budget for 1970, military and civilian, was $515·7 million representing an increase of about 12 per cent on the previous financial year and about 22 per cent on the Federal budget for 1968. The budget requested for 1972 amounted to over $600 million.

This brief mention of national investment in marine resources leads to the main theme of the book, which is an attempt to show just what the oceans hold in store for those who turn to them. *The Last Resource* is not a book about oceanography as such, but an account, in the true sense of the word, of a vast territory which has been bequeathed to man.

Chapter 1

Food in Abundance?

The gap between the rich and the poor nations of the world
grows greater every day. This unattractive situation is
further aggravated by the population explosion with its
prospect of even more mouths to feed in years to come.
Today more than 3·5 billion people inhabit the earth. By
the year 2000 this population will have more than doubled.
And yet already many people have to survive on paltry
diets, children grow up dwarfed and crippled, while millions
more do not live to see their fifth birthday. Approximately
1·5 billion people, largely in tropical and sub-tropical areas
of the world, rely on one staple food, generally a root or
cereal crop the protein of which is lacking in one or more of
eight amino acids essential to human nutrition. In contrast
to this, in North America only about a quarter of the diet
consists of such foods; in Britain the proportion is slightly
higher, 31 per cent; and in Europe as a whole it is about 50
per cent. In other words both quantity and quality of food
supplies in developing countries must be improved if the
present alarming toll of human life is to be decreased.

One way of improving the quality of the human diet is to
redistribute available supplies to ensure a properly balanced
diet; instead of relying on the single inadequate staple,
people would have a vegetable 'cocktail' which ensured that
they received the essential amino acids and other constituents of a healthy diet. A second and perhaps more feasible
solution is to supplement the predominately vegetable diet
with animal protein. Very little of this high-grade supple-
mentary protein is needed – some 10 to 20 grams per person
per day. And this is where man might turn profitably to the

sea. The world fish catch of 1964 contained enough protein to supplement the diet of two billion people. It would have been more than sufficient to eliminate the chronic protein deficiency extant in the equatorial zone of the world at that time – assuming, of course, that the people there could have been persuaded to eat fish!

The potential supply of protein held in the seas and

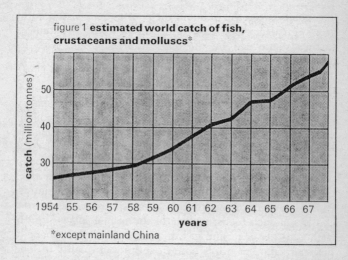

figure 1 **estimated world catch of fish, crustaceans and molluscs***

*except mainland China

oceans is enormous – the Atlantic Ocean alone could prob- ably provide the protein equivalent of 20,000 world grain harvests. The world catch of fish has doubled since 1960 and is still rising (see figure 1). The final harvest, however, is a matter of some debate. Figures vary from a total catch of about 80 million tons of fish to more than 140 million tons. Obviously the final figure would rely on advances in fish- eries equipment as well as the discovery of new stocks of fish. One must also bear in mind the possibility that develop- ments such as marine farming might curtail any final full- blooded assault on the sea's larder. Nevertheless, it is worth remembering that the catch of fish over the last twenty years has increased at a faster rate than the world's population.

Yet the marine harvest can never solve all man's food problems. If the whole of the present world catch were used directly by man, it would only supply little more than an eighth of the total protein needed by the world. In practice a large proportion, probably greatly more than a quarter, is converted into fishmeal which is used as a high-protein source in animal feeds. It therefore adds only indirectly to man's food supplies and during the chain of events from fish, to meal, to livestock, to man, most of the original food value is dissipated. Processing, with its attendant loss of valuable protein, is probably inevitable if the fish are to be stored, transported and distributed. For example, a large proportion of the fish caught off the coast of Peru is converted into meal – these fish are too small and too numerous to be handled and sold as 'fresh fish', but as meal they can be distributed over a long period of time for use in animal and poultry feeds. Recently, fishmeals, or rather protein extracts, suitable for direct use by man have been devised The extract added to traditional diets may well make a major contribution to stamping out malnutrition, particularly among the young people of the world.

A report on the World Food Supply produced by the US Science Advisory Committee in the summer of 1967 did not share such optimism for the role of unconventional sources of protein in solving the world's problems. Members of the Committee felt that the answer lay in birth control, increasing the land under cultivation and improving the yield per unit area. Considering that less than half of the Earth's potential arable land has been cultivated over the past twenty years and specially bred plants such as hybrid maize can almost double the yield per acre, one can appreciate this point of view, but the results of agricultural development can be very disappointing. In a report issued in the autumn of that same year, the Food and Agricultural Organization of the United Nations revealed that the bad seasons of 1965 and 1966 had effectively wiped out the advances made by the developing nations over the previous decade!

The web of life

The story of protein production in the sea starts, just as it does on the land, with the capture of the sun's energy by plants in the process of photosynthesis. Photosynthesis progresses in two stages: first water is broken down to release its hydrogen, which then combines with carbon dioxide. Carbon, hydrogen and oxygen form the basis of both sugar and starch (carbohydrates) as well as oils and fats (hydrocarbons). To produce proteins and other constituents of the living cell a variety of mineral elements must be incorporated into the carbon, hydrogen and oxygen building blocks; twelve mineral elements are known to be essential to the nutrition of plants. Only traces of some of these vital elements are needed, but several, such as nitrogen, potassium, sulphur and phosphorus, are required in relatively large quantities. On the land, the soil acts as the mineral storehouse for growing plants, but in the marine world the sea itself provides the vital soup of nutrients.

The most conspicuous marine plants are the tangles of seaweeds which fringe rocky shores all over the world. But they are of little importance in the food cycle of the sea when compared with the much smaller plants, many of them no more than a single cell, which drift in the surface waters – the phytoplankton. As long as the sunlight continues to reach it, the phytoplankton flourishes – a cup filled from the surface water would contain countless thousands of these simple plants, all of which belong to the group known as algae. This group includes both large and small marine plants, but it is the microscopic algae such as diatoms with their curious silicon cell walls which form the hub of life in the sea. The diatoms provide grazing for countless small animals – the zooplankton. The 'vegetarian' members of the zooplankton become food for the carnivorous ones which in turn are preyed upon by other marine animals including some of the fish eaten by man. The most important members of the zooplankton are the copepods. Some 70 per cent of zooplankton consists of these small crustaceans; they are the 'insects' of the sea, and some fish feed almost entirely on them.

This sequence of events by which energy is transferred from the primary producer (the phytoplankton) to the herbivores and then to carnivores is usually described as a food chain, but in nature such a simple sequence is rarely if ever found. Instead, ecologists talk in terms of a web. Each linking point in its mesh is occupied by one or a group of species all having in common the way they feed and the way they are preyed upon by animals at a higher level. At each of these points, energy 'changes hands' and in the process probably as much as 90 per cent of it is lost. In other words 1,000 pounds of plants will support 100 pounds of vegetarians which in turn will support 10 pounds of carnivores – a yield of one per cent! Even this is probably an optimistic figure.

Much remains to be learned about these fundamental equations but, ultimately, the energy passing through the marine food web depends upon the state of the phytoplankton. Anything which affects the growth of marine plants causes repercussions throughout the marine life dependent upon it. While the phytoplankton flourishes all is well. In temperate waters there is a spring 'flowering' of the phytoplankton, but this loses its impetus as the season progresses. More and more of the mineral nutrients essential to plant growth become locked away within the living cells of the plankton. When the animals and plants die, their cells become the targets for marine bacteria and the dead and decaying matter sinks slowly into deeper waters. This continuous rain of material naturally includes a high proportion of nutrients and, as stocks become depleted in the sunlit surface waters, plant growth slows down. It does not stop completely; supplies of nutrients such as those in the excreta of the zooplankton are enough to tide the phytoplankton over the summer shortage. In the autumn the storms churn up the waters sufficiently to return nutrients to the surface and the plankton flourishes again until the shorter days rob them of another vital component – the sunlight. During the winter, mineral nutrients accumulate in the surface waters until the warmer, longer days of spring when the cycle starts again.

The key to the seasonal changes is the separation of the warmer surface waters from the colder water below them in a region known as the thermocline. The creation of the thermocline stems from the physical fact that as water (above $4°C$) is heated, it expands and becomes lighter. The warmer, lighter water floats on the colder denser water so that no mixing takes place: the strata are stable. In the early summer the thermocline lies within about 40 feet of the surface and the difference in temperature between the two layers is some $4°C$ – the difference between about $16°$ and $12°C$. As the summer progresses some heat is inevitably passed across from the warm water to that immediately beneath it, and so the thermocline moves slowly deeper. However, the main point here is that the thermocline forms a real barrier to the exchange of the mineral nutrients which drift down over the year into the colder water. Thus these nutrients are lost until the surface water begins to cool, causing the thermocline to break down, and storms churn up and mix the waters.

In other parts of the oceans the fertility of the surface waters is maintained by mineral-rich water welling up from below. Such up-wellings occur along the eastern edges of the oceans, for example on the Pacific coast of North America and the Atlantic coast of South Africa, where prevailing winds literally push back the surface water, allowing the colder water from below to take its place in a continuous cycle of replenishment. Naturally enough the phytoplankton and hence other members of the food web flourish and the presence of most up-wellings can be detected by areas of colder surface water and an abundance of fish. Off the west coast of South America, the cold, mineral-rich Humboldt or Peru Current wells up as it moves towards the equator. The shoals of anchovy which thrive on the phytoplankton in the area of this up-welling support the largest single-species fishery in the world. In 1967 Peru became the first nation to catch more than 10 million tons of fish, largely anchovy, in a year. And even with this massive capture, enough fish escape to provide more than adequate food for an estimated 25 to 50 million birds living in the region. Many of these birds breed on arid rocky islands and their droppings, known as guano, build up in sufficient quantities to form the basis of a fertilizer industry. Many other famous fishing grounds such as the Grand Banks of the north-west Atlantic and Dogger Bank in the North Sea owe their existence to permanent up-wellings and the mixing of nutrient rich waters with depleted ones.

Some scientists have suggested that a more direct use of the plankton should be possible. They point out that many of the animals belonging to the zooplankton occur in concentrations sufficiently large to be commercially exploited. Krill, a prawn-like animal two to three inches long, provides the major source of food for the blue whale, the largest animal ever to inhabit the Earth, with specimens reaching up to a hundred feet or more in length and weighing over 150 tons. If the swarms of krill can feed such huge creatures they must certainly be possible contenders as a new source of food for man. These and other crustaceans are at least five to ten times as abundant as conventional marine resources. Russian experiments show that krill can be caught in large numbers quite easily and processed to produce animal feed. Between January and April, krill form large shoals in the sub-surface waters of the Antarctic Ocean. The Soviet trawler *S.S. Knipovitch* has reported catches of up to six tons for half-hour trawls. An even greater advance will be made if ways of removing the horny body-shells and preventing rapid decay of the flesh can be found; with suitable packaging and presentation, the meat which tastes like other shrimps and prawns should find a ready sale.

Is it possible to conserve energy even further by harvesting the primary producer? 'Planktonburgers' have been suggested. Unfortunately, the people who have eaten plankton do not rank them as a gastronomic delight and there is always the risk of a new kind of food poisoning. Certain of the phytoplankton – particularly members of a group called dinoflagellates – are highly poisonous. One species of dinoflagellate found in the Gulf of Mexico, *Gymnodinium breve*, can occur in such large numbers that the water looks red. The toxin of this red-tide organism probably accounts for considerable kills of fish as well as presenting a potential danger to people. Laboratory test animals have died when fed on shellfish which had ingested the dinoflagellate. In May 1968, unusual conditions off the Northumbrian coast led to the 'flowering' of another dinoflagellate, *Gonyaulax tamarensis*, and more than eighty people became ill after eating shellfish contaminated with its toxin. Some 80 per cent of the breeding population of the shag in the area and numerous other sea birds died as a result of this unusual bloom. Obviously, then, any attempts to harvest phytoplankton would have to be looked at very carefully, although there is probably no reason why some of these marine plants should not be cultivated on special farms where conditions and species could be rigorously controlled.

For the moment, the biggest contribution of plankton to the world's food resources is as the start of the sea's food cycle. However, this is not their only asset. The various associations of animals and plants found in the plankton can tell the fishery scientist a great deal about the movement of waters and more particularly about the prospects for fisheries. One of the most intensive surveys of plankton

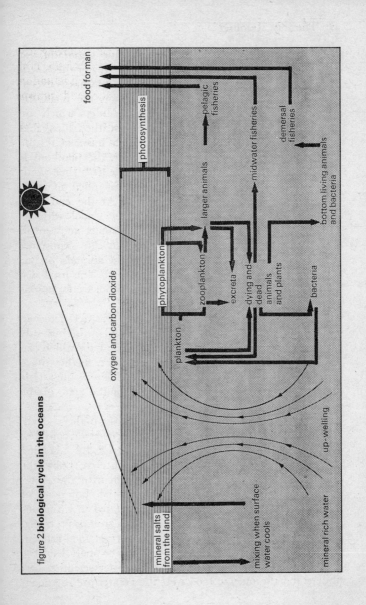

figure 2 **biological cycle in the oceans**

is being carried out at the Oceanographic Laboratory at Edinburgh; this laboratory continues a survey of the North Sea started by Sir Alister Hardy in 1932. The work is exceptional in that the collections of plankton are made by machines called continuous plankton recorders which are towed behind merchant ships, ocean weather-ships, and fishing vessels in the course of their normal business. As the recorder moves along through the water, the plankton is sieved out on to a moving ribbon of gauze. It is then sandwiched with another ribbon of gauze as it is rolled up inside a formalin-filled tank in the machine. At the end of a voyage of perhaps 200 to 300 miles, the spool with its enmeshed plankton is taken out of the sampler and sent to the laboratory where the marine biologists can reconstruct the journey of the recorder in terms of the animals, plants, fish eggs and larvae which it has collected. The total distance sampled in this way during 1965–66, for example, was 112,000 miles.

Until recently the plankton recorder was restricted in both its sampling depth – 10 metres – and in taking only plankton samples. Now machines are being built which can undulate between depths of 10 and 100 metres as they move along. At the same time they record other oceanographic data enabling a more complete survey of the zone of the sea populated by the plankton.

Studies based on the collections made with the conventional plankton recorder have already proved of considerable importance to the commercial fisheries. In a herring survey which has been carried out since 1947 by the Oceanographic Laboratory in conjunction with the Aberdeen Marine Laboratory, fluctuations in the abundance of some planktonic organisms have been related to variations in the number of fish available. Other research has revealed differences in the feeding habits of important food fish, information which may ultimately help in the analysis of the fluctuations in their populations. The better scientists can understand the marine food web, the greater are the possibilities for more efficient exploitation of the fish stocks and the brighter the prospects for developing marine farms.*

Hunting for fish

Catching fish must rank among man's oldest ways of exploiting the sea and yet, in spite of a wide range of edible marine fish, only a few species such as cod, haddock, plaice, anchovy, herring and tuna support really large commercial fisheries. Generally speaking, these fisheries belong to one of two groups: one catching demersal (bottom-living) fish and the other catching pelagic (surface-living) fish. By far the most important demersal fishery is the one for cod – over three million tons are caught each year in the North Atlantic alone. The haddock and flat fish such as plaice, sole and flounder are other examples of demersal fish. Of the pelagic fisheries, the Peruvian one for anchovy has already been mentioned. The tuna and the herring also support large pelagic fisheries. Pelagic fishing can be done anywhere around the world where sufficient fish are found, but demersal fisheries can operate only in shallow regions such as the continental shelf or where great banks rise up from the sea bottom. Because the greater proportion of continental shelf is found in the northern hemisphere, the demersal fisheries predominate in the temperate regions, while in the tropics and southern hemisphere the pelagic fisheries are more important. Much of the recent growth of the world fish catch is explained by the expansion or creation of new pelagic fisheries south of the equator.

To catch fish one must first find them in sufficient numbers for the profitable deployment of expensive vessels, equipment and manpower. In the past, success or failure rested almost entirely on the skill and experience of the skipper. Over the years he gained an intimate knowledge of the fishing grounds and how conditions such as weather and sea state might influence the fishing. A mixture of

* See Chapter 2 for a treatment of marine farming.

fishing lore, superstition and sound commonsense provided the ingredients for his decision, but the final test remained, as it does today, the size of the catch. Since those times, science and technology have intruded into the business. Most fishing vessels carry some kind of fish detection system, usually sonar, or echo sounder. Now, instead of wrinkling his nose and watching for 'signs', the skipper reveals his skills in the manner in which he interprets the information arising from such instruments.

Sonar systems all work on the same basic principle: a sound, or more accurately, an acoustic signal is transmitted towards the seabed or ahead of the boat and the echoes returning from obstacles in its path are recorded and displayed. The time-lapse between the initial signal and the echo gives the distance to the obstacle, in this case fish. The picture may be confused by echoes from larger members of the zooplankton in the surface and mid-water but it is in the search for demersal fish on or near the bottom that the picture becomes really complicated. To detect demersal fish, a very narrow receiving beam is needed to prevent echoes returning from collections of fish from being obscured by a general mass of seabed echoes. However, it would take the skipper a very long time to scan the fishing ground using such a narrow beam. How can such apparently contradictory demands be satisfied?

At the University of Birmingham in England, a team of scientists under Professor D. G. Tucker have been working on this kind of problem for many years. They have found a solution which takes advantage of the ability to switch electronically between a number of narrow beam receptors – a product of the revolution of 'solid-state' electronics. A wide beam 'floods' a sector with the acoustic signal. This sector is then rapidly scanned by a narrow beam receiver which collects the returning echoes and displays them on a screen in a complete picture of the sector. This visual display lacks the detail that a hunter on land might require, but it does represent a considerable advance. During experimental trials the equipment showed fish moving about the cooling water intake of a power station, and individual fish could be seen and followed. Other experiments have shown that the echoes from different fish may vary according to the frequency of the signal and the species. Thus scanners can be developed which will inform the skipper of the presence of fish and, further, the species.

Professor Tucker's group is not the only one concerned with providing underwater 'eyes'. For example a system known as 'Bifocal' has been developed at the British Admiralty Research Laboratory. This system, which gets its name from an ability to switch from scanning a wide area to examining a small sector within it, has been used to study the movements of a trawl being towed through the sea. Several commercial companies are also involved in improving present fish detectors and are devising new ones. However, most of these systems still have a long way to go before they graduate as fish detectors. With the present devices, the catch may bear little relationship to the sonar evidence. One reason for this discrepancy is that one can never be sure that the fishing net will move through the same path as that surveyed by the fish detector. Another is the effect of the skipper's skill and experience in using the data provided by the instruments.

Just as the basic reliance on the skipper has not been seriously eroded, so the major fishing industries continue to depend on methods which in many respects have changed very little possibly for centuries and certainly for decades.

One of the oldest organized fisheries is that for herring – records of an English herring fishery go back to Saxon times. The principal gear used in herring fisheries is a gill net known as a drift net. This net, made up of sections some 50 yards long and 10 yards deep, may extend for three miles or so. The top corners of each section hang from large floats while the rest of the net's top, which is about six feet below the surface, is buoyed up with a line of corks. A heavy cable or warp holds down the bottom. Stretching like some giant tennis net, it is towed gently along by the fishing boat drifting with the wind. During the night the herring move into the surface waters to feast on the plankton there. When they meet the net barrier, they try to swim through, but the mesh is so gauged that only small fish escape through it. The larger, marketable fish are retained, caught by their gill covers as they try to retreat out of the mesh. At first light, the net is hauled in and the captured herrings – several thousand or possibly more – are shaken free on to the deck.

Seine fishing has also probably changed very little over the years. In a sense, this method moved on to a new stage in hunting; instead of lying in wait for the fish, the fisherman uses the net to surround surface-swimming shoals. When operated at sea, one end of the long net is attached to a buoy and the fishing boat then moves off in a wide circle slowly paying out the net. On arriving back at the buoy, the two ends of the net are brought together and the warp running along its base is drawn in, an action known as 'pursing' the seine. The net is now hauled.

The final stage in fish hunting comes with the pursuit of prey typified by trawl fishing. However, it is one thing to encircle fish with a net and quite another to collect them in a trawl net pulled along the bottom at a majestic speed of three knots. The first trawls were cumbersome affairs with a heavy beam placed across the top or head of the net to keep it open. To complete the framework around the mouth of the net side-pieces were added to the beam. Eventually metal runners, like those on a toboggan, joined the side pieces so as to help the heavy trawl slide over the seabed. These beam trawls were heavy enough when dry, but once wet and full of fish they were almost impossible to handle.

The real 'breakthrough' came in the nineteenth century with the introduction of the so-called otter boards. When pulled through the water the boards, one on each side of the net, sheer away from each other like kites and keep the mouth of the net open. The cumbersome beam could be dispensed with, and the use of otter boards spread rapidly first from Irish and British fishermen to Europe and then to more distant parts of the world – by 1905 Japanese fishermen had otter trawls. The first trawls had the boards fastened to the webbing at the side of the net. Originally this webbing had helped to increase the spread of the net by funnelling fish towards its mouth, but with the wider opening of the net made possible by the boards this webbing could be reduced. In fact, there was no reason that the boards should be attached to the net at all, and the Vigneron-Dahl trawl was designed with long wire bridles between the net and the boards to give an even more extended mouth to the net. Today numerous designs of otter trawl exist. For example there are the Granton and Aberdeen trawls favoured by the British and the Skagen or S-wing trawl used increasingly by European and Canadian fishermen.

When nets are not used, the commercial fisheries fall back on equipment more often associated with the sports fisherman – hooks and lines – and in some cases such as tuna fishing the techniques are not so very different. When a shoal of tuna has been spotted breaking the surface, the fishing boat slowly approaches the fish and releases live bait from special compartments. At the same time, the boat churns up the water to conceal its presence and to attract the tuna to the bait. The excited tuna feed voraciously in the swirling water, snapping at anything which flashes in the water – including unbaited hooks. Teams of fishermen working from platforms lowered over the side cast their lines as fast as they can go. Each line ends with a barbless hook so that as soon as a fish bites, the fisherman can pull it out of the water and land the fish in such a way that it falls off the hook. Even as the tuna falls to the deck, the hook is sailing back through the air towards the shoal of threshing fish. The use of hooks and line, this time for demersal and mid-water fish, does not seem quite so exciting but it is just as profitable. Long lines with as many as five hundred

branches are lowered in the water. Each branch carries a
barbed hook baited with a tasty morsel such as a piece of
squid or a small fish, guaranteed to tempt a cod or a haddock. Once the line has been shot the upper end is made
fast to a marker buoy and the fishing boat moves off to lay
down more long lines.

Gill nets, seines, trawls and long lines all belong to the
large-scale operators, but fishermen in various parts of the
world have exploited practically every conceivable way of
catching fish, from woven basket traps to enlisting the aid
of fishing birds such as the cormorant and shag. In local
terms such methods may be entirely sufficient, but they are
not likely to make any impact on the major fisheries. However, other methods such as electric and pump fishing
might well make their mark in years to come.

So far electric fishing has been restricted largely to fresh-
water localities. It relies on the so-called anodic effect; in an
electric field fish tend to align themselves with the anode
and move towards it, but, before reaching it, they usually
become stupefied. To obtain the best results a direct current
must be used. Unfortunately sea-water with its high content of salts conducts electricity far more easily than fresh
water and, to have the necessary influence on the fish, very
high currents and therefore very high powers are required
– up to 10,000 kw to give a fishing range of only 30 feet
radius. However, a discovery that pulses of electricity not
unlike those of electric fishes can be effective offers prospects of a saving in the power needed for the process.
Although the anodic attraction is not so strong, another
effect helps counteract this deficiency; low-frequency pulses
at a rate close to the natural swimming rhythm cause more
swimming activity. The overall result is to bring the fish
towards the anode where they can be netted or pumped on
board the fishing boat.

Some experts argue that using the anodic effect is an unnecessary complication. They suggest firing electrodes into
the middle of shoals, delivering a short, sharp shock and

collecting the stunned fish. This seems a drastic and not very selective technique. Far more ingenious is a system being developed by the US National Marine Fisheries Service to collect brown and pink shrimps. The shrimp fleets have to spend half their time lying idle over the fishing grounds because the shrimps stay buried in the muddy sea-bed until the evening, when they come out to feed. By patient study, the American scientists have found out how much electrical stimulation is needed to force the shrimps out of their mud burrow. They have even worked out what strength and frequency is needed to make the crustaceans move to a suitable height for a particular speed of trawling. The prototype electric trawl – a converted Gulf of Mexico trawl – has five electrodes which stretch in front of its mouth dragging over the sea floor. The electrodes deliver pulses of electricity at a rate and power which are varied according to the nature of the bottom. Apart from this promising technique, the only commercial use of electricity in marine fisheries is on some tuna lines. Once the fish is hooked, the fisherman gives it a short sharp shock to cut short its struggles.

Pump fishing combined with a light lure provides more evidence than electric fishing of its potential value to commercial fisheries. After all, fishermen in the Caspian Sea have been using this technique for many years. The lights bring the fish within the range of a suction pump which draws them out of the water and dumps them in the holds of the boat. No one knows how lights attract fish; the area illuminated by even the most powerful lamp is fairly limited. It seems that they attract and hold the attention of fish which accidentally come within their range. An altern-ative explanation is that light has an indirect effect by lur-ing the small animals on which the fish is feeding. In American experimental fish-rearing programmes, copepods needed to feed larvae of pelagic fish such as the mackerel and Pacific sardine were gathered using a 1,000-watt under-water light connected to a pump which was suspended several feet below the surface. But whatever the explanation, the fact remains that lights do attract fish. The US National Marine Fisheries Service has carried out experiments with a combination of four submerged 1,000-watt lamps and a 1,500-gallon-per-minute experimental pump in the eastern Caribbean. Off Grenada the system delivered 234 pounds of anchovies and sardines in an hour.

Undoubtedly pump fishing and the like have a part to play in fisheries of the future, but traditional techniques can still be significantly improved, particularly by employing the reliable and comparatively cheap man-made materials now available. Twines made from substances such as polyamide, polyvinyl alcohol, polyvinyl chloride, polyethylene and polypropylene are bringing about a revolution in conventional gear. These new materials resist rotting. In static tests carried out by the US Naval Civil Engineering Laboratory manilla rope left at depth in the sea for little over a year was severely damaged by micro-organisms, and boring animals, whereas nylon and polypropylene ropes emerged practically unscathed from similar conditions. Man-made fibres are strong, elastic and do not soak up water. As a result nets constructed from them can be made larger and last longer. Seine nets now exist that could envelop the 365-foot high St Paul's Cathedral. Gill nets of transparent plastics have been shown to catch more fish in clear waters than those made from conventional twine, and terylene drift nets are now standard in most fisheries. In Western Australia crayfishing activities are being extended through the winter season from April to August by fishermen moving into waters previously considered beyond the range of their 'lobster pots'. Only the strength of propylene rope used to lower the weighted pots hundreds of feet down has made this possible. In fact new materials together with a virtual doubling of power in modern fishing vessels like the distant-water trawlers have brought the entire design and use of fishing gear under close scrutiny.

In the past, fishing gear was improved largely on a trial and error basis, but the development of at least one modern trawl has passed through as many stages as a new aircraft or boat. After the first design came tests with models in tanks where conditions met by the working trawl could be simulated. After that, it was back to the drawing board and further tests until eventually the design 'wrinkles' were all 'ironed out'. Now came tests with larger prototypes, and finally the first trawl was ready for its trials. Apart from avoiding the need for excessively expensive modifications, the detailed preliminary work does much to compensate for the uncertainties inherent in observing the action of large trawls moving through murky waters at a depth of approximately 500 feet.

Advances in net design coupled with progress in electronics have brought renewed prospects for increasing the exploitation of mid-water fish. Apart from long-line fisheries which have expanded considerably in recent years, the mid-water region has been largely neglected; fishermen have concentrated on pelagic and demersal fish. This apparently myopic view stems mainly from the lack of suitable trawls for mid-water fishing and the difficulties of operating in a region unbounded by either sea floor or surface. How can one be sure of the position of the net in the mid-water region? Are fish escaping by ducking underneath or rising above the approaching net? Can the net be kept 'on station' or will it undulate out of control? These are typical problems facing the prospective mid-water trawl man. Because they operate in 'three dimensions', mid-water trawls usually have a square mouth. In some, the bottom of the net protrudes like a jutting lip to prevent fish from diving beneath it, others have elaborate floats and hydrofoils to keep them in position, and the majority have specially designed otter boards to hold the mouth of the net wide open. Their depth is controlled by a combination of speed and the length of towing warp let out from the trawler.

Since the performance of mid-water trawls is still largely a matter of chance, various acoustic devices have been tested to feed back information on the net's progress through the water. The Netzsonde, invented in 1958, is typical of these and works on the echo-sounder principle. It is fitted on to the headline of the trawl and relays information to the boat by a cable connection. By the signals returning from this device the fisherman can learn how wide the net is opened and how deep the trawl is lying. It even gives some indication of fish entering the trawl. However, many vital questions still remain to be answered, for example the speed at which the trawl moves through the water. In British trials, a mid-water trawl towed at 10 knots caught a large proportion of herring that had been detected in its area, but at half this speed the operation was only about 60 per cent successful.

Recent progress in nets and similar gear would have been impossible without accompanying innovation on board fishing vessels themselves. The introduction of the power block – a hydraulically powered winch slung on the end of a derrick – has produced extraordinary results in seine fishing. Larger nets can be handled by fewer men than in the past. It has been argued that the power block was instrumental in promoting the fantastic growth of the Peruvian fisheries where the catch increased five-fold in the decade after 1953. Mechanical handling and automation are becoming part of everyday life in advanced fisheries. They reach their peak in modern trawlers but, before looking at these, it is advisable to consider what a relatively simple change from primitive craft to specially designed fishing boats can do for a developing fishery.

At the request of the Ceylon Government, the Food and Agriculture Organization of the United Nations sent a naval architect, Erik Estlander, to design a fishing boat suitable for operating in their waters. In 1960, after trying numerous different models, Estlander came up with a 26-foot boat with an inboard motor – the E-26. The boat carries a crew of five, and its average daily catch during the monsoon between December and April is about a thousand pounds of fish – about ten times the catch of other boats. Even during the off season, the E-26 far outstrips its closest local competitors, with catamarans by far the largest. An unmotorized 'cat' takes about 10 to 12 pounds of fish per day. The addition of an outboard motor increases the catch ten-fold. In the past a catch of 20 pounds was the occasion for a celebration!

In spite of examples such as the E-26, the stern trawler must take the prize for the most important advance in fishing boat design. As the name suggests the net is handled over the stern instead of over the side as in conventional trawlers. This breakaway from conventional design resulted directly from the experience of a British whaling company, Christian Salvesen of Leith. Finding their ventures after whales in the Antarctic Ocean becoming less profitable, the company decided to see if experience gained in handling and processing these giant mammals could be of any value in the wider context of fishing. The end of these deliberations was seen in 1954 when the first stern trawler, the *Fairtry*, went into operation. The *Fairtry* boasted the stern ramp of the 'factory' ship used in whaling, and like this it carried a surprising array of equipment for processing the catch. It was to be the first of many similar vessels built by fishing nations all over the world. Not all of the subsequent boats have been of this 'factory' ship design; since the early sixties a smaller breed of stern trawler with a swinging gantry instead of the ramp has also appeared on the scene. The ability to pull the net up over the stern using powered winches has several advantages: the low sides needed in conventional trawlers for manhandling the loaded net on to the deck can be replaced with higher, more protective sides; and fewer crew are needed for hauling in. The stern trawler may carry half the number of crew found on a comparable, conventional trawler.

The large factory trawlers are part of a new dimension in

the highly industrialized fisheries. They trek to distant fishing grounds to take the larger catches needed for their economic operation. Trips of several months or more are not unusual. As a result they have come up against a basic problem which has taxed fishermen ever since more fish were caught than could be eaten – the problem of preserving the catch. The earliest techniques, pickling and salting, have lost ground steadily in the face of the increasingly 'refined' demands of the home market where the cry is for 'fresh fish'. The housewife picks and chooses for the best quality fish where the flesh is not discoloured but looks 'fresh and wholesome'. Unfortunately, as soon as a fish dies its flesh starts to undergo irreversible changes which lead inevitably to a loss of quality and value: hence the emphasis on fish processing equipment in the *Fairtry*. The very large factory ships such as those found in Soviet fishing fleets have been completely converted to the role of mother ship. They receive and process fish taken by smaller catcher ships which are in turn serviced by the larger boat.

One method of preserving the catch which appears to have the least effect on the actual taste is freezing, and since the Second World War the number of freezer trawlers in operation has increased rapidly. But not all trawlers have facilities for freezing and in this event the catch is usually kept in ice. Even with the most efficient use of ice, however, fish such as cod cannot be landed in good condition after more than twelve days in ice. Antibiotics such as chlorotetracycline and oxytetracycline added to the ice can extend this period by five days or so by preventing bacterial spoilage. Unfortunately they cannot halt other natural changes within the dead fish.

Spoiled fish which are discoloured and perhaps rancid are easily detected at the port, but how can the remainder of the catch be tested for freshness? In common with other sections of the food industry, the final decision frequently depends on the human senses of sight, taste and smell. Teams of professional tasters visit the ports and sample the fish. (Anyone doubting the effectiveness of such subjective testing would do well to recall the skills of the trained and experienced wine merchant who can trace a wine's origin down to the hillside on which the grape was grown.) The fish tasting panels have also been known to check the effectiveness of fish sampling instruments. Most of these instruments detect chemical changes which occur in the fish either immediately after death (e.g. the production of hypoxanthine) or after bacterial attack (e.g. the production of trimethylamine). However, the simplest tests so far developed, such as the German Intelectron Fish Tester, measure physical changes in the fish flesh. As yet no truly rapid, simple and foolproof technique exists for testing fish, and sensory evaluation remains the final judge of quality.

The bacteria causing spoilage need moisture to grow and multiply, and drying is often sufficient to prevent deterioration. Fish contain from 66 to 84 per cent water. In the United Kingdom, the first real attempt to investigate fish drying probably occurred during the Second World War in the search for an easily transported form of fish which could be imported into the country after being processed elsewhere. These early attempts were not entirely successful; they produced ingredients which were suitable for 'fish cakes' but would have had little sale in peacetime. More recently scientists at the Torry Laboratory in Aberdeen have devised a system of dehydrating fish by passing it through a drying tunnel which becomes progressively hotter. The secret of the process is to ensure that the temperature does not rise so rapidly that the fish cooks in its own juices. The first commercial-scale operation of accelerated mechanical drying started at Aberdeen in 1966. The Torry Laboratory has also been responsible for improving on other traditional methods of preserving fish such as 'smoking'.

In some parts of the world, particularly the Far East, the chemical changes which occur in fish after death or as a result of bacterial action have been harnessed to produce fermented products. The art of this type of treatment is to arrest the succession of chemical changes which occur at a point when the product is sufficiently stable to be stored but has not become so degraded that its food value has disappeared. According to R. C. Cole and L. H. Greenwood-Barton writing in *Tropical Science*, 'Three types of fermented product are generally recognized. In the first of these the fish is not comminuted and retains much of its original shape because only a slight degree of fermentation is permitted. This group includes the Cambodian fresh water fish, the Colombo cured mackerel of India, the *Makassar* fish of Indonesia and the *pedah siam* of Thailand. The second group includes the pastes in which fish or small shrimps are pounded to a paste before and during fermentation. This group includes the *ngapi* of Burma, the various *mam* of Cambodia and the *belachan* or *trassi* of Malaya and Indonesia. If fermentation is continued beyond the stage at which the pastes are produced, the protein is reduced to a liquid containing the degradation products. These sauces are similar in composition to soya bean sauce and are used in much the same way as condiments. The group includes the *nuoc mams* of Indo-China, the *shiokara* of Japan and the *chenchalok* of Malaya.'

In addition to traditional fish-processing techniques, a new method – solvent extraction of fish protein – has recently come to the fore. The US Bureau of Commercial Fisheries, for example, has devised a process for producing fish protein concentrate (FPC) from various species of hake. The concentrate, which contains 85 per cent protein, is highly nutritious and is practically tasteless and odourless. British scientists have devised a method which uses a detergent (sodium dodecyl sulphate) to extract protein from herring. Once more, the final product has a high nutritive value and a bland taste with no hint of soapiness. Other countries have also developed extraction processes; in 1968 Sweden started sending major consignments of FPCs made by the pharmaceutical company, Astra, to Ethiopia as part of an aid programme. The Swedish concentrate contains 83 per cent full value protein and 13 per cent mineral substances and is soluble in water. FPCs are not intended as food in their own right, but as additives to more traditional dishes in areas where diets do not contain the balance of proteins essential to complete nutrition. Even in the UK and the USA, countries not normally associated with malnutrition, disturbing cases are reported every year often as a result of ignorance in choice of food. In fact the Swedes have expressed the hope that FPC will be accepted as an additive in the industrialized countries as a prelude to a major marketing effort in the developing countries. The problem is to persuade people of the benefits to be gained from eating 'reinforced' foods. One suggestion is that FPC should be added to processed foods of the 'breakfast cereal' type which are often firm favourites of children. Young children, it is felt, tend to have fewer prejudices about what they eat and, more important, protein malnutrition has its most damaging effects during these formative years.

Under new management?

Without proper management the considerable progress in fisheries technology – detecting, catching and processing – witnessed in the past twenty years or so may well lead to a considerable decline in the very industry it has been developed to support. During what scientists have called the 'Pleistocene overkill', some ten thousand years ago, our ancestors probably accounted for the extinction of more than a hundred of the large mammals native to the North American continent. In the last century, a reputedly more civilized breed of man has been emulating his primitive forebears by mustering the full force of his technology to hunt relentlessly those large mammals, the whales, that live in the southern polar seas. Recently, responsibility for the number of whales caught each year has rested with the International Whaling Commission. For many years it was claimed that these quotas were set too high, but the scientists invited by the Commission to assess available supplies, who advised that the quotas should be drastically reduced, were consistently ignored. As a result a once-profitable industry has been brought to its knees. In a five-year period from 1961 to 1966 the number of whaling expeditions to the Antarctic fell fom twenty-one to ten, while in the 1968–69 season, only two countries – Japan and the USSR – sent fleets to that region. Whaling activities then switched to other waters: in the 1966–67 season 15,265 whales were taken in the Antarctic compared with 31,470 whales caught elsewhere.

Our ancestors may be forgiven for their lack of concern during the Pleistocene Age, but little sympathy can be extended to those nations who for immediate gain continue to over-exploit the Antarctic whales. At the meeting of the Commission in July 1963, the scientific committee advised that hunting of the blue whale and the humpback should be prohibited and that the annual kill of finback whales should be limited to 5,000 or fewer. If this were not done, they warned, in the coming season the industry would harvest not more than 8,500 blue whale units (one blue whale unit equals one blue whale, two finbacks or six sei whales) and then only at the expense of some 14,000 finbacks. The advice was ignored. The Japanese commissioner proposed a quota of 10,000 blue whale units and was supported in this by the Russian commissioner. If anyone doubted the ability of the scientific committee to give an accurate account of available whales, they should have been convinced when in that season the industry processed 8,429 blue whale units including 13,870 finbacks. And yet the following year, Japan, the USSR, the Netherlands and Norway again chose to ignore its advice, settling privately for a limit which in the event they failed to achieve. Since that disastrous season the quotas have been progressively lowered. Six species of whale are now protected, including the humpback and the blue whale. Whether this restraint on the part of the Commission has come in time to save some of the Antarctic whales, particularly the blue whale, from extinction remains to be seen. In 1971, the Antarctic population of blue whales, at approximately 6,400 animals, is believed to be 4 per cent of the population prior to the onset of whaling.

The scientific committee's accurate estimates of whales reflect the growing insight into how marine populations increase, decline and generally regulate themselves, which leads naturally to considerations of how such populations, particularly of fish, can best be exploited by man. The procedure relies basically on finding the optimum number of animals which can be culled annually without producing large-scale fluctuations in the population. In any population of fish a difference exists between the numbers born (or reaching a catchable size) and the numbers dying from natural causes. This difference represents the sustainable catch. If the stock is small, the recruitment of replacements will be slow, and therefore fewer fish can be caught each year. The sustainable catch is also small when the population is very large, because under these competitive conditions death rates tend to be higher and reproductive rates lower than in small populations. The maximum sustainable catch lies somewhere between the high and the low levels. Therefore the aim of scientific management is to bring the population to this level and then to hold it there by fixing the number of animals caught each year.

According to the British scientist, Dr J. A. Gulland, a member of the International Whaling Commission's scientific committee, the industry could have culled some 30,000 whales annually if the stocks had been properly managed. This catch would produce a third of a million tons of oil and a quarter of a million tons of other products, yielding in all some £50 million per year.

One of the greatest factors contributing to over-exploitation of the Antarctic stocks of whales was the tremendous capital investment involved in providing factory ships and their attendant fleets of about a dozen catchers. One can

imagine the chagrin of Japan, who bought up the whaling
fleets of the UK and the Netherlands together with their
share of the annual quota, when tighter restrictions on whaling were advised.

The problem is not restricted to whaling; earlier, mention
was made of the greater mechanization of the fisheries with
freezer and factory trawlers and the like. What effect will
this growing fishing power have on stocks? How much
further, if at all, can the catches be increased? Are any new
regulatory measures needed at this stage? These are the
kinds of questions over which fishery scientists are now very
concerned – and one can see that they do not differ greatly
from questions which went answered but unheeded by the
whaling industry.

Particular attention is being paid to the value of preventing small fish from being caught, by increasing the size of
mesh used in nets. Just how such a simple restraint could
improve a fishery has been well demonstrated in British
studies of a small fishery for cod within twenty miles of the
Tyne estuary off the north-east coast of England. Tagging
experiments have shown that these fish form a fairly well
defined stock – few of the tagged cod have been caught
outside the grounds. Tagging has also shown that more
than 60 per cent of the population are caught within a year.
Censuses of the age of these fish reveal that about 70 per
cent of the fish are removed from the population each year.
Therefore death by natural causes could account for not
more than one seventh of this loss compared with six
sevenths from fishing. In other words, six sevenths or 85 per
cent of the cod living in the Tyne area are caught sooner or
later. With this information the benefits which accrue from
letting the small fish go can be calculated by balancing the
weight of the small fish released against the weight of the
85 per cent (less the few which will die before attaining the
new size) which will be caught later. Because these Tyne
cod are caught when very small, but could grow very
quickly to a good size, the fishery scientists have estimated

that protecting the small fish could probably double the weight of the catch. In the North Atlantic cod fisheries an increase in the mesh size of only a few per cent has led eventually to increases in the catch worth an estimated £10 million.

A reduction in total exploitation would be even more beneficial in some of the particularly heavily fished areas. It has been estimated that if the number of trawlers fishing in the Northeast Atlantic could be halved, then, after a short period, the remaining fleet would take 10 per cent more than the total previous catch and the cost per ton might be more than halved. However, the history of Antarctic whaling bears witness to the difficulties inherent in bringing about international agreements of this kind even in the face of the strongest evidence. Most major fishing grounds lie over international waters and nations involved in their commercial exploitation do not like to curtail their efforts, thus sustaining heavy losses, so that all can benefit in the more remote future, by which time much of their present fishing gear would be 'written off' anyway.

Only the briefest respite from over-exploitation may be sufficient to enable the stocks of fish to recover. Unlike the female whale which produces one young every two years, a single female fish has at least the potential to produce thousands. Although it is not often practical to stop fishing to allow a particular stock to recover, falling returns from a failing fishery may be enough to divert fishermen to other kinds of fish. The plaice fishery in the North Sea has enjoyed such a fortuitous turn of events and has improved considerably. Finding the plaice fishery becoming less remunerative, Danish fishermen, for example, have now developed an extensive fishery for sand eels and young herring, subsequently converting these smaller fish into meal suitable as animal food. Alternative food fish are available for exploitation in many other cases: probably nowhere is this better seen than in the United Kingdom.

By tradition, British people are noted for conservatism of

taste – at least where fish are concerned. Housewives tend to think of only a few species of fish, such as cod, haddock and plaice, when buying, and to ignore other types like coley and redfish. British companies have large, expensive trawlers built for the long trek to distant fishing grounds in the pursuit of cod, while no more than a couple of hundred miles away there are relatively abundant supplies of coley (saithe), a fish related to it. To make matters worse, the low demand for these other fish does not encourage the same marketing care as the more valued species receive, so they do not arrive in the shops looking as fresh as they might. And yet the British White Fish Authority has found during trials carried out at schools and industrial canteens that, properly cared for, coley and redfish are quite acceptable. In fact some schools continued to serve redfish after the trials had ended.

The White Fish Authority has been especially active in promoting the increased consumption of fish, particularly those species not normally eaten in Britain, and has developed a whole range of novel products using mainly coley, redfish and dogfish. These are a few examples taken from one of the Authority's bulletins: *frying sausage* – 'similar in taste and appearance to the usual pork sausage'; *slicing sausage* – 'reproduces some of the characteristics of meat products such as boloney, etc., which are sliced cold and consumed cold'; *frankfurters* – 'smoked, skinless sausage'; and *fish crisps* – 'crisps similar to products made from shrimps and prawns which are sold in some restaurants'. The demand for these unusual items has been subject to market research and on the whole the results were favourable, with crisps the most successful and the slicing sausage the least so. The results of these trials, together with recipes and specifications for their preparation, have now been passed to commercial food manufacturing companies.

The value of novel products capable of competing with more conventional ones will undoubtedly grow not only in Britain but in countries where shortages of meat may put an impossible premium on other high-grade protein foods. But no matter how manufacturers choose to disguise fish products to promote otherwise poorly utilized fish, this can never be an excuse to run down the fisheries for more prized types of fish such as turbot, halibut and Dover sole. And if the present heavily exploited grounds are to be maintained in a highly productive state they must be managed and controlled far more rigidly than hitherto.

One noteworthy example of how a fishery can be kept in a viable state over an extended period of time is provided by the Canadian and American one for halibut in the Eastern Pacific. This joint fishery off Cape Flattery, Washington, began in 1888. By the turn of the century the annual catch amounted to some 10 million pounds of fish. Unregulated it continued to increase until in 1915 the catch was about 69 million pounds. Thereafter things did not go so well and, in spite of greater fishing effort, the catch declined to 44 million pounds by 1931. A fishery commission was set up by the two countries involved, and as a result of its measures stocks have increased three-fold since 1932. Without this joint action, present catches would probably be in the order of 30 million pounds of halibut per year, paralleling conditions in the unregulated fisheries of Europe and Japan. Just as in Europe, there would be a high proportion of young fish weighing five pounds or less, caught chiefly by trawls in the course of harvesting other species of fish. The maximum sustainable yield of the North American fishery is estimated to be about 70 million pounds of fish per year. And all that this has involved is proper management of the resource backed by the modest investment of about $5 million which the governments combined have given to the Commission since 1930.

Apart from such encouraging results, the overall picture of the world's fisheries is a dismal one (see figure 3). No one has yet found a completely satisfactory solution to the problem facing most traditional fishing areas – namely overfishing. Commercial fisheries still seem destined to suffer the

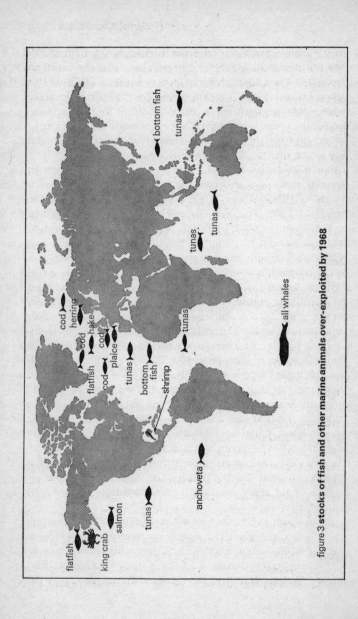

figure 3 stocks of fish and other marine animals over-exploited by 1968

same inexorable exploitation: first an unexploited stock is discovered; the catches are good; more fishing boats are attracted to the area; the total catch remains more or less steady even in the face of the increased effort; then, finally, the catch begins to fall as the stock of fish becomes depleted.

As fishing becomes less profitable new stocks of fish have to be found. One expanding fishery is that for hake off the south-west coast of South Africa. Total landings from this fishery have risen considerably in recent times. A potentially rich fishery, again for hake, lies in the area of the Patagonian Shelf, off Argentina. However, the size of the stock, its distribution and the effects of increased exploitation must all be determined to develop the fishery. Armed with such data, fishery scientists will be in a position to predict the maximum sustainable yield, and to forecast the long-term prospects for the fishery. Elsewhere in Latin America new resources of deep-water shrimp, lobster and 'langostino' have been found. Another interesting area is the South China Sea. An FAO survey in the waters off South Vietnam has shown valuable stocks of fish which were virtually unexploited. One shoal of mackerel found by their survey boat extended over an area 45 by 30 miles. Good catches of demersal fish have also been reported.

Several other scarcely exploited fisheries are to be found in various parts of the world; examples are the stocks of anchovy off California, the ocean perch (redfish) in the Gulf of Alaska, the tuna in the Atlantic and various demersal fish in the Bering Sea. The waters off South Arabia offer the potential for large catches of yellowfin and other tuna, shrimps, lobsters and sardines. The problem is how and by whom these stocks should be exploited. India, for one, could certainly benefit from a fishery in the South Arabian area, but how can she exploit it without trawlers and factory ships? In common with other countries hungry for high-grade protein India lacks the financial resources to build up such a fishery. Similarly for South Vietnam to exploit the fish found on her doorstep, a new trawler fleet must be built. All too often one finds the established fishing nations moving in and removing valuable fish protein practically from the doorsteps of the hungry.

To raise primitive fisheries to a level at which they can compete directly with fleets and industries developed over decades, even centuries, makes fantastic demands on already over-taxed economies. It is one thing to provide engines for boats, nylon twine for nets, portable winches for beach seine fishing, kilns for drying and refrigeration plants for freezing fish, but it is quite another scale of operation to supply, say, factory trawlers and similar equipment of the modern industrial fishery along with the distribution network so typical of the 'home market' which supports their effort. In addition, considerable build up of the world's fishing fleets would make the management of available fish stocks well nigh impossible, so that present fish populations might well be destroyed. Obviously some kind of compromise is essential. One solution might lie in persuading the handful of nations which dominate the fisheries to contribute aid according to their individual share of the total world catch. This aid, among other things, would help poorer nations to improve their existing fisheries and, where possible, might be used to encourage the direct transition from primitive levels of fishing to marine farming. In this way, emergent nations bordering on the seas could build up a growing and renewable source of marine food.

Chapter 2

Farming the Sea

The old belief that there are as many good fish left in the sea as ever came out of it is no longer tenable, as old established fisheries decline, weakened by over-fishing. To recover, the depleted stocks of fish must be rested but, even then, the great catching power embodied in modern fishing fleets makes impossible any return to uncontrolled exploitation. Only the relatively untouched populations of oceanic fish can support large fleets without too much control or management, but gear and techniques have yet to be devised for most potential oceanic fisheries and, moreover, the need to deploy fleets over such a wide area will inevitably make costs high, perhaps prohibitively so. From all points of view, the days of the marine hunter appear to be numbered. In his place must come the 'estate management' of highly regulated international fisheries and, of course, the marine farmers.

For some time at least one marine fish, the yellowtail, has been reared quite extensively in Japan. The fish which are 'fattened' in enclosed areas of the sheltered Inland Sea are caught in the open sea while still young. This fry, caught during the spring, is reared to a marketable size for the following winter. Every year several million fish are released in the growing places. At Comacchio, south of Venice, a similar method is used. In this old-established fishery, which may date from pre-Roman times, fish are trapped in enclosures set up in a shallow lagoon. They remain in them during the summer and winter. Shades protect the fish from the summer sun and in the winter fresh water running over the surface of the lagoon freezes to

form an insulating layer from the very cold air which
would make the sea-water colder still. Just as in the
Japanese system, some fish are netted outside and brought
into the enclosures. In other parts of the world, fish are kept
alive in enclosures for a few days or weeks after being
caught, not so much to improve their size but to maintain
them in a marketable condition. In none of these cases are
fish artificially raised from the egg.

The real breakthrough for marine farming occurred with
the recent development of techniques for stocking marine
fields with domestically hatched and reared fish. This opens
up the possibility of achieving the same kind of revolution
in aquiculture as Robert Bakewell achieved in livestock
breeding in England during the eighteenth century. Bakewell, a Leicestershire farmer, produced by astute breeding a
remarkable increase in productivity of cattle and sheep
which led to his animals being bought and bred all over
Britain. The same might be done for fish and shellfish. The
specially bred animals would be reared in marine 'fields'. In
this way, two types of fishery could develop: on the high
seas fleets would cull the wild fish populations – somewhat
as some African countries crop the wild animals in the
national parks; and, nearer home, the marine farmer would
cultivate 'domesticated livestock' in the inshore pastures of
territorial waters.

The marine farmer

The earliest attempts at hatching and rearing marine fish
were not specially geared to stocking marine farms;
pioneers in the late nineteenth century planned to release
young fish over existing fishing grounds. Biologists argued
that hatchery fish could more than make good the effect of
increased exploitation by the expanding fishing fleets. Unfortunately the plans were hasty and ill conceived. The
newly hatched fish could not be fed once their store of yolk
had been used and the very young fry had to be released

into the sea where they probably fell easy prey to their natural enemies. Some claims were made that fishing improved as a result of these releases but the evidence was inconclusive and, as enthusiasm and financial support waned, most of the hatcheries closed or were converted into fishery laboratories.

In spite of such setbacks, dreams of enriching the seas persisted. They were encouraged by the work of Dutch and British scientists who studied the effects of transplanting fish from poor to rich feeding areas of the sea – a system which avoided the previous hatchery problem. In typical experiments, the British scientist, Professor Walter Garstang, took young plaice from crowded breeding grounds off the Dutch coast and released them into the fertile waters swirling around the Dogger Bank in the North Sea. He found that the plaice released over Dogger grew three to four times faster than those left to fend for themselves in the breeding grounds. Encouraged by such results, Garstang proposed that such transplantation should be carried out on a large scale, but his political experiment was not nearly so successful – no one wanted to invest large sums of money on improving fishing grounds in which any nation could fish. Nevertheless, some sixty years later, fish are being transferred from one region to another by some countries. The Russians, for example, have carried out numerous experiments in removing fish from one area or sea to another. They have taken the hump-back salmon from the Pacific to the Atlantic, the flounder from the Baltic to the Caspian, and they have even suggested releasing herring in Antarctic waters to feed on the rich suppy of plankton found there.

One important step towards marine fish farming occurred just before and during the Second World War. In 1938, a Norwegian scientist, Gunnar Rollefsen, discovered that marine fish larvae would feed quite happily on newly hatched brine shrimps. These little crustaceans can be reared conveniently from dry (but viable) eggs collected in their millions from the margins of salt lakes in various parts of the world. Then, during the war, Dr F. Gross of Edinburgh University showed that when the chemical fertilizers, sodium nitrate and superphosphate, were added to isolated sea lochs the biological productivity improved. First the large seaweeds and phytoplankton showed greater growth, followed later by the zooplankton and finally the bottom-living animals. Plaice and flounders released in the fertilized lochs grew two to four times faster than those in unenriched areas. These two developments provided the basic ingredient for fish farming: evidence of enhanced growth in fertile marine 'fields'; and a source of food for the very young fry to help tide them over until they could be put out to pasture. All that was needed to complete the picture was a supply of young fish.

In 1952 James Shelbourne and his co-workers at the Ministry of Agriculture, Fisheries and Food's laboratories in Lowestoft began looking into this very problem. Their main concern was to raise flatfish, such as plaice and sole, from eggs and beyond the stage of metamorphosis. At metamorphosis the larval plaice undergoes a singular change: the right side of its body becomes pigmented, the left eye migrates slowly across to this coloured side and the body becomes flattened. By the end of the process the larva has been transformed into a miniature adult about the size of a thumb-nail. After metamorphosis the growing plaice changes its habits as well as its appearance. It forsakes the surface waters – and the most dangerous period of its existence – to take up life on the sea floor where its natural camouflage helps it to avoid undesirable attention from potential predators. In other words, survival beyond metamorphosis is the key to success. If the young fish have to be released before this stage they are hardly better off than the very young larvae released in the earlier hatchery experiments.

Working in laboratories at Lowestoft and Port Erin on the Isle of Man, the British scientists systematically investi-

gated the conditions essential to successful rearing. They
'juggled' with various factors of the environment such as
light intensity and temperature, but for some reason survival of fish was below 30 per cent of the initial eggs. Then
they tracked down the cause of the trouble – marine bacteria. Conditions in the rearing tanks were ideal for
microbes which settled on the eggs, either killing the growing embryos or so seriously weakening them with toxic substances that few larvae survived long after hatching. In the
spring of 1962, Shelbourne added a mixture of antibiotics –
penicillin and streptomycin – to the water circulating
through the tanks. The results were spectacular, with over
65 per cent of the fish surviving to metamorphosis. The
scene was set for a further expansion of the work and with
the help of the White Fish Authority a pilot-scale hatchery
was established at Port Erin.

Adult plaice and sole, living in two large sea-water ponds
adjacent to the hatchery, supply the eggs which are scooped
from the surface during the spawning season (from mid-
February to May) and transferred to rearing tanks stacked
in racks in the hatchery. Since a female plaice may produce
100,000 eggs or more, there is no shortage of supplies. Each
egg is a small ball about two millimetres across. Inside its
tough outer case lies a cluster of cells – the developing fish –
together with a store of yolk. The fish larvae, which hatch
after about three weeks, still have a small supply of yolk
remaining in a sac hanging from the belly. After a few days
the yolk is used up and the growing larva takes its first meal
of brine shrimp. In the early stages each fish takes about
ten shrimps daily. Within three months this figure increases
to 200 or more. Part of the hatchery's success has, therefore,
depended on constructing an automated plant for the bulk
cultivation of the shrimps. More than 2,000 plaice can be
reared to metamorphosis on one square metre of tank
bottom and the total capacity of the plant is in the region
of a million fish a year.

In 1965 the British scientists moved on to the next phase

in the experiment – the 'seeding' of a marine 'field' with hatchery fish. The 'field' which they used is a dammed-up arm of a sea loch at Ardtoe in Scotland. Gross's earlier experiments had indicated some likely problems, but even so the new study started rather shakily. Heavy rainfall diluted the sea water, rotting vegetation robbed the lower waters of oxygen, and predators such as crabs and eels made a meal of the hatchery plaice, many of which for some unknown reason lack the usual protective colouring. Very few fish survived and the result is best described by one worker's comment that an excellent way had been found of growing the shore crab – a valueless creature. And yet with so many variables involved, some bold step such as this had to be undertaken for further progress to be made. The faults discovered in that first year in 1965 have been corrected. The results so far suggest production rates of 50kg of fish every two years from one cubic metre of enclosure.

Nor is this the only experiment. In the cold waters around Britain, fish grow very slowly, if at all, during the winter months. To overcome this challenge to productivity, fish are now being kept in tanks supplied by sea-water warmed by the generating plant of power stations. Under such conditions plaice have attained a marketable size in less that two years – half the time taken under natural conditions. Although chlorine has to be added to power station water to curtail marine growths, by the time the water reaches the fish tanks the level of chlorine is only 0.5 parts per million, which the fish can apparently tolerate. They are fed on chopped boiled mussel.

In these and other ways we are moving steadily towards marine fish farming, although it is still too early to make a reliable guess at when it might become economical. Take the question of feeding. To produce one pound of edible fish requires five pounds of food so that a farmed plaice might easily cost £1 per pound. In the future, specially bred hybrid fish may give better conversion rates or the farmed fish may be weaned on to cheaper foods, perhaps fishmeal made from fish or fish waste not suitable for human consumption.

In the marine 'fields' one cannot even be sure that all the food reaches the fish. The Danish marine scientist Professor Gunnar Thorsen has thrown some light on the fate of potential fish food, although his studies relate to the open sea. He found that three quarters of the food which could be eaten by fish, in this case flounders, is in fact eaten by other unwanted animals such as starfish, molluscs and crabs. And what is more, they do not even compete on equal terms. Weight for weight, these 'pests' eat four times more food than the flounders. Various suggestions have been made as to how these pests can be controlled, but the fact that many of them start life floating in the plankton aggravates the problem. It is rather like trying to cultivate a field surrounded by a hedge of flourishing weeds and being powerless, for territorial reasons, to remove it. However, before despair sets in, it is worth remembering that the experimental cultivation of plants and animals on the land has been carried out for several centuries whereas the very first fish farms belong to the 1960s.

What form the final marine 'fields' will take is still a matter of debate. Much of the marine 'field' at Ardtoe lies within the influence of the tides so that dams had to be built to prevent it from becoming too shallow; a depth of at least six to ten feet of water is essential to develop a standing crop of phytoplankton using fertilizers. With this 'closed' system, scientists can study the various factors influencing the conditions within the field and the growth of the fish, but there may well be less demarcation between open sea and commercial marine farms. In Japan, for example, fish and crustacea are reared in areas enclosed with nets. Other barriers have also been suggested. 'Curtains' of air bubbles have been used in the USA to herd fish shoals towards nets. The fish only break through the screen of bubbles coming up from a perforated pipe towed by a trawler if the shoal is herded too closely or the fish are badly frightened. The Russians have simulated sounds produced by feeding fish to bring them within range of their nets. Perhaps a barrier produced by transmitting 'alarm' signals could keep fish penned in the marine field. Even electrical barriers have been considered.

One of the most successful ventures in marine farming so far is the rearing of the Japanese prawn *Penaeus japonica*. The key figure in this work is Dr Motosaku Fujinaga who until 1954 was Director of the Research Bureau of the Japanese Fisheries Agency. Dr Fujinaga has devised methods for hatching eggs obtained from 'berried' female prawns brought in by fishermen. One female may lay anything between half a million and a million eggs. Just like the British fish breeders, he also had to develop ways of cultivating masses of food for the larvae – they eat the diatom *Skeletonema costatum*. After feeding on this microscopic plant, the growing prawns move on to graze on animals such as copepods and brine shrimps and, when two centimetres long, the prawn is ready to be put out to pasture. Because the prawns do not grow much more than eight or nine inches long, they do not require the extensive 'fields' envisaged for the plaice. The largest sea-water pond used for their cultivation is 100,000 square metres (about 24 acres). Each square metre yields two to three mature animals – about 9,000 per acre – and each year more than 100 tons of prawns are sent to the Tokyo market. Before being dispatched the prawns are dipped in cold water to slow down their metabolism so that the small amount of water trapped in their gills supplies sufficient oxygen to ensure that they reach the market alive – an essential requirement for a ready sale in Japan.

The success of this Japanese venture rests largely on two criteria: sound experimental work on the best methods of farming and favourable marketing conditions. And of the two, the high selling price is the decisive factor. Even during the summer, when ocean-caught prawns are plentiful, prices are several times higher than in the United States or the United Kingdom. Out of season the price increases still further, sometimes reaching £2 per pound. Such prices more than cover the additional expense of cultivation and give the marine farmer with his continuous supplies an opportunity to exploit the market situation. No doubt if similar conditions prevailed for plaice and sole in the British markets, present fish farming effort would be greatly accelerated.

The only marine farming done on a world-wide scale is the cultivation of shellfish and, in particular, the oyster. During the Roman occupation of barbarous Britain, one of the few things endearing it to Rome is said to be the output of 'native' oysters, *Ostrea edulis*. Apparently no banquet was complete without oysters and, with records of at least one civilized Roman consuming a thousand at a single sitting, it is hardly surprising that some came from as far afield as Richborough in Kent. After the British oyster lost its enthusiastic Roman following little was heard of it again until the Tudor period by which time an extensive fishery had been established in the river estuaries around Colchester near the East Coast. Thereafter stocks of oysters here, and in other coastal sites, apparently thrived until by the 1850s the oyster had become a poor man's food with hundreds of millions being sold in London. But such thoughtless predation could not last long; the oyster beds were over-exploited and pirated with disastrous results.

Attempts to restock the depleted beds with new oysters, including some from overseas, made matters worse by introducing pests such as a marine snail, the oyster drill (*Urosalpinx cinerea*) and the slipper limpet (*Crepidula fornicata*) from the USA, an Australian barnacle (*Elminius modestus*) and the 'red worm', really a degenerate crustacean (*Lytilicola intestinalis*). Today the production of oysters in the United Kingdom is only some one per cent of that in the heyday of the industry just over a hundred years ago. However, British oyster beds have not been the only ones in danger. During the time of Napoleon III, the situation in France became so serious that Professor J. V. Coste of the Collège de France was sent on a fact-finding mission to other oyster-growing areas. More recently, the oyster beds in the United States have become seriously depleted, often as a result of apparently unaccountable diseases. Moreover polluted rivers in these and other countries carry increasing quantities of waste which have serious effects on shellfish.

Abundant supplies of 'seed' oysters are needed to maintain viable oyster beds. Like so many marine animals, part of the oyster's early development takes place in the surface waters. Eggs held in the gill cavity within the twin shells or valves are fertilized when sperm released in the surrounding water is drawn in during respiration (and feeding). The fertilized eggs undergo a series of changes leading eventually to small, free-swimming larvae that leave the gill cavity and move into the plankton. After a sojourn at the surface, the larvae known as 'spat' settle in suitable sites on the bottom within the inter-tidal zone. A considerable oyster industry in the Arcachon area of France and other parts of the Biscay coast has built up as a result of the successful collection of newly settled spat and the development of techniques for rearing it to a size suitable for laying down on the oyster beds.

For many years little was done to improve the British oyster beds, other than to provide clean shell on which the spat could settle, and the natural-spat fall has been small. In the United States, too, spat from established oysters has not proved adequate to restock the ravaged beds. Therefore, fisheries scientists in both countries have investigated the possibility of establishing oyster hatcheries. Dr V. L. Loosanoff of the US Fish and Wildlife Service has pioneered a system whereby the adult oyster is induced to spawn and, after hatching, the larvae are fed, just like the newly hatched Japanese prawns, on specially cultured single-celled plants – in this case the flagellates *Isochrysis* and *Monochrysis*. In the United Kingdom a pilot-scale oyster hatchery has been set up at Conway by the White Fish Authority. This hatchery, using techniques developed by scientists at the Conway Laboratory of the Ministry of Agriculture, Fisheries and Food, is capable of producing settled spat on a commercial scale and at economic prices. In May 1967 about 50,000 young oysters from the 1965 hatching reached seed size sixteen months after settling.

Not all oysters are laid out in beds on the bottom; Japanese, and more recently American, growers have employed a system of hanging cultivation. Oyster shells containing spat are tied to wires, each one holding a dozen or so shells. The wires are then suspended from a wooden raft which is anchored in waters deep enough to prevent the lowest shells from touching the bottom. Out of reach of predators and pests the oysters grow rapidly with the abundant supplies of food found in the deeper, less crowded, waters. Under such favourable conditions, the mortality rates fall and the oysters attain a marketable size in about half the normal time. One American oyster producer claims that hanging cultivation can produce about 64,000 pounds of oyster per acre – several times the traditional harvest.

Hanging cultivation has already helped another shellfish industry to prosperity. Mussels are reared in large quantities from rafts moored in the shelter of the fjord-like 'rias' which cut into the coastline of the province of Galicia in north-western Spain. The industry started in 1946 when Manuel Trigo introduced the first rafts to the Ria Arosa. Since then the industry has expanded rapidly until now about 1,500 rafts produce over 75,000 tons of mussels per year. The rafts carry a framework from which esparto grass ropes are hung at intervals of two feet. On the average each raft carries 800 ropes from sixteen to twenty feet long according to the depth of the mooring. The ropes are changed several times through the life of the mussel from seed mussel (one twentieth of an inch) to market mussel (three inches). Each time the shellfish have to be removed from the rope, to which they become attached by thread-like secretions called byssus threads, and tied to the new one by hand. The mussels take from nine to fourteen months to reach a marketable size.

The Spanish system contrasts sharply with the mechanization of the mussel industry in the Netherlands – the major mussel producer in Europe. The Dutch use boats and mechanical dredges to move the growing mussels from one area to another just as the Spanish growers of Galicia transfer them from one rope to another. Wild-seed mussels settle first in dense patches in the Waddenzee; from there they are moved to nursery and then to fattening areas. With their large boats pulling several dredges at once, the Dutch can handle colossal quantities of mussels in a rapid, economical manner – a single boat can pick up as many as 40 tons of the shellfish in an hour. Similar reliance on mechanical power is found in the soft clam (*Mya arenaria*) fishery in the Chesapeake Bay area. The Americans use powerful hydraulic dredges to reach the shellfish which lie buried in the sand and mud.

But the cultivation of bivalves like clams, mussels and oysters does not end when they are gathered; the animals must be cleansed of possible harmful contaminants before they are sent to market. These shellfish feed by filtering out small particles, largely phytoplankton, from the water drawn into the gill cavity during respiration. The large fleshy gills are covered with microscopic whip-like appendages called cilia which, beating rhythmically, push food particles trapped in a mucous secretion towards the mouth. Although this filter mechanism selects the size of particles eaten, it cannot prevent potentially harmful bacteria from being ingested along with the normal food of the shellfish. Therefore, where the water is polluted, particularly with human sewage, these microbes may collect within the shellfish and on its gills and mantle – the fleshy lining of the shell. Fortunately it has been known for some time that such contaminated shellfish can be purged of these unwanted microbes by flushing with sterile, running sea-water

– indeed mussels have been cleansed on a commercial scale in Wales since 1928.

Different shellfish require different conditions and times to cleanse themselves, but in mussels the procedure is as follows: the shellfish are kept in sterile sea-water for a day, during which the gut and gill cavity are cleared of bacteria. They are discharged along with other detritus bound up in strings of mucus. The contaminated water is then replaced with freshly sterilized sea-water. After a further day, the mussels are collected and their outsides washed with chlorinated water. Finally, the shellfish are checked to ensure that they are clean and then packed ready for market.

Modern cleansing techniques are definitely adequate to handle everyday bacterial contamination of shellfish, but do they also remove disease-causing viruses? Some cases of infectious hepatitis (a liver disease producing jaundice and fever) have been attributed to eating oysters infected with the virus causing this disease, but evidence has been inconclusive partly because the virus is difficult to study even in the laboratory. Far more evidence relates to polio viruses which make more convenient experimental subjects. Several scientists have demonstrated that the oyster will take up these viruses – in one study the viral concentration became 10 to 60 times that in the surrounding water. Equally, other evidence indicates that, during cleansing, viruses are expelled at a rate which closely parallels that for bacteria. One must also remember that the concentrations of viruses used in many experiments exceeds that normally found over commercial shellfish grounds. Strict rules govern where shellfish may be taken for human consumption. On the whole, then, there seems no cause for alarm, but oysters and other shellfish growing in the neighbourhood of sewage outlets should be regarded with suspicion by the amateur collector.

At least two contaminants do resist effort to remove them: the marine toxin known as paralytic shellfish poison (PSP) and pesticides. PSP is accumulated by the shellfish which feed on members of the phytoplankton such as the red-tide organism which contain the toxin. Vast areas of clams off the north-west coast of the USA cannot be exploited because they are known to be heavily contaminated with PSP – even transplanting such clams to unaffected areas has not been successful. The pesticides, however, arrive in the water which runs off from agricultural land and can occur in high concentrations where intensive seasonal spraying such as occurs in fruit growing is carried out. As the following table shows, shellfish can rapidly build up stores of these toxic chemicals.

Species	Amount of DDT in the environment	Exposure time in days	Amount of DDT in tissues
Eastern Oyster *Crassostrea virginica*	10,000 ppm		151 ppm
Eastern Oyster	1,000 ppm	35	17 ppm
Pacific Oyster	1,000 ppm	7	20 ppm
Hard Clam *Mercenaria mercenaria*	1,000 ppm	7	3–9 ppm

No account of marine farming would be complete without some mention of the larger seaweeds which fringe rocky shores all over the world. In some coastal areas they increase agricultural yields indirectly when spread as a rich organic manure over farmland – weight for weight they contain twice as much potassium as farmyard manure although they have only a third the phosphorus. However, their cultivation as a direct source of food for man is much more restricted. Sir Maurice Yonge has described the seaweeds eaten in and around Britain: carrageen or Irish moss (*Chondrus crispus*) in Ireland and the Hebrides, dulse (*Rhodymena palmata*) in Scotland, and laver (*Porphyra laciniata* or *P. vulgaris*) in England and Wales, and also in Ireland where it is called sloke. One has to go to eastern countries such as China, Japan, Malaya and some South Pacific islands to find peoples who value seaweed at all highly as food. By way of contrast, the Atlantic provinces of Canada have five species which provide total harvests worth a million dollars a year, but of these only one, dulse, is sold for direct human consumption – the remainder are processed for use in the food and pharmaceutical industries.

The Hawaiians are reputed to have been among the first to cultivate seaweeds, growing them in special marine gardens, but the Japanese were certainly the first to grow them on an extensive commercial basis and to sell extracts from them all over the world. There was a time when Japan supplied most of the world's agar – a dried bleached seaweed extract which forms a clear jelly when water is added. Agar is extracted from 'red seaweeds' (particularly *Gelidium gracilia* and *Pterocladia* sp.). Today the main supplies of agar come from Japan, South Africa, Ceylon, Australia, Macassar and the USA. It is used in the manufacture of a variety of foodstuffs from canned meat and fish to dessert jellies and salad dressings.

A different group of algae, the 'brown seaweeds', particularly the oar weeds (*Laminaria* sp.), supply another range of complex substances – alginic acid and the alginates derived from it. If anything, the alginates are more versatile than agar and in some cases they are replacing it. Sodium alginate for example is now used to thicken soups, sauces and creams – including ice cream. But agar still has one universal use which is unlikely to be changed – as a base on which microbes can be grown. Agar remains undigested by most bacteria and since the end of the last century it has been used with the addition of suitable nutrients to cultivate bacteria, moulds and, more recently, isolated tissues. Agar is therefore found on the shelves of most laboratories where microbes are studied. In this way, material extracted from seaweed is having an impact, indirect though it may be, on medicine, and there is now a growing interest in finding other medical allies from marine organisms.

Poisons and palliatives

Although the sea has not provided natural drugs comparable to those from the land, marine animals have figured prominently in research into some fundamental questions such as how the nerve conducts its message and how the brain works. The sea has also been the source of important food additives which have helped to prevent certain deficiency diseases. Iodine, once extracted from seaweed, prevents goitre, and the vitamins extracted from fish-liver oil still provide that extra boost for many growing children. Several groups of scientists are now making exhaustive searches for other useful medical materials among the animals and plants found in and around the sea.

One long-standing source of curiosity on the part of scientist and layman alike is the variety of deadly poisons liberally scattered among marine animals. Dr Bruce Halstead has described many of these marine creatures that are poisonous when their flesh is eaten or venomous because of their stings or bites: the sea snakes of the Pacific and Indian Oceans are more venomous than the notorious cobra; the sea wasp, a jelly-fish, has a sting that kills within three to eight minutes; marine snails such as the cone shells inject venom through a hollow harpoon-like structure; the toxic blooms, like the red-tide organism mentioned earlier, wipe out millions of fish; and over 300 species of fish which are poisonous to eat lie in wait for the unwary or the ignorant.

These poisons can be placed in one of two groups – protein or non-protein. The protein poisons are generally more potent but one well-studied non-protein poison, tetrodotoxin, is at least more toxic than that of a rattlesnake, although it is still 100,000 times less lethal than the notorious botulinum toxin produced by the bacterium *Clostridium botulinum*. Tetrodotoxin comes from the puffer fish (so-called because they can inflate themselves with air or water) of which at least forty species are known to be poisonous. The poison is not spread throughout the body but is generally concentrated in the gut, liver, reproductive system and, to a lesser extent, skin. The muscles of the back are not poisonous and are considered something of a delicacy by the Japanese. In fact this infatuation with such a potentially dangerous food has greatly advanced the knowledge of the poison – and the way in which its unfortunate victims die. The earliest symptoms appear in the first parts of the body to come into contact with it: the lips, tongue and inner surface of the mouth. A numbness, coupled with a tingling sensation, in the mouth is followed by paralysis of limb and chest muscles. The blood pressure falls, the heart beats more rapidly than usual and the pulse is weak. The victim may be dead within half an hour of eating fugu, as the puffer fish is known in Japan. Fortunately the cases of fugu poisoning are on the decline today because trained chefs prepare the fish which is served only in specially licensed restaurants.

Various delights have been ascribed to eating fugu from hallucinations which give the sensation of riding on a cloud to heightened or restored sexual powers, but the true value of the tetrodotoxin may lie in medicine. As far back as the early 1900s a Japanese scientist Yoshizumi Tahara, who gave the poison its name, advocated its use as a pain-killing drug. Since then the toxin, in a purified form, has been used as a muscular relaxant and as a palliative for terminal cancer patients. As might be expected from the symptoms described earlier, tetrodotoxin acts on the nerves and the muscles. Its first action, is to block the passage of impulses along the nerves and later it spreads to the muscles, preventing their fibres from contracting. If it blocks a nerve-carrying sensation from a particular area of the body then that part becomes anaesthetized. Unfortunately the toxin's ability to migrate to tissues in other parts of the body probably rules out its direct use as a local anaesthetic. Instead scientists who have now worked out its chemical structure are trying to find the part which produces anaesthesia. Such information might provide the chemical 'plan' on which greatly improved local anaesthetics could be modelled.

Another animal toxin, holothurin, this time from the sea cucumber, has some interesting properties. The Guam islanders collect sea cucumbers – long sausage-shaped animals related to sea urchins and starfish – crush them and throw the pulverized mush into coral pools. Holothurin released from the crushed animals paralyses fish, making them easier to catch. However, the property more relevant to this discussion is the toxin's ability to interfere with the growth and development of cells. In this context, treatment with holothurin has caused certain tumours in mice to regress. Once more there is the problem of separating the beneficial part from the dangerous part of the chemical. Even if this is impossible, the discovery of this remarkable property in holothurin suggests that potential anti-cancer drugs may well be sequestered in the bodies of other marine organisms.

The poison produced by that notorious jellyfish, the Portuguese Man-of-War, has already helped to make an important contribution to medical science. Experiments in which animals were fed successive doses of extracts from this jellyfish led Charles Richet to the concept of shock or anaphylaxis. According to this, the initial exposure of a person to a biological material can increase the sensitivity and shock arising from further exposure to it. This line of reasoning led Richet to an understanding of allergic reactions which earned him a Nobel prize.

Not all marine poisons have such an obvious Jekyll and Hyde potential. Take for example the mysterious fish poisoning known as ciguatera. Unlike tetrodotoxin and most other poisons, true ciguatera occurs in fish such as the red snapper which are ordinarily edible. Often these potential booby traps are restricted to particular localities and in some cases it is even possible to say that fish taken from, say, the north side of an island should be safe whereas those from the south are deadly. This kind of restricted distribution suggests that the presence of poisonous fish is related to the occurrence of some other marine organism which flourishes in these areas, but all attempts to identify it have so far proved inconclusive. One of the difficulties may be that several organisms are involved, in which case examples of poisoning now grouped together may vary in detailed symptoms and origin. Some investigators lay the blame on the blue-green alga, *Lyngbya majuscula*, which occurs in the plankton. One important piece of evidence implicating a member of the plankton is the similar type of contamination found in shellfish. Paralytic shellfish poison is also restricted to specific localities and is apparently the result of the shellfish's ability to accumulate the toxic products taken from phytoplankton growing there.

From minute algae which apparently pass on their poison we now move to large seaweeds which offer prospects as beneficial drugs. Some of the earliest applications of algae in medicinal herbs were in the treatment of gastric disorders, including those resulting from infection. In some cases scientists have been able to isolate active ingredients from such algae. The Japanese took preparations of the seaweed *Digenea simplex* as a vermifuge (worm remover) and a substance, 'kainic acid', with this property has been isolated from it. Today a drug incorporating some kainic acid extracted from *Digenea* is marketed as a vermifuge in Japan. Carrageenin, a substance extracted from Irish moss, has been shown to prevent gastric ulcers from forming in experimental animals. Agar, because it remains undigested by humans as well as microbes, can be used to treat diarrhoea and similar ailments. This ability of agar and certain alginates to pass undigested through the stomach has also been exploited in the preparation of 'delayed action' drugs. The active drug ingredients are coated with, say, sodium alginate so that the pill passes through the stomach to the lower part of the guts before releasing the contents.

However, so far very few drugs derived from marine algae are on the market, although in the light of recent events the position could change rather rapidly.

It does not seem long since the first antibiotics were prescribed, but already disease-causing bacteria show signs of becoming resistant to them. The reason for the widespread appearance of this resistance is still a matter of debate but the widespread use of antibiotics in both medicine and agriculture probably makes a large contribution. Under such conditions certain strains of bacteria can become resistant to many commonly used antibiotics and, to make matters worse, they may pass on this resistance to other strains and species – a condition known as infective-drug resistance. Some warning voices have already pointed out that unless something is done about this alarming development the world may find itself rapidly reverting to the conditions existing in the pre-antibiotic days of medicine. However, chemists might keep one jump ahead of the microbes by synthesizing new antibiotics. Nevertheless, greater controls are being imposed on the use of antibiotics in animal feeds. At the same time the search for new antibiotics becomes more important – and this is where the marine algae may once more be important.

Dr Paul Burkholder, an eminent American botanist who brought to light the antibiotic chloromycetin, has compiled some interesting examples of antibiotic effects shown by marine algae. He writes:

The first scientific demonstration of [marine] antibiotic substances was published by Pratt and associates, who demonstrated inhibition of *Staphylococcus aureus* [found commonly in boils and carbuncles – and hospitals], *Escherichia coli* [common intestinal bacterium some strains of which cause disease] and *Pseudomonas pyocyaneus* [another pathogenic bacterium found in pus] by several species of seaweeds collected on the California coast. These investigators obtained particularly striking inhibition of various laboratory strains of bacteria with extracts of the red alga *Rhodomela larix* ... Antibacterial properties of marine phytoplankton in Antarctica have been studied in relation to the microbial ecology of penguins and other animals feeding directly or indirectly upon plankton ... Investigations of marine algae in Japanese waters and along the coast of Mexico suggest that antibiotic substances in seaweeds are widely distributed ... A bloom of dinoflagellates collected in Puerto Rico, apparently *Gonyaulax tamarensis*, has been found to produce three different biologically active substances. One of these is lethal for mice, another inhibits growth of *Staphyloccus aureus* and a third is inhibitory for *Candida albicans* [a pathogenic fungus] ... Blooms of the planktonic diatom *Skeletonema costatum* have been reported to be inhibitory for certain marine bacteria and *E. coli*.

Several marine extracts have been reported to have antitumour or cancer-preventing properties. Whether these are related to an anti-viral property is not clear. What is certain is that this possible role of marine extracts has been only marginally explored in research so far. For example, C. P. Li of the US National Institutes of Health has extracted a substance that he calls *paolin* from shellfish. This substance acts against bacteria and viruses and has been found to prevent tumours in hamsters. Sponges have yielded a substance that is apparently highly effective in the treatment of leukaemia in laboratory animals, as is another substance, this time from the sea squirt. Finally, A. C. Schmeer has reported that a substance, which she has named *mercenene*, extracted from the liver of the hard clam (*Mercenaria mercenaria*) is active against human cancer cells. Mercenene may not be a natural product of the clam itself but may be derived from plankton or some other food material of the mollusc.

Potential marine drugs are not restricted to those which are swallowed or spread on the skin and directed against disease-causing microbes. Since scientists worked out the chemical structure of heparin – a chemical which prevents blood from clotting – a new use as anti-coagulants has become apparent for some seaweed extracts such as laminarin sulphate. Laminarin sulphate injected into dogs has been found to be about a third as potent as heparin which is normally prepared from lung or liver tissues. Other related algal extracts have also been shown to prevent blood clots from forming. One alginate, by preventing the deposit of radioactive strontium in bone, offers the promise of protection from damage by the consumption of foods contaminated with this product of nuclear fall-out ... and so the list of uses continues to grow.

The sea, it seems, is a virtually untapped source of potentially useful medicines and several groups of scientists in various parts of the world including the USA, the UK, Japan and Canada, are systematically searching for them. Some groups have devised 'mini' labs which can be taken to areas of scientific interest. Some scientists take advantage of every possible marine cruise or expedition to collect material, while others at central laboratories investigate specimens sent from collectors in different parts of the world. In this respect, the search for drugs is becoming very like that involved with terrestrial organisms. These systems have all produced results – Paul Burkholder came across the natural source of chloromycetin, for example, in a soil sample from Venezuela. There is plenty to choose from in the spectrum of living things haunting the oceans and, if the marine search follows the pattern of discovery on the land, there will be little cause for complaint.

Chapter 3

The Earth's Reservoir

Although every age can boast prophets of doom, the world, with its increasing population, does seem to be moving towards a crisis: a serious shortage of water. In all probability this crisis will involve countries which so far have not felt the pinch of prolonged drought – at present the doubtful privilege of peoples living in semi-arid and desert regions. But the need for water is not restricted to special groups or nations; it is an essential raw material for agriculture, industry and homes alike, the very stuff of civilization. Every gallon of gasoline produced takes about 10 gallons of water. A ton of steel is made at the expense of 4,400 gallons. The figures grow even more alarming when agriculture needs are considered. A ton of wheat alone consumes 300,000 gallons of water during cultivation. By comparison, a man's annual consumption of 220 gallons of drinking water seems modest, until one starts to count the heads. The message is clear: the world needs considerable quantities of fresh water.

Inevitably, as the collective thirst of the world's population and attendant agriculture and industry increases, tighter controls will have to be enforced on the use of water. Already in some areas and cities the water supplies have to be metered to alleviate the problem of a threatened shortage. But such measures are little more than stop-gaps; for lasting benefit, efforts must be made to conserve and increase available supplies. Conservation involves the improved treatment of industrial waste and sewage, so that water can be re-cycled many times, the more efficient capture of water running off the land and the prevention of loss by evaporation – to give but a few examples. Undoubtedly, astute and scientific management can produce considerable savings, and in many cases may completely remove the danger of a water shortage – a point not always made by parties interested in promoting new sources of water supply. There is no doubt that industrial and political publicity has thrown up smoke-screens, which have confused both the public and the popular press. Yet the very distribution of water over the surface of the Earth suggests that desalination has a distinctive role to play in raising the hopes, health and prosperity of many different peoples.

The oceans hold in the region of 97 per cent of the Earth's total supply of water. Of the remainder, over 2 per cent is locked away in ice and snow, less than 1 per cent is found in rivers, lakes and ground water, while the atmosphere holds about 1/1,000 per cent. However, these figures give little clue to the great 'hydrologic cycle' responsible for the movement of water about the Earth. The seas and land masses are continually giving up water vapour as a result of solar heating. This vapour rises high in the atmosphere and is carried by surface winds until it descends once again as rain, hail, sleet or snow. Some of the precipitation falls on the land and makes its way either directly or indirectly to the sea: it seeps into the surface to join with the ground water, or drains into rivers and streams.

To obtain his water supply, man can interrupt this cycle at any stage. So far this interruption has consisted largely of building dams and reservoirs to hold the surface waters, but much still remains to be done by way of tapping available water supplies; even in the United States only 7.3 per cent of the annual precipitation is estimated to be used. The building of dams holds considerable promise in many places which, though starved of water and power, have large rivers flowing through them; but where land is at a premium it could well be that the cost of building the necessary dams and buying the land to be drowned rules out this solution, and water supply companies may eventually find it easier and cheaper to look at the major reservoir of water, the oceans. In such times, the know-how and plant for desalination will literally control the destinies of nations, irrespective of their past prosperity and importance. Small wonder then that the traditionally 'well-watered' countries are seriously investigating the various methods of 'sweetening' the seas. Small wonder too that a political shadow hangs over current investment in desalination and water supply engineering in general.

The raw material

Although water is not a 'universal solvent', comparatively few materials remain unaffected by prolonged contact with it. Consequently, the water in rivers, streams and wells carries dissolved mineral salts washed out from the rocks over which it has passed. In fact accurate measurement of the mineral salts dissolved in a stream coupled with a knowledge of its course provides a relatively cheap way of geological surveying and prospecting. Generally, the water in rivers and streams has quite a low mineral content because most of the easily dissolved materials have been washed away long ago. Before this water is ready to drink, debris, any dangerous bacteria and undesirable odours and taste must be removed. Well water and other standing waters which have spent some time in contact with the ground usually present the additional problem of large quantities of dissolved materials. Frequently, matter dissolved in this water exceeds 500 parts per million (p.p.m.) by weight, the limit for potable water. Since the composition depends largely on the materials with which the water comes into contact, brackish waters vary considerably in salinity and mineral content. For example, water at Buckeye (Arizona) has a salinity of 2,200 p.p.m., at Bahrein it is 3,400 p.p.m. and at Welkom (South Africa) 3,000 p.p.m.

Sea-water also varies both in total salt content and composition, but the fluctuations are not as great as those of brackish waters. In the open oceans, away from the influence of river estuaries, the total dissolved mineral content is about 35,000 p.p.m. In more confined areas such as the Red Sea this increases to about 43,000 p.p.m. The table below shows that although in this chapter desalination is discussed largely in terms of sodium chloride, there is far more in the basic raw material than salt and water – a fact which we shall see can cause some serious difficulties in the design and economical operation of desalination plant.

COMPOSITION OF SEA-WATER
(Dissolved solids 36,000 p.p.m.)

Approximate percentage composition by weight

Chloride	55
Sodium	30
Sulphate	8
Magnesium	4
Calcium	1
Potassium	1
Other dissolved constituents	1

In many countries the public water supplies are governed by strict regulations which cover the permissible levels of dissolved salts among other things. The United States Public Health Service, for example, states that the total salt content of drinking water *should not* exceed 500 p.p.m. but *must not* exceed 1,000 p.p.m. The various dissolved constituents are also tightly controlled. Nevertheless, sometimes a situation arises where such restrictions are not possible. How much higher can the salinity rise? Experiments during the Second World War on survival kits for emergency life rafts showed that – subject to the concentrations of common salt, sulphate and magnesium being within certain limits – water with up to 1,500 p.p.m. total dissolved solids was acceptable.

Unfortunately the amount of water consumed directly by man is very small compared to the vast quantities used in agriculture and industry, both of which are rather less adaptable when it comes to the matter of salinity. Although some salt-resistant plants are being bred on experimental stations, most crops are very sensitive even to brackish water. The presence of dissolved salts in water used by industry can lead to increased costs from corrosion and impaired efficiency, for example by forming hard mineral scale on heat-exchanging surfaces. Practically all industrial users of water would prefer to have water completely free of dissolved salts. In many cases this could save the additional expense of pre-treating water supplies to ensure that dissolved impurities remain in solution or, more rarely, of removing them completely.

Methods of desalination

In the past, two processes – distillation and electrodialysis – have been commercially exploited in desalination. Of these only distillation has been used extensively to sweeten the seas; electrodialysis has been confined largely to the treatment of brackish and similar waters. However, there may be more processes to choose from in the future; at least a dozen newer ones are being investigated. As research progresses and more critical evaluation becomes necessary, some processes have come to the fore, but so far none has successfully challenged the two mentioned above. The story of the search for cheaper, more efficient desalting of sea-water seems to progress in a series of optimistic peaks interspersed by severe depressions as the weaknesses of a particular process become painfully apparent. There will be more to say about this in the next section, after this summary of various methods, both tried and experimental, which are being considered for desalting the seas.

Generally speaking, the methods fall into three groups: processes involving a change of phase, for example from water to ice or to steam; those using membranes; and finally a loosely connected group of chemical processes.

They all have one thing in common: they require energy to remove the salt. Since books have been written about desalination alone, what follows can be only a sketch of the basic principles involved.

1. PROCESSES INVOLVING A CHANGE OF PHASE

Distillation. Apart from being the major process, distillation must be one of the oldest. The sailors of Ancient Greece knew about it; there are references to the use of wooden stills on sailing ships; and, with the advent of steamships, the process became firmly established. Essentially all that is involved is putting energy (heat) into salt water and removing it from the salt-free steam to give water. What could be more simple? On board ship, the saving in cargo and passenger space given by removing the need for water storage is obvious; but on land the economics become quite different. On land, energy is usually expensive and water cheap. Therefore the guiding force in the evolution of distillation methods has been to make the most economic use of available energy.

In its most primitive form a distillation unit need consist of nothing more than a large kettle with a coiled cooling tube sloping away from the spout. But this wastes that valuable heat energy: the heat released from the condensing steam is lost to the atmosphere. A simple solution in a continuous process is to use incoming sea-water to cool the steam. In the early marine units, steam was allowed to by-pass the ship's boiler and pass through pipes submerged in a pool of sea-water. Steam distilling from the pool condensed on other pipes which carried sea-water to the pool. This submerged-tube type of distillation reached the peak of its development on the land in the construction by the British company G. and J. Weir of plant producing a total of 2,240,000 Imperial gallons per day (g.p.d.) at Aruba (1 Imperial gallon = 1·201 US gallons).

Advances in the late 1950s, particularly by the British

company Weir Westgarth, were soon to make the submerged-tube system obsolete. In 1957 Profesor R. S Silver
patented a new advance in another distillation process, flash
distillation. Flash distillation works on the principle that
water subjected to a lower pressure than normal boils at a
lower temperature – the kind of problem met by moun-
taineers when they try to make a good cup of tea or coffee.

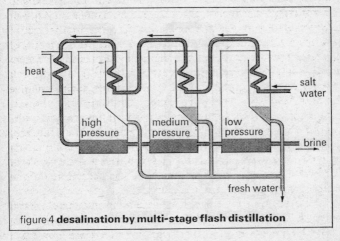

figure 4 **desalination by multi-stage flash distillation**

When heated sea-water is fed into a low-pressure chamber,
steam 'flashes' out of solution leaving behind cooler and
more salty brine. It is not difficult to see that if this brine is
passed to a chamber at an even lower pressure more steam
will flash out. Just as in pool distillation, incoming sea-
water is used to condense the steam and to conserve heat
energy. Unfortunately effective cooling requires far more
water than can be desalted. Only part of it receives a final
boost of heat and, with the recirculating brine, enters the
first low-pressure chamber in the series; the remainder is
rejected (see figure 4). The basic secret of Professor Silver's
success was in determining the number of stages required
for the most efficient performance.

Multi-stage flash distillation is not the only system to use repetitive units in which distillation and condensation occur at progressively lower temperatures and pressures. In long-tube vertical distillation, heated sea-water passes down tubes which are surrounded by steam. During its journey some of the hot sea-water boils and the steam generated is passed on to a second chamber where it surrounds another

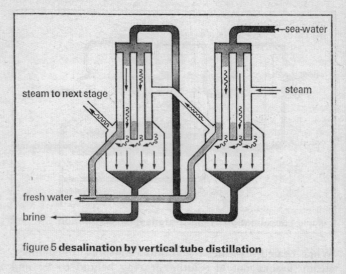

figure 5 **desalination by vertical tube distillation**

set of vertical tubes carrying brine which failed to vaporize in the first one. The tubes in this second chamber are maintained at a lower pressure than those in the first one so that steam condensing and giving up heat on the outside of the tubes provides the energy needed to evaporate more brine. The steam generated passes on to the next set of tubes in the series and the process is repeated (see figure 5). In one experimental plant the sea-water enters the first chamber at 121 °C and the brine enters the last at 32 °C.

The final distillation process differs from those above because it uses mechanical effort and not steam to supply the energy for evaporation. When a vapour is compressed its temperature and pressure increase and its volume decreases. In the vapour-compression process a compressor pump draws off water vapour from the top of a distillation chamber. The compressor raises the vapour's temperature and pressure before passing it through a heat exchanger submerged in the brine itself. The release of heat from the

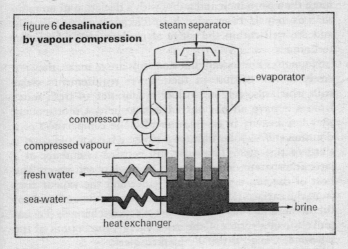

figure 6 **desalination by vapour compression**

steam separator

evaporator

compressor

compressed vapour

fresh water

sea-water

brine

heat exchanger

compressed vapour encourages more evaporation within the distillation chamber (see figure 6).

Humidification. Diffusion-humidification units use both mechanical and direct heat. The basic structure resembles the tuning unit of a radio; rotating discs are interleaved with stationary plates. The lower part of the discs dip into a pool of saline water which is warmed by an immersion heater. As the discs rotate, they become covered with a thin layer of warm salt water. The vapour coming from the wet discs condenses on the stationary plates which are kept cool by cold water running inside them and drops of water run down into collecting troughs.

The efficiency of the diffusion still depends on keeping the gap between the discs and condenser plates as small as possible while avoiding any contact between the surface films of fresh and 'raw' water. A full-sized test unit built by the General Electric Company in the United States had a design gap of 0·094 inch. Engineers had to make a condenser surface which deviated from perfect flatness by no more than 0·010 inch and a disc with a deviation of no more than 0.020 inch. In practice, both tolerances were easily met and are well within the range of modern mass-production techniques.

No matter how cheap diffusion stills are to make, they are costly to run because of their power requirements. Solar stills which also rely on surface evaporation of fresh water from salt have an obvious advantage here. Unfortunately they lose heavily in comparison with the compactness of a diffusion still. A solar unit for a 120-acre farm would cover a third of this area. The solar still consists essentially of a large transparent dome covering a trough of salt water. The heat of the sun evaporates the water and the vapour rises from the surface. The vapour condenses on the underside of the dome and runs down to a collection channel. To improve the absorption of the sun's energy, the bottom of the salt water trough is usually painted black.

Even under ideal conditions solar stills produce fresh water very slowly – about one pint of fresh water can be obtained each day per square foot of energy-absorbing surface. A study completed by the Battelle Memorial Institute in the United States in 1965 shows that solar stills can compete with other forms of distillation only where small amounts of fresh water are needed. Nevertheless water could be provided more cheaply than by conventional flash or vapour-compression processes in certain areas of the world providing that the demand was less than 50,000 g.p.d.

Freezing. Long ago the Eskimos learned that the first ice which forms when sea-water freezes contains very little if any salt. The Russian emigrant Alexander Zarchin who designed the freezing plant at Eilat in Israel is reputed to have watched Russian peasants living in coastal villages skimming the ice from the surface of shallow bowls which they had filled with salt water. Ice forms on the surface of a solution containing 35,000 p.p.m. salt at $-2.2°C$. As the temperature falls even lower, more ice forms. Salt does not start to be deposited from the brine until $-21.1°C$, although other impurities may be released from solution at $-8.3°C$. Fortunately both temperatures are below the normal working ranges of present processes – direct and secondary refrigerant freezing.

In the direct-freezing method, the sea-water is cooled by feeding it into a vacuum chamber. On entering this chamber some of the water flashes and cools the remainder. Approximately half of the water entering the chamber freezes. The mixture of ice and brine is then pumped to the bottom of a separating column where the ice crystals float to the surface. This collection of ice forms a core inside the column. As the core is pushed upwards by ice collecting beneath it and the pressure of the brine, it is washed free of salt. Finally the core's top surface is scraped and the scrapings are passed into the melting tank (see figure 7).

The secondary refrigerant process uses a gas which has been cooled to the liquid state to freeze the water. The liquefied gas is added to the salt water and allowed to evaporate. Again the heat of evaporation extracted from the salt solution causes some of the water to freeze. Just as in the direct-freezing process the brine/ice slurry passes on to a separation column, where the ice crystals are separated from the brine, washed and passed into the melting chamber. The boiling point of the gas that has been evaporated is raised by slightly increasing the pressure. It then flows to the melting chamber where it condenses, liberating heat which melts the ice. The water and the remaining liquid gas do not mix and so are easily separated in a decanting chamber (see figure 7). Using butane as the secondary

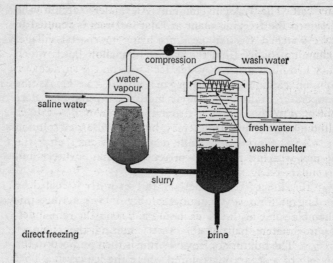

figure 7 **freezing processes for desalination**

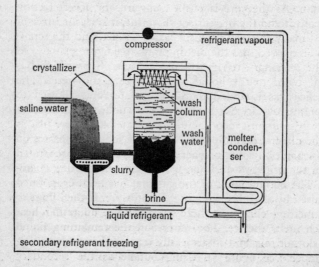

refrigerant the freezer and separating column can be operated at nearly atmospheric pressure, which avoids some of the expensive problems involved in constructing vacuum chambers of the type used in direct freezing.

2. PROCESSES USING MEMBRANES

Electrodialysis. When salt dissolves in water it breaks up into charged particles or ions, the sodium ions being posi-

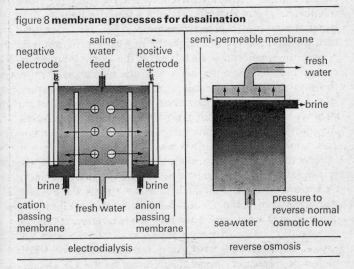

figure 8 **membrane processes for desalination**

negative electrode · saline water feed · positive electrode

semi-permeable membrane

fresh water

brine

cation passing membrane · fresh water · anion passing membrane

brine · brine

pressure to reverse normal osmotic flow

sea-water

electrodialysis · reverse osmosis

tive and the chloride negative. If a current of electricity is passed through the solution the negative ions move to the positive pole and positive ions move to the negative pole. Electrodialysis exploits this fundamental behaviour and enhances its effect by placing special membranes in the path of the migrating ions. Membranes which allow only positive ions through them alternate with membranes permeable solely to negative ions and as a result alternate compartments of concentrated brine and desalted water slowly build up (see figure 8). Because the amount of energy required by the process depends directly on the number of ions being pushed along and because electrical energy is generally expensive, electrodialysis is used mainly to desalt brackish, less salty, water.

Reverse osmosis. In contrast to electrodialysis, in which the salt ions are moved through the membranes, in reverse osmosis it is the water which passes through them. If a sugar solution is separated from water by a semi-permeable membrane – one that allows only water through it – the water moves into the sugar solution. This movement will continue indefinitely although the rate at which the water crosses the membrane will fall off as the sugar solution becomes diluted. The only way to stop the migration of water through the semi-permeable membrane is to apply a pressure equal to the 'attractive force' or osmotic pressure of the sugar solution on the sugar side of the membrane. An increase beyond this osmotic pressure not only stops the flow of water into the sugar solution side but actually reverses it, squeezing water back through the membrane. This is the principle behind desalination by reverse osmosis (see figure 8). Unfortunately it is difficult to make a membrane which will let water through but hold back the sodium and chloride ions which are only very slightly larger than the water molecules.

C. E. Reid first suggested using reverse osmosis for desalination in a research proposal submitted to the US Department of the Interior. Of the various membrane materials which he and his co-worker E. J. Breton tried, commercial acetate films proved the most impermeable to salt. In a typical experiment using a pressure of 100 atmospheres, the concentration of salt in the effluent was approximately 5 per cent that of the feed solution. The most serious drawback was the very slow rate at which the water moved through the membranes – about a tenth of a gallon per square foot of membrane per day. Attempts to improve on this by using very thin films failed. Some other way of increasing the flow was indicated. In 1960 S. E. Loeb and F. Milstein of the University of California described a specially cast cellulose acetate membrane through which water flowed 50 to 100 times faster. This membrane rejected some 98·5 per cent of the salt and, since the rejection was geared to the pressure, it was theoretically possible to reach a point where no salt was allowed through.

3. CHEMICAL PROCESSES

Ion exchange. Records going back to the time of Aristotle indicate that sand filters have been used to purify salt water and make it drinkable. Sir Francis Bacon described experiments in which he passed salt water through pots filled with earth to remove the salt – he even mentioned imaginary water treatment plant in *The New Atlantis* (1623). In spite of this early start, the first quantitive information on ion exchange came not from the development of water purification but from experiments with farm manure. Farmers and scientists wanted to know, for example, why chemicals such as potassium and ammonium salts were held by the soil sufficiently firmly to prevent the rain from washing them away and yet remained available to the growing crops. From their experiments grew a new body of information on how such ions behave – information upon which purification by ion exchange ultimately depends.

Modern desalting systems do not rely on natural substances capable of exchanging various chemical ions; instead they use specially developed synthetic resins. As might be expected from the earlier mention of electrodialysis these ion exchangers have to process both positive ions (cations) and negative ones (anions). Beds of cation and anion exchangers are placed in series – the sea-water first passes through the cation exchanger, where sodium ions are exchanged for hydrogen ions, and then flows through the anion exchanger where chloride ions are replaced by hydroxyl groups. The hydrogen and hydroxyl combine to make more water. As long as the ion exchange resins remain active, fresh water from the sea together with that formed by the combined ions will flow, but the resins gradually lose their supply of exchangeable ions until eventually they can no longer remove the salt. At this point, the conversion process must be halted and the ion exchange material regenerated. It is washed with chemicals which remove the unwanted salt ions and replace them once more with hydrogen and hydroxyl ones. This can be quite a costly process. Therefore, just as in dialysis the amount of salt in solution is a critical factor – the more salt, the more often the ion exchange beds have to be regenerated. Not surprisingly, apart from their use in life raft survival kits and other relatively small marine units, ion exchange systems are generally restricted to the desalting of brackish waters.

Solvent extraction. If the chemistry of ion exchange seems complicated, that of solvent extraction techniques should appear very simple. All that is required is a solvent which takes up either salt or water, but not both. Most of the materials tried have had an affinity for water. The water is removed from the solvent which is used again. So far, simplicity has not been much of a bonus. None of the chemicals has been used on anything greater than a laboratory scale; even then it has proved excessively expensive, largely because few solvents have a great affinity for water and most of the solvent materials have been very costly.

Hydrate formation. A hydrate is a crystallized substance formed by water and certain ions. Liquefied propane gas, a hydrating agent currently under investigation, forms a solid crystal with water in the ratio of seventeen molecules of water to every one of the gas. The hydrating agent is mixed with saline water in a reactor vessel where it forms crystals composed solely of pure water and the agent – only salt is left behind. After separation and washing, just as in the freezing processes, the crystals are decomposed by heat, melting to yield fresh water and the original hydrating agent. They divide into two distinct layers, just like oil and water, and can easily be separated. In many ways the hydrate process resembles freeze separation, but ultimately it depends upon the formation of chemical bonds to separate the fresh water from the salt.

Problems galore

The fact that some desalting processes are available commercially does not mean they have been perfected. The success of multi-stage flash distillation, for example, results largely from compromises in design and working temperatures which avoid rather than overcome major difficulties implicit in desalting sea water. And several of the methods currently being developed may never go beyond the pilot-plant stage. They will be left straddled between laboratory and consumer, held back by problems inherent in the process or created by the sea-water itself. This abundance of problems is confirmed in reports from the many laboratories investigating desalination. Even the most cursory glance at their pages shows that research aimed at improving present commercial methods of distillation and electro-dialysis continues alongside the development of other, as yet unproven, processes.

The calcium and magnesium salts dissolved in sea-water create serious problems for distillation processes. When untreated sea-water is heated to about 70°C, the salts start to come out of the solution and encrust the heat exchange surfaces. This mineral coating or scale forms a barrier to the transfer of heat from the hot to the cooler water and therefore reduces the efficiency of the plant. Flash distillation avoids the worst problems of scale formation by operating at comparatively low temperatures, but it does not escape completely. The sea-water feed must be pre-treated to remove various minerals and oxygen which increase the corrosive action of sea-water. Usually, acid is added to convert the chemical troublemakers into a harmless form, or the calcium and magnesium may be removed from the seawater by other chemical additives. Some workers have even suggested that the sediments from 'de-scaled' sea-water might be used to make chemical fertilizers – one treatment would produce 37 tons of fertilizer for every million gallons of sea-water.

The formation of mineral scale is not the only block to efficiency: as the steam condenses, a film of water spreads over the metal surface of the heat exchangers and acts as an insulator slowing down further condensation. The only way to prevent this is to break the layer up into tiny droplets. Certain organic chemicals can be added to the seawater to promote this so-called dropwise condensation but it is far more satisfactory if the surface itself can bring about this more efficient type of condensation. More than thirty years ago scientists showed that a very thin layer of water-repellent material would increase condensation, but only recently have suitable surface coatings such as the plastic Teflon been discovered. Work along these lines at the Franklin Institute in Philadelphia has led to some rather remarkable suggestions. Scientists there have suggested that gold-plated heat exchange surfaces could be the solution; copper pipes coated with a layer a few thousandths of an inch thick of silver, gold, rhodium, palladium or platinum have produced increases in condensation rates of 50 per cent or more.

The membrane processes also have their weaknesses. Most of the membranes in electrodialysis consist of a base material such as polyethylene or polystyrene which is treated chemically to devlop the necessary properties. Once more the chemicals, other than sodium chloride, in the sea or brackish water play havoc with the process: insoluble salts collect on the membranes and block them or change their chemical composition. Whereas in distillation heating above certain threshold temperatures leads to scale formation, in electrodialysis the interaction of the migrating ions causes the trouble. Local reactions occur in the compartments where the ions collect particularly at the surface of the membranes. As the membranes become more resistant to the flow of ions through them – a process known as polarization – more and more energy is needed to push them along until eventually the process 'grinds to a halt'.

Israeli scientists at the Negev Institute for Arid Zone Research have developed one possible line of attack against polarization of the membranes and its attendant deposition of insoluble chemicals; they reverse the flow of electricity for brief periods. The reversed pulses drive the main concentration of ions fractionally away from the surface of the membranes. It does not prevent their interaction, but the scale now forms in the stream of brine and can be flushed away. Inevitably such solutions reduce the efficiency of the plant, but savings in terms of membranes and the time lost during their replacement can more than cover this.

So far, the choice in electrodialysis seems to rest between membranes which are cheap to make but have a short life and those which are expensive but last longer. Obviously a considerable pay-off awaits the company which manages to produce membranes combining efficiency, long life and cheapness. One of the more successful membranes so far is 'Selemion', developed and manufactured by the Asahi Glass Company of Japan – as early as 1964 this company was turning out some 15,000 pairs of membranes per month. The Selemion membrane seems to prevent much of the deposition of calcium sulphate on its surface in the compartments of concentrated brine.

The membranes for reverse osmosis have not even reached this stage. Evidence suggests that the osmotic powers of the cellulose-acetate membranes gradually tail off when sea-water is treated, and that under the high pressures needed to ensure a reasonable purity physical changes occur which lead to a further deterioration of their property. Numerous groups, particularly in the USA and Britain, are engaged in the search for new materials which will yield membranes superior to the cellulose acetate ones – but so far with very little success. In the August 1966 issue of *Science Journal* Dr Alan Sharples of Arthur D. Little Ltd described four basic requirements:

The first is a material which can dissolve water to a limited extent (and hence transmit it by diffusion) but which has a reduced affinity for sodium and chloride ions ... The second is a process for casting the material in the form of a suitably flexible film, with the special structure characteristic of the high throughput membranes developed by Loeb and Sourirajan ... The third is ability of the structure to withstand high pressures ... and finally, it must be free from defect pores ...

One promising approach being pioneered by Du Pont replaces the flat membrane by a mass of fine hollow plastic fibres. The input water, under high pressure, flows over the outside surface of the fibres and a portion of the water passes through into the inside. This product water, containing very little salt, is then run off from the fibres at the same time as the salty water surrounding the fibres. Known as 'Permasep' permeators, units built on these lines can demineralize brackish water when operated at a pressure of 600 pounds per square inch.

Hope for reverse osmosis lies in the growing understanding of how the membranes work and in exploring the diversity of materials and structures available. Unfortunately, understanding is not always enough: scientists know how brine becomes trapped in spaces between ice crystals which are closely packed together, and they know how to vary the rate of formation of ice and the size of the crystals, but for many years problems met in experimental plants prevented the freezing processes from achieving their theoretical advantages over other processes – for example the low theoretical requirement of energy and the reduction of corrosion. One American pilot plant has been 'moth-balled', and the freezing plant at Eilat was slow to come into full operation, although it now operates at more than the original design output of 240,000 g.p.d.

In the early 1960s freezing processes had an enthusiastic following. In a scientific paper given in 1961 Hugh Simpson and Professor Silver ranked it, together with reverse osmosis, as a process likely to be cheaper than multi-stage distillation for desalting sea-water. They arrived at this conclusion using a general theory based on energy requirements and theoretical engineering costs. However, early experience was not encouraging and interest waned. Only in the late 1960s did the process show signs of becoming a successful commercial venture with several British companies leading in its exploitation. We have here an example of yet another problem area in desalination; the difficulties of reliably assessing the merits of the various processes when so few of them have reached any sizeable productive capacity.

Dollars and pounds

We now have a working knowledge of the contenders in the desalination race, but multi-stage flash distillation remains the proven leader in large-scale desalination. In certain circumstances electrodialysis competes favourably, but usually not in the context of desalting the sea – the main concern here. In any race, the man in search of a likely winner must have some basis for a choice, and the desalination stakes are no exception. The decisive factor here is, in a word, cheapness. In most countries water is a cheap raw material, a gift from the heavens, which does not command any great respect until time of shortage. Therefore, its price is usually far below its real value to the community, a point well made by Dr Roger Revelle in an amusing but relevant comparison of costs. In the United States, water costs $10 to $20 an acre-foot (325,872 US gallons), compared with wholesale prices of $22,000 for petroleum, $100,000 for milk and $1 million (not including taxes) for bourbon whisky.

Making financial comparisons between water from conventional sources and that from desalination is not quite so easy. The pitfalls are many and Dr D. G. Miller of the British Water Research Association has pointed out two sources of serious error. Unlike water rates, estimates for desalination do not usually include distribution and storage, yet distribution costs may account for as much as 50 per cent of the total. Yet current costs for conventional supplies are often based on old production plant which would cost considerably more to replace than it originally did to build. The only fair comparison, it seems, is between the total cost of a completely new supply by each method. When this is done, fresh water can still be piped over considerable distances at a cost of far less than that involved in the conversion of sea-water, particularly where large volumes are required. As a result, large-scale desalting has been restricted to special areas where other factors have counterbalanced its comparatively high costs.

For example, when oil companies began to exploit new fields in Kuwait they found a situation where the main source of drinking water was the Shatt-el-Arab river at Basra, some sixty miles away. The supplies, brought each day by boat, were inadequate for their needs, and in 1950 the Kuwait Oil Company installed its first desalination plant – the savings were obvious because the fuel was very cheap. Within a year the government was buying water for domestic supply from the company. Shortly afterwards it commissioned the first of what was to be a whole series of distillation plants. In a more temperate climate, the island of Guernsey invested in a desalting plant to protect its important tomato crops – and its considerable tourist trade – from shortages of water. Malta, another island held to ransom by an acute water problem, constructed its first desalting plant with an output of over one m.g.d. in 1967, and further plant has now been installed there. And so the story continues: Curaçao, Cyprus, Aruba, Nassau in the Bahamas, Kingley (Bermuda) and Key West (Florida), all have desalination plants. It is not possible to name every installation but the total production of fresh water throughout the world is mushrooming from tens to hundreds of millions of gallons per day. Nevertheless, desalination is still an expensive business, and that final economic barrier which will make it competitive with conventional supplies has still to be crossed in most parts of the world.

Two main routes to cheaper desalination exist. One is to keep capital costs to a minimum, and the other is to make the best possible overall use of energy supplied to the plant. Unfortunately these money savers tend to oppose rather than complement one another: more efficient processes involve further research and development and more sophisticated design and structures, and all this adds up to higher costs. On the research investment side Dr H. Kronberger of the United Kingdom Atomic Energy Authority and Professor Silver have pointed out that a cost reduction of the order of 25 per cent might rely on a technological advance which would probably cost several million dollars for research and development. A change in interest rate from 5 per cent to 4 per cent could achieve the same effect on the cost of water, while a change from a 4 per cent to a 5 per cent interest rate could wipe out the improvement. However, financial juggling apart, in the end the designer must make a compromise to arrive at the best possible total cost for a given output of water.

Experience has shown that capital costs per unit of production become smaller as the capacity of the plant increases. This particular trend was seen in the submerged tube installations and is being repeated with the multi-stage flash process. An important point here is that the flash process offers so much more scope for exploiting this 'capital gain'. The 2·6 m.g.d. distillation unit built by Westinghouse at Key West ranks as the largest single unit in the world at the time of writing; but installations with capacities of 100 m.g.d. or more may be installed in Southern California, Israel, the USSR and New York. This fifty-fold increase could cut the daily cost per gallon by more than half – it is figures like these, theoretical though they may be, that have led to considerable optimism about the prospects for cheap water by desalination.

Another source of optimism is the possibility of combining nuclear power generation with desalination. This helps to overcome restrictions imposed by considerations of the total cost on the full use of the available energy. The major British companies involved in desalination have long been aware of the fact that distillation is more economical when the production of fresh water is combined with the generation of power. All major installations built by Weir, apart from the one on Guernsey, are of this dual-purpose type. Water produced in this way has a price comparable to that of water from more conventional sources in some parts of Western Europe – about 60 cents per thousand gallons.

Why is it cheaper to have dual-purpose plant? The answer lies in the very simple principle laid down by the nineteenth-century engineer N. K. S. Carnot (1796–1832), which states that to operate any kind of heat engine, heat must be rejected. He worked out mathematically that the efficiency of this process of taking heat, making it work, and then rejecting the balance depends upon the difference between the initial working temperature and the final temperature at which the heat is rejected, divided by the initial temperature. In combined power-generation and distillation, these differences, and hence efficiency, remain the same but the hot water coming from the turbo-generators is channelled into distillation units operating at comparatively low temperatures. In other words the power-generation is kept the same, but the efficiency of the combined processes is improved by exploiting a general weakness of desalination units – the inability to operate at very high temperatures.

At last scientists and engineers seem to have resolved the apparent dichotomy between efficiency and capital costs: dual-purpose plants permit the construction of large units. Combining the nuclear power station with flash distillation has obvious attractions for countries like Israel, which need both fresh water and energy. However, this does not mean that the green light is necessarily showing for desalination and that it is just a question of building the monster installations. The fact remains that so far no really large dual-purpose plant has been built and therefore much of the 'dollars and pounds' talk remains an extrapolation from very much smaller conventional installations.

Even though a convention of costing new projects has been developed, estimates can vary considerably. The dual-purpose nuclear power and desalting plant proposed for California provides an example of this. Scheduled for construction on an artificial offshore island a few miles south of Long Beach, California, the plant was to have provided 150 m.g.d. (enough water to meet municipal and industrial needs of a city of 750,000 people) and generate electric power at the rate of 1,600 megawatts (sufficient power for a city of almost 2 million people). However, as the project progressed to detailed analysis, the water cost of 22 cents originally estimated was found to be highly optimistic in view of the tremendous construction costs. In July 1968 the project was cancelled. In that year only one large dual-purpose nuclear plant was under construction – this was at Shevchenko close to the Caspian Sea. The plant which is located about a mile and a half from the shore has the capacity to generate 150 megawatts of electricity and to provide about 33.5 m.g.d. This installation, small in comparison to the other suggested dual-purpose plant, is intended as a pilot plant for much larger ones.

In Britain, it has been estimated that water supplied from established sources costs about 15 cents per 1,000 Imperial gallons, while that from new reservoirs can cost 24 cents or more per thousand gallons with pumping costs. But even though the giant dual purpose plant may bring the costs down to a few cents per 1,000 gallons, the water is still too expensive for irrigation purposes. The FAO has said that, except for special cases, the use of desalted water for irriga-

tion will not be economical as long as its production cost
without subsidy is above 10 cents per 1,000 gallons. For
large-scale agricultural use, the cost will have to be about 3
cents per 1,000 gallons. Add to this the observation that, in
most agricultural regions where the need for water is great,
the demand for energy is very small, and one begins to
understand why the research effort into desalination continues to increase throughout the world.

The international front

'No water-resource programme is of greater long-range importance than our efforts to find an effective and economical
way to convert water from the world's greatest, cheapest
natural resources – the oceans – into water fit for consumption in the home and by industry. Such a breakthrough
would end bitter struggles between neighbours, states and
nations; and bring hope to millions who live out their lives
in dire shortage of usable water ... though living on the
edge of a great body of water throughout their parched
lifetime.' This was how the late President Kennedy expressed his belief in the American desalination programme.
President Johnson was to reiterate this credo when he took
office, and the body responsible for desalination, the Office
of Saline Water of the Department of the Interior, has gone
from weakness to strength. It began in 1952 with an appropriation of $175,000 and by the end of the financial year for
1967 (30 June 1967) had a total appropriation of $111,309,000.
Of this, $91,865,000 was spent on research and development
and the remainder was invested in construction, operation
and maintenance of plant.

British participation in desalination has not enjoyed
such massive financial encouragement from Government
sources. Apart from joint studies with the Dutch on electrodialysis in the 1950s, official quarters have been slow to
appreciate the commercial and political gains involved in
this area of process technology. In 1963 the then Depart-

ment of Scientific and Industrial Research set up a committee to review desalination, and research grants were awarded shortly afterwards to the Water Research Association and the Heriot–Watt University in Edinburgh. In the following years the Government showed greater interest, and in 1965 the Minister of Technology directed the Atomic Energy Authority to undertake a 'substantial programme' of research into methods of desalination. The Committee on Desalination Research was also placed under the Authority and the project launched with a three-year budget of £1·3 million. However, this project was not the start of the country's interest in the subject; by this same year, a handful of British manufacturers had installed some 60 per cent of the world's land-based units. The British Government wanted to see this lead maintained. In December 1967 a second programme was announced involving an estimated £4 million over the period ending in spring 1971. This further expansion of the desalination effort included the development of commercial designs prepared during the previous programme. Since then the Government has continued to support desalination on a reduced scale. For example, it assisted in the installation of a vertical tube evaporation plant in Gibraltar. In 1972, however, desalination was under review.

In Israel, where the present water supplies fall short of the potential demand by as much as 50 per cent, the impetus for developing methods of desalting the sea and brackish water derives from the question of survival rather than commercial interest. Under the guidance of the country's Sea Water Conversion Commission, the Israelis carry out an extensive research programme which they hope will lead them eventually to emancipation from the threat of serious shortages of water. The country already boasts several desalting installations including the Zarchin desalination plant at Eilat.

A shortage of quite another kind prompted Japan's initial interest in desalination – lack of natural deposits of salt.

Today a million tons of salt are taken from the sea every year. On the whole there is no shortage of water, but sometimes unusual circumstances do lead to a demand for fresh water as well as salt. On a small island near Sasebo City the population has been swollen by the labour needed for a coal mine. The Sakito Salt Manufacturing Company has been able to exploit this unusual situation by building a desalting plant which provides salt and the water needed by the island populace. With their considerable marine interests, Japanese companies have also concentrated over the past twenty-five years or so on the construction of desalting units for use at sea, particularly compact units suitable for small ships. Apart from such commercial enterprises the Government Chemical Industrial Research Institute at Tokyo and the Japan Monopoly Corporation (responsible for the supply and price of salt) are engaged in research into most aspects of desalination.

The list of nations who have their sights set on economic desalination does not end with the mention of four countries; many others such as Australia, France, Germany, Holland, Italy and the USSR are involved. Many millions of dollars are being spent throughout the world each year in the search for the breakthrough dreamed of by President Kennedy. The research varies from laboratory tests producing a few precious drops to the installation of demonstration plant producing a million gallons per day.

At Shevchenko the Soviet authorities have set up an experimental test range to evaluate various methods of desalination. The US authorities, as a result of the Demonstration Plant Act of 1958, have built four plants at various sites, and three of these are still in operation. A fifth one also constructed under this programme contains more experimental features than in the other demonstration plant, and is generally classified as a large pilot plant. The British engineers and scientists have tended to rely more on their experience with large commercial installations. However, Professor Silver has suggested the construction of a large distillation unit financed at a low fixed-interest rate, in which the difference in financial terms between this low fixed rate and the more usual levels is regarded as a research investment.

In the end, no matter what financial wizardry is brought into play, the fact remains that desalination is moving to a new, more expensive phase where scientific and technical know-how gained in the laboratory and pilot installations must be put to the test in more ambitious projects. Extrapolation has its limits, and eventually someone has to decide to go ahead and build. This decision will impose a heavy financial burden and therefore the ranks are beginning to close – and in addition to the proliferation of published papers on desalination, the number of international agreements on various projects is also growing. The USSR and the United States, for example, have agreed to cooperate and exchange information, and their experts have already inspected each other's installations. Meanwhile, the world still awaits the construction of the first really large dual-purpose plant – not until this is done and the new problems created by handling water and steam on an unprecedented scale have been solved will the pundits be able to give the final verdict on current efforts to sweeten the seas.

Politics and perspective

In 1964 the United Nations Department of Economic and Social Affairs announced the results of a world-wide survey made to establish where economic desalination might be possible. The survey indicated that at least fifty areas merited further, more detailed investigations. It also revealed some surprising anomalies in the price paid for water supplies – in some cases people paid more for their water than the cost of desalted water. Many of the areas covered by the investigation suffered both a shortage and a serious lack of quality in their fresh water. Such lack of quality frequently expresses itself in a high incidence of water-borne diseases and other ailments stemming from the lack of adequate personal hygiene. For example, the number of deaths each year in the developing countries from diarrhoeal disease among children under the age of one year is estimated to be nearly five million, a high proportion of which stems from poor water supplies.

Clearly water can have considerable political content – one has only to recall the example of the Aswan High Dam. This dam, which is capable of retaining for Egypt the average annual flow of the Nile, was built with Soviet financial and technical aid, as an international political gambit whose pay-off came in the promotion of political ideology and power within a key Arab area. The same possibilities may well exist with large-scale desalination. The United States has been quick to recognize the value of being able to provide sources of cheap fresh water. The Water for Peace Conference held in Washington in May 1967 is an indication of this. This international meeting of desalination experts was held under the auspices of the US State Department and not, as might be expected, the Office of Saline Water. No Soviet experts were present, for the USSR also appreciates the value of cornering the water-supply market in developing areas of the world.

If this political interpretation is correct, considerable expansion in water supply propaganda and the investment of even greater sums of money in desalination can be confidently anticipated. However, in the midst of their banner waving, the advanced nations of the world may find that their own water supply situation gives little reason for complacency. In the United States the use of water is growing at a rate of 25,000 gallons per minute and is expected to rise from a daily rate of 359 thousand million gallons in 1965 to 453 thousand million gallons a day in 1975. In south-east England, which supports the higest density of people per acre of catchment area in the world, water must be taken from farther and farther afield. Large industrial centres in other parts of the country must also collect supplies from distant, less populated catchment areas – it is now almost a regular sport for dissident Welsh nationalists to blow up a pipe or two taking water from the hills of North Wales to slake the thirst of Liverpool sixty to eighty miles away.

Speaking at a symposium on nuclear desalination in London in October 1967, A. F. Rowntree, director of the British Water Resources Board, forecast that the first nuclear dual-purpose plant would be in operation in Britain within ten to fifteen years. In 1967 the then US Vice President, Hubert Humphrey, inaugurated the world's largest single-unit desalting plant at Key West. But at present there is no need for any widespread use of desalting – better use of existing supplies could do much to relieve many threats of serious shortages of fresh water.

The whole question of desalination needs to be put into perspective against the supplies of fresh water which are already available but poorly exploited. The table below

ESTIMATE OF WORLD'S WATER SUPPLY

Location	Water volume (cubic miles)	Percentage of total water
Fresh water lakes	30,000	0·009
Saline lakes and inland seas	25,000	0·008
Average in rivers and streams	300	0·0001
Soil moisture and near-surface ground water	16,000	0·005
Ground water within depth of half a mile	1,000,000	0·31
Ground water lying deep	1,000,000	0·31
Ice caps and glaciers	7,000,000	2·15
Atmospheric water	3,100	0·001
World oceans	317,000,000	97·2

(United States Geological Survey)

gives some indication of the unequal distribution of water between land and sea.

Although rivers supply a large proportion of the water

used today, they still pour millions upon millions of gallons
back into the sea. Something like a quarter of the Nile's
water ends its journey in the Mediterranean. But, as mentioned earlier, the Aswan High Dam is intended to bring
this vast potential supply under stricter control; the periodic
flooding of the Nile valley will cease as the mighty river
stores its load in the dam. When the water is released it will
be made to work, turning generators as it falls to the level
of the dam's base. The power it produces – more than a
million kilowatts – will supply homes and industry as well
as the pumps pushing water into the irrigation system.
Another great dam, the Kariba, completed in 1960, has a
total water capacity of some 180 million cubic metres. This
is enough water to supply a population of 50 million for
fifty years at a rate of 200 litres per person per day without
any refilling. These then are the giants of the water supply
and power generating business. In 1900 there were approximately 1,000 large dams in the world. Since then the number has doubled every twenty years until today there are
over 8,000.

Dams are an obvious way of capturing and holding water
until it is needed; not so obvious is the use of porous rocks
beneath the earth's surface as an underground reservoir. It
is hoped that underground storage of water in the upper
reaches of the Thames catchment area will help to prevent
future shortages anticipated for south-east England. The
water contained within the upper half mile of the Earth's
crust amounts to some 3,000 times that at any given time in
the world's rivers. Compared with this largely untapped
mass of fresh water, the water stored in dams and reservoirs
is comparatively puny. Unfortunately it takes time to track
down the hidden subterranean supplies, and even when
they are found the problem of how they can be exploited
remains. In some cases removal of too much water irreversibly damages the water-storing rocks, drastically reducing their ability to soak up further supplies of ground
water. Even where there is little danger of altering the

physical properties of the underground storehouse, over-exploitation can lead to an influx of brackish or salt water which contaminates the remaining water. Some underground supplies in Israel, a country which relies heavily on underground sources of water, are already in danger. One solution may be to use desalting units along the coast like kidneys, rejecting the unwanted impurities before feeding water into the underground reservoirs. The Israelis have even considered over-exploiting their subterranean supplies to stave off the need for desalting plant. New developments in desalination might occur in this interim period which would save them from having to use present more expensive methods. However, the consensus seems to be that waiting would be unwise; most experts do not envisage any process which will replace present distillation methods in the very large units.

Barrages across rivers or bays provide another method of storing fresh water. In the Netherlands the Barrier Dam, which is twenty miles long, has forced the North Sea to retreat fifty miles and has shortened the coastline by nearly two hundred miles. Behind its massive walls the Zuyder Zee has become a fresh water lake, the IJsselmeer, and over half a million acres of new land have been reclaimed. After the disaster of 1953, when the sea broke through the Dutch defences and inundated a considerable area of their land, the Dutch authorities drew up a new project to give them more control over the sea. Called the Delta Project the scheme involves damming off four major sea arms and three rivers, the Rhine, Meuse and Scheldt. It is scheduled for completion in the early 1980s. Their ambitious system of dams and dikes will prevent the incursion of salt water into canals and drainage channels, and will provide further reservoirs like the IJsselmeer as well as valuable reclaimed land. In Britain, barrages have been suggested for Morecambe Bay, the Wash and the Solway Firth. The construction of barrages across suitable bays and estuaries may well provide cheap sites for large reservoirs as the cost of land-based ones becomes prohibitively high. These reservoirs need not be confined to containing fresh water flowing from the land; they could be kept full by large desalting installations working continually at maximum efficiency. Unlike the great river dams where the annual flow of water is uncertain, these shoreside reservoirs could be designed to hold a specific output of water from the plant.

But there is more to water engineering than finding and containing the supply. These days water-supply engineers also talk about conservation and re-use. Many people argue that if less water were wasted there would be no need to worry about supplies for many years to come. The problem is to persuade people who have become accustomed to cheap water to have more respect for this vital raw material. One way of doing this is to meter supplies and charge more for them. A survey of 136 American towns and cities with populations exceeding 25,000 gave illuminating results in this respect. Where 10 per cent of the supplies were monitored the daily consumption per person was 650 litres compared with 265 litres in areas where 50 per cent or more houses had metered supplies. In Gibraltar, the inhabitants pay a realistic price – about ten times that in Britain – for their metered water although they receive a piped seawater for such uses as water closets and washing free of charge.

There is no doubt that when realistic prices are charged for water, people soon become experts in making the best use and re-use of it. Many industrial concerns, particularly those which have to pre-treat their water, have known this for a long time. They simply cannot afford to waste water. On the average the petroleum industry re-cycles water six and a half times while individual refineries may re-use water as many as thirty times. As water becomes increasingly expensive such re-use must become more widespread on the domestic front. This will mean more treatment of polluted water. In Britain, some municipal supplies rely on water courses half of which are processed sewage effluent.

Desalination must be regarded as only a part of a larger problem of finding sufficient fresh water, and the case for its widespread use is not so great as some writers and authorities would have us believe. However, there are many places where desalination is already, or soon will be, economical. The issue is further confused by the incomplete knowledge of the world's water resources. The International Hydrological Decade which started in 1965 has as one of its aims the preparation of an accurate balance sheet of the world's water. However, even in the absence of accurate figures one can be fairly sure that new sources of fresh water will be found in the years to come. How easily they can be exploited is impossible to guess – it might be cheaper to build desalting plant. In the end some kind of criterion must be applied and one could do worse than insist that the development of any water resource be justified in terms of human well-being. In other words, the provision of a supply of fresh water should not be regarded as an end in itself. This test goes beyond propaganda and seeks out tangible rewards such as improved agriculture or industrial productivity. A cheap way of desalting the seas will free men from the chains of poverty and thirst, but it must not be allowed to commit them to just another form of bondage.

Chapter 4

A Mineral Storehouse

Diamonds, gravel, platinum and tin are dredged up from the sea floor in shallow coastal areas; natural gas, oil and molten sulphur are piped up from the underlying rocks; bromine, common salt and magnesium are extracted from sea-water itself; and still the store of marine minerals is hardly touched by man. Every year rivers flowing from the land add close to 3,300 million tons of material all of which eventually comes to settle on the ocean floor. In addition nearly four million tons of meteoritic and other material rain down from outer space. Minerals are being deposited in the oceans faster than man can hope to collect them, providing a renewable resource which will last beyond the foreseeable future. In fact, the oceans form a global chemical plant in which practically every conceivable chemical is being processed and finally stored.

The grandeur of the global mineral resources is matched only by the problems they present to any would-be marine miner. Take those sediments accumulating on the ocean floor. Red clays containing enough copper and aluminium possibly for a million years lie there but the average depth of the oceans – 2·36 miles – places them well beyond the reach of conventional dredging machinery. Or consider the valuable minerals dissolved in sea-water. The prospect of collecting gold dissolved in sea-water led the Germans in 1924 to dispatch the *Meteor* to survey this marine bullion. They hoped to pay off their war debts with it, but the scientists found that the cost of extracting the estimated 10 million tons of gold was more than the metal's worth. It is easy enough to talk of millions and sometimes trillions, of tons of valuable minerals sequestered in the marine world, but the expense of collecting and processing them rarely falls to a level where the effort is worthwhile. In many cases the necessary equipment for the job does not exist.

The truth of the matter is that man has no real incentive to take minerals from the oceans when alternative supplies are available on the land. Yet where a nation does not have adequate supplies or where for political reasons its foreign source may be uncertain, the marine reserves may be seriously considered or at least investigated more fully, perhaps with a view to future contingency planning. Such a case could be put forward for the manganese found in the form of potato-sized nodules in all of the world's oceans. The United States has no high-grade deposits in the land and must import over 90 per cent of her manganese. In theory, American industry could become emancipated from its foreign suppliers of manganese and other minerals contained in the nodules. The problem is whether the cost of retrieving the nodules can be reduced to a level which will enable industries using minerals from this source to remain competitive. In practice, the nodules nearest to the American coast appear to be very low in manganese while those rich in the mineral lie in much deeper, distant waters. Whether these more remote sources of manganese could be exploited must depend on international law as well as technology.

Generally speaking, many of the more important minerals taken from marine areas represent little more than a continuation of exploitation that has already started on the land. The recent developments in the North Sea show this well. On 14 August 1959, the Slocherren No. 1 well in the Groningen province of the northern Netherlands reached rocky strata, rich in natural gas. Since then, this field has proved to be the largest one in the world, beating even the Panhandle field in the United States. Naturally enough, the major oil companies, spurred on by the Dutch discovery, searched for further supplies of geologically related areas. The search took them northwards into the North Sea. On 21 September 1965, the drilling rig *Sea Gem* struck gas, and this discovery was followed later by other rigs. By early 1967 the first gas was being piped ashore from the marine field to the United Kingdom.

What will happen in marine mining in the immediate future is anybody's guess. Where the rewards can be plainly seen, as in the case of North Sea gas and more recently oil, the finance needed to develop the resource can always be made available, but when it comes to less easily accounted prospects the picture is not nearly so clear. Large companies are slowly moving towards the idea of exploiting the oceans; some are already searching for new mineral deposits, but no matter how strong the current emotional sway towards this neglected resource, the number of commercial marine activities is likely to remain restricted to a few paying propositions for some years to come.

Surveying and prospecting

A serious shortage of detailed information about the surface of the sea floor and its underlying geology has presented a considerable barrier to the discovery and exploitation of marine mineral resources. A mining company moving into practically any part of the land masses can expect some kind of geological plan to be available, whereas in the oceans even the shallow continental shelf regions are often virtually unsurveyed. When the search for natural gas moved from the Netherlands into the North Sea, for example, the oil companies had to carry out preliminary surveys and mapping – and this in an area almost enclosed by advanced nations with strong maritime traditions. Little is known about the chemical and physical forces at work in the marine environment except where they impinge on the land to shape the coastline. And this general impoverishment of marine geology was, until very recent times, reflected in the small basic kit of instruments and techniques available for underwater investigations.

On the land, four basic geophysical techniques are used to investigate geological structures: electrical, gravitational, magnetic and seismic. These have provided the starting points for the evolution of marine systems. In some cases – for example, magnetic techniques – little alteration of already-existing equipment has been necessary; but with what is probably the most important technique, seismic profiling, advanced systems have been developed to take advantage of the larger amounts of data which can be obtained in the marine environment.

Electrical techniques rely essentially on changes in naturally occurring or induced electrical currents brought about by the geological structures through which they pass. Theoretically they show considerable promise, but even on the land electrical techniques are generally restricted to probing structures near to the surface (including the detection of archaeological remains). At present greater restrictions apply to their application in marine investigation due to the high conductivity of sea-water. Of the three remaining categories, seismic techniques are probably the most widely used but, before considering these, a word or two on gravitational and magnetic surveying.

Gravitational methods are based on the way in which the 'gravitational pull' of the Earth on an object suspended above it varies from place to place according to the density of the underlying material and its distance away from the object. In other words, the weight of an object at a given latitude and altitude depends on the nature of the rocks lying beneath the surface in that locality. In general, the older rocks which have become compacted with time tend to exert the greatest influence. By plotting lines of equal attraction the gravitational contours of the underlying strata can be drawn.

Magnetic techniques also favour the study of older rocks; igneous (volcanic) rocks and metamorphic rocks (sediments converted into compact rock by pressure and heat) contain sufficient quantities of magnetic minerals such as ilmenite, magnetite and pyrrhotite to produce detectable changes in the Earth's local magnetic field. The more recent sedimentary rocks generally contain relatively few of these magnetic minerals. However, being of geologically recent origin, the sedimentary rocks lie on top of the igneous and metamorphic layers so that changes detected in the older, basement rocks will influence the overlying sedimentary rock.

Oil companies, as a result of investigations on the land, know the types of geological formations which favour the accumulation of oil and natural gas. Where possible, it helps to know from the outset the form of the basement rocks in the prospective areas. In the case of the North Sea search ten companies banded together to share the cost (over £350,000) of producing a magnetic map of the entire area from southern Norway to the Straits of Dover, a total of 144,000 square miles. The survey was carried out from an aircraft using a magnetometer to measure the strength of the magnetic field.

Seismic methods give a picture of the underlying rocks irrespective of their origin. The name comes from seismology, the study of earthquakes. In seismic surveying an artificial earthquake is created, sending out waves of energy which surge downwards through the Earth. The velocity at which these shock waves pass through rock depends upon the latter's elasticity, density and composition. Whenever these properties change – as, for example, from one rock stratum to another – some of the energy is reflected back to the surface. These 'echoes' are picked up by 'geophones' to give recordings which, with suitable processing, can be built up into a picture of the various layers and structures beneath the surface.

Seismic surveying on the land is a laborious process involving carrying large amounts of equipment from one place to another, drilling holes for the explosive used to create the shock waves and perhaps skirting round obstacles such as rivers, lakes and objecting land owners. At sea the job is much easier. The seismic charges are detonated just beneath the surface, movement from place to place is easier and, by paying out the cables carrying the geophones at the same rate as the forward speed of the boat, the cable remains stationary during the recording of the echoes although the recording craft can be making a steady speed all day (see figure 9). Small wonder then that the cost per mile of seismic surveying at sea is only about a quarter of that on the land and that sixty miles or more can be covered a day.

In marine-seismic systems a wide variety of energy sources other than conventional explosive charges has been used, including rapid discharges of compressed air, gas 'poppers' created by an explosion of a gas/air mixture, exploding wires caused by a sudden release of electrical energy into a thin wire, 'sparkers' where an open spark passes through the water, and 'boomers' in which an electrical force propels an aluminium plate rapidly against the water. All produce a shock wave which travels through the water and into the sea floor. The development of such sonar profiling devices has been one of the major developments in geophysical exploration over the past decade or so. They have been employed in anything from mapping sediments to surveys of the English Channel as part of investigations into building the Channel Tunnel.

One of the earliest uses of sonar, however, was related to work of a different nature but which has also come to play a part in mineral surveying – deep-sea photography. Once the technical problems of building undersea cameras and providing them with appropriate light sources had been solved, there arose the question of controlling their position relative to the bottom. The solution was to use a sonar 'pinger' which transmitted a direct signal giving the depth of the camera and a reflected signal giving the depth of the sea floor. In this way the height of the camera could be con-

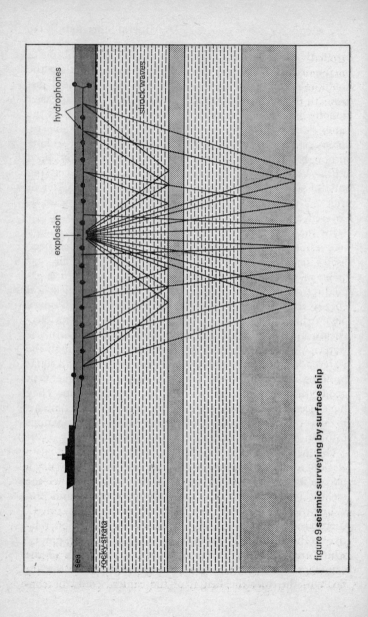

figure 9 seismic surveying by surface ship

trolled and the camera prevented from being held too high or, conversely, from burying itself deep into the ocean floor sediments. This 'near the bottom' pinger also provides additional information about the nature of the sea floor – hard rock gives a weak signal, with irregular side echoes, because it rarely presents a flat surface perpendicular to the pinger, whereas mud with its flat surface has a strong signal.

At some point in any survey some kind of quantitive estimate must be made. In the case of surface deposits samples can be taken fairly conveniently with dredges, grabs, corers and, in recent times, by manned submersibles. But once deposits below the immediate surface sediment are considered, the difficulty of making such assessments assumes quite a different scale. Oil and natural gas do not present too much of a problem; the size of the field can be estimated from the results of comparatively few test drillings and evaluation of the gas or oil flow. However, mineral ores can be mapped only after a considerable number of samples have been collected. Unfortunately at present satisfactory drilling techniques for investigating ore bodies just do not exist – the kind of rig used by the oil companies is far too costly because of the loss of drilling time during the necessarily frequent shifting. To assess an ore deposit would involve drilling shallow holes 100 to 700 feet in solid rock at intervals of hundreds of feet rather than miles. According to one expert, the evaluation of a large ore body would require a minimum of 50,000 feet of drilling in the form of approximately twenty holes, and to maintain exploration at a viable level this would have to be done at a cost below £50,000. In fact, unless a cheap drilling system is devised, the prospects for exploring in search of marine ore bodies must remain very poor indeed.

This discussion has concentrated on the geological detective work which goes into finding and assessing mineral resources, but it must be remembered that such activities have to be located accurately on the Earth's surface. On the land the production of maps, aerial photographs and the like enable results from surveys to be accurately located, but this kind of aid is not always available out at sea. In fact, before any survey or exploration can commence, a navigational grid may have to be established so that results can be pinpointed and related one to another over the entire area under study.

Natural gas and oil bonanza

Some 200 drilling rigs are at this very moment probing the continental shelves in various parts of the world in the search for natural gas and oil. In the Gulf of Mexico, the Bass Strait between Tasmania and Australia, the Mediterranean, the Gulf of Suez, the Sea of Japan, the Black Sea, the North Sea, the Sulu Sea in the Philippines, the search continues with drilling bits gnawing into promising structures found in surveys. And as the search widens, moving into the deeper waters, the risk to men and equipment grows. Violent storms arise suddenly in the Arabian Gulf, ice floes create problems off Alaska and hurricanes wreak havoc in the Gulf of Mexico. Like any other push into new territory, this expansion of the oil industry into the sea is taking its toll of men and equipment. One wintry day the rig *Sea Gem*, the first to find natural gas in the North Sea, foundered with the loss of half its crew. Fortunately alongside such disasters come improvements in rigs, equipment and techniques to make the job safer and easier. And the goal of this effort? Geologists estimate that the continental shelf holds supplies of oil at least equal to those on the land – some 1,000,000,000,000 barrels!

Although their origin is still disputed, most geologists believe that oil and natural gas are formed from animals and plants which flourished in the warm seas millions of years ago. Remains of these marine organisms together with sand, silt and other debris formed a thick carpet over the sea floor. As time went by more sediments collected, layer upon layer, compressing the material lying under them.

With the great pressure and temperature involved, the dead creatures were crushed together, and without the oxygen needed to bring about complete decay their cell matter was slowly converted into hydrocarbons. This chemical conversion was also helped by various minerals which had collected with the dead organisms and which acted as catalysts to speed up the process. If the overlying rocks formed an impenetrable barrier and if sideways movement was also prevented, the hydrocarbons remained, together with water, in the pores of the rock in which they were formed. The oil and gas traps sought by the petroleum geologists are often nothing more than the crests of folds in oil-bearing rock which have been 'capped' by an impermeable rock. The gas or oil originally dispersed throughout the rocks has migrated upwards to occupy the top of the fold while the water fills the remainder of the reservoir. Another kind of trap occurs when masses of rock salt have forced their way upwards, distorting the hydrocarbon-enriched strata into arches and at the same time sealing them off with an impenetrable layer of salt.

As long ago as 1896 an oil well was drilled off the coast of California. By the 1930s drilling was being carried out in the lakes and bays of Louisiana where in 1938 the first off-shore oil was struck. The first drilling rigs used in the swamps and marshes were nothing more than strong platforms mounted on wooden piles; everything – the drilling equipment and the crew – was situated on them. Later the whole rig was mounted on a barge which could be towed to the drilling location and then brought to rest on the shallow sea bottom. But neither pile platforms nor barges were suitable for the deeper locations which began to be explored after the Second World War, and a new generation of drilling platforms which could be moved from one place to another was evolved. Some of these steel islands have long legs which can be lowered to lift the platform well above the waves. Typical of such 'jack-up' rigs is the *Neptune-Gascogne*. This rig can work in up to 170 feet of water. Its hexagonal platform is almost half an acre in area and stands on legs 350 feet tall. Another type has legs incorporating ballast tanks which are flooded to bring them to rest on the sea floor. The *Kerr McGee 54* can sit on the bottom in this way at depths of water similar to those of the *Neptune-Gascogne*.

As the search moved into still deeper waters, it became apparent that systems which relied on the sea bottom for support would eventually reach their economic or technical limit. The answer was to develop floating rigs. At first surplus naval vessels were converted for drilling; the drill was lowered through a hole in the centre of the vessel, or over the side. Although quite satisfactory – one of these floating rigs did the preliminary drilling for the ill-fated Mohole project – the need for greater stability in rough seas led to the semi-submersible floating unit. The platform of such a rig stands well above the surface of the sea but its float lies deep enough in it to escape the forces of waves whipped up by storms. The full force of the waves passes through the rig rather than against it and semi-submersible rigs can operate in the roughest seas; one such rig, *Blue Water 2*, has operated in twenty-five-foot seas without excessive pitching or rolling while another, *Ocean Driller*, rode out waves fifty feet high when Hurricane Hilda swept through the Gulf of Mexico in 1964.

With the sea forever on the move, drilling rigs, even those that stand on the seabed, are in continual danger of being swept off station. The flexibility of the drilling pipe allows some leeway but the movement this permits is limited – generally to about 5 per cent of the length of pipe in the water in any one direction. Obviously, the problem is most serious with floating and semi-submersible rigs, and ever since these rigs were conceived, experiments have been carried out to find the best way of holding them on station. The Shell Oil Company, for example, has devised a mooring system whereby the rig is held by eight lines connected via spring buoys to anchors on the seabed. The tension in the mooring lines is monitored continuously and can be adjusted using electrically operated winches. Another system does away with the anchor lines and instead uses a propeller, which can swing in any direction to keep the rig on station. Any change in position is recorded by instruments which feed the information direct to a computer in the control room. The computer then calculates the necessary correction and instructs the propeller controls accordingly.

One of the greatest searches for oil and natural gas involving these islands of steel centres on the continental shelf beneath the North Sea. The search started officially in 1964 when the British Government invited applications from oil companies to explore and exploit this area of the North Sea. Five major gas fields have now been located and within the next three years will be supplying 15 per cent of the country's total energy requirements. Already by May 1972 a natural gas network, 1,726 miles of it, had been constructed and the Gas Council was predicting that by 1975 over 90 per cent of all gas consumers would have been converted to its use. At present 90 per cent of all gas used in Britain is natural gas, although, of course, not all of it comes from the North Sea.

The gas generally occurs in the layers of porous rock known as the Rotliegendes sandstone. Since this particular bed of rock seems to have been deposited originally under desert conditions, the gas is unlikely to have originated there. However, the Rotliegendes lies immediately above coal measures; the gas has probably migrated gradually out of the coal into the porous sandstone. Above the Rotliegendes is a formation called the Zechstein which consists of thick layers of common salt and layers of limestone. Where the impermeable layers overlap the coal measures, they have trapped the hydrocarbons in the sandstone layer sandwiched between them. In some places the Zechstein rocks are themselves broken and porous and where capped by rock salt have become reservoirs for natural gas. Some gas has been found in even higher layers of the North Sea rocks (see figure 10).

The main constituent of natural gas is methane ('marsh gas'). The other constituents vary considerably from one gas field to another. North Sea gas is on the average 90 to 95 per cent methane with about 4 per cent nitrogen, small amounts of more complex liquid hydrocarbons, and traces of benzene and sulphur compounds. There is also a considerable amount of water mixed in with the gas. All of the solids, and some of the water, are usually removed at the well-head and, before piping the gas ashore, other substances may be added to prevent hydrates from forming a scaly deposit inside the pipeline. As the gas passes towards the shore installations, liquids separate out and collect at low points in the pipe. Periodically these collections of impurities are swept away by sending spheres or other plugs, known in the business as 'Go-devils' or 'Pigs', along the pipe to push them out. After the removal of any remaining undesirable impurities, at the shore terminal, the gas is ready for conventional processing, distribution or storage.

The search for oil in the Gulf of Mexico has led to development of another mineral resource. Drilling down to a promising salt dome, the Humble Oil Company of the United States came across considerable quantities of sulphur in the limestone capping the dome. The deposit, which stretches over several hundred acres and varies in thickness from 220 to 425 feet, is the third largest in the United States. It lies under about 2,000 feet of sediments about seven miles seaward of Grand Isle, Louisiana. The sulphur is now being mined using a modified Frasch process. Dr Herman Frasch, a petroleum engineer, came to the aid of sulphur miners in the 1890s. The miners had found extensive terrestrial deposits of sulphur, but the lethal hydrogen sulphide gas found with the sulphur prevented it from being excavated. Frasch hit upon the idea of making use of the low melting

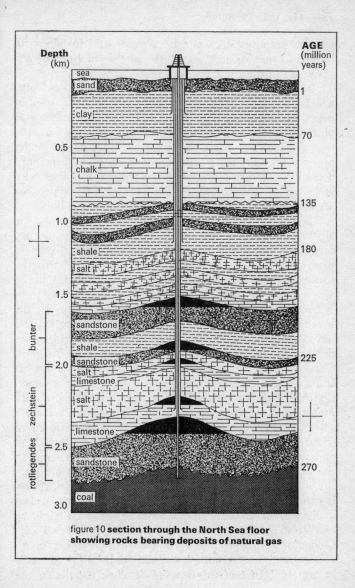

figure 10 **section through the North Sea floor showing rocks bearing deposits of natural gas**

point of sulphur. Why not, hé argued, send in hot water instead of men to melt and flush out the sulphur? By the early 1900s his process was a commercial success.

The secret of its success is a special 'three-in-one' pipe which is sunk down through the cap-rock into the sulphur deposit. The outer jacket of the pipe encloses another pipe of half its diameter which, in turn, surrounds an even smaller pipe. The outer sleeve carries water heated under pressure to about 330°F down to the bottom of the sulphur deposit. Some of the sulphur melts and, because it is twice as heavy as water, moves to the bottom of the pipe. The pressure behind the hot water tends to force the liquid up the middle sleeve of the pipe. The sulphur does not come all the way unaided, however, for to complete its journey compressed air is forced down the small central pipe to foam and hence lighten the sulphur and carry it to the surface. Here, the still-molten sulphur is separated from the air.

To exploit the sulphur deposit found by Humble, the Freeport Sulphur Company constructed the largest steel island ever built at sea. It cost some $30 million and houses drilling and production equipment, a power plant, heliport, offices, and sleeping and recreation quarters for 120 men. It is a self-contained community out at sea. From the island the molten sulphur is pumped ashore along a heated submerged pipe.

It is not a very large step in the imagination to move from the Frasch process to another for the recovery of oil and natural gas using underground explosions. Whereas in the Frasch process superheated steam under pressure frees the sulphur, the explosion would break up the rock releasing the trapped hydrocarbons so that they could be drawn to the surface. In other cases, the energy released might be used to extract oil from oil shale. In the Peceance Basin, Colorado, such a technique might yield anything up to 160,000,000,000 barrels of oil, assuming only half of the oil is recoverable! In fact the deposits of oil-rich shales in the

United States alone might provide yields equivalent to several 'Persian Gulfs'. Project Gasbuggy, the first American experiment using a nuclear explosion to release natural gas, took place in December 1967 when a 24-kiloton device was set off at a depth of 4,000 feet in New Mexico. The Russians are known to be experimenting with large charges of conventional explosives, along similar lines to those used by the United States.

Could these techniques be extended to the retrieval of minerals in the bed-rocks of the sea floor? It is tempting to hope so, but both the Frasch and the explosive processes rely on the fact that the end products will flow through a pipe. Of course solids can flow if they are suspended in some transporting fluid such as water. Such a mixture, known as slurry, can be made to flow along a pipeline providing that sufficient pressure is exerted on it to maintain flow and prevent any settling. In the case of slurries, such as finely crushed coal or clay, the liquid tends to buoy up the powdered solid and settling is not usually a problem; but most slurries, including those of metallic ores, quickly settle and block the pipe if they are not kept moving fast enough. The speed of flow needed to prevent settling depends, among other things, on the size of particles involved; whether ores would be pulverized sufficiently by, say, an underground explosion to allow them to be retrieved in a sea-water mixture is a matter of speculation. Of course, some minerals might be made to flow by dissolving them in acid, or even water.

In view of the almost science fiction nature of these proposals, the retrieval of minerals from the rocky strata beneath the sea is likely to remain restricted to the few deposits such as coastal veins or coal and iron ore which can be reached by sinking shafts from the land. These deposits will need to be surveyed from the sea; the British National Coal Board uses a special drilling rig to assess the coal deposits beneath the sea off the north-east coast of England. However, if man ever takes to living in underwater settlements, it would not be beyond his ingenuity to develop underwater mines. At first these might be 'open cast' ones where the minerals are scraped from the sea floor; later deep mines might be carved in the bedrocks.

Scraping a living

Even conservative estimates of the minerals lying on the deep ocean floor and the continental shelves involve quantities almost beyond comprehension. In many instances they are counted in terms of billions, trillions and, sometimes, quadrillions of tons. Dr John Mero, author of *Mineral Resources of the Sea*, has presented some astonishing estimates of the various minerals locked away in one type of deposit – manganese nodules – on the floor of the Pacific Ocean. According to him, the nodules hold enough aluminium to supply man for about 20,000 years, cobalt for 200,000 years, copper for 6,000 years, manganese for 400,000 years and zirconium for 100,000 years (as based on 1960 rates of consumption). In addition, the Pacific manganese nodules are estimated to contain some 207,000 million tons of iron, 113,000 million tons of lead, 25,000 million tons of magnesium, and so on. In fact, some of these metals appear to be accumulating faster than they could at present be used. And, these manganese nodules are not restricted to the Pacific – they are also found in the Atlantic and Indian Oceans.

As if these figures were not impressive enough, other even more extensive mineral deposits are found on the deep ocean floor. Calcareous and siliceous oozes and red clays are by far the most abundant sediments (clays hold less than 30 per cent organic remains and oozes contain more than 30 per cent of these remains). There are some 10,000 million million tons of calcareous oozes lying over some 128 million square kilometres. This ooze, which lies at depths up to about two and a half miles, consists largely of the skeletons of planktonic animals called foraminifera (mainly the species *Globigerina bulloides*). These microscopic animals have coiled shells not unlike those of a snail except that instead of a single foot they have long filamentous processes which extend from the sieve-like walls of the shell. If the ooze were mined, it would provide sufficient calcium carbonate for literally millions of years. The siliceous oozes also come from organisms in the plankton, but in this instance both animals, such as the radiolaria, and plants, such as the capsules of diatoms, contribute to them. The remains of diatoms which lived in prehistoric seas are already mined and used to make ceramics and linings for furnaces. Finally, the red clay, which also occurs in the deeper waters, may contain significant amounts of metals such as copper and aluminium as well as several of the rare earth elements. This red clay is all that remains after the calcium carbonate and less resistant substances have been leached out, but deposits of it probably equal the calcareous oozes in total quantity.

In spite of their abundance, neither red clay nor calcareous and siliceous oozes are being considered for exploitation; manganese nodules are claimed to be the ocean's nuggets, although the average depth at which they are found – about 13,000 feet in the Pacific – makes conventional dredging out of the question. Dr Mero suggests that giant dredges controlled from the surface could sweep up the nodules from the ocean floor. According to his calculations, these machines would cost some $4·8 million or more and the processing equipment would cost perhaps five times this. Undeterred by such costs, Dr Mero claims that a profit of around $17 a ton should be possible and that most of the industrially important minerals in the nodules could be made available at three quarters – or, in some cases, less than half – the cost of more conventional supplies. For example, satisfying the demand of American industry for nickel would result in the production of three times the managanese and five times the zirconium used in the country.

So far, companies scraping a living from the sea floor have restricted themselves to the more accessible deposits found on the continental shelf: most manganese nodules raised from the ocean floor still arrive at the surface in the oceanographers' grabs and dredges. In one case phosphorite nodules were successfully collected from concessions off the coast of California until other less welcome types of deposits were discovered: the area had been used as a range by the US Navy and live shells came up in the dredges. Very rich deposits of phosphorite exist beyond the continental shelf which, according to John Mero, should give an annual return on investment of around 40 per cent after paying all taxes!

Among the traditionally 'glamorous' minerals found in the shallow waters of the continental shelves are tin, gold and diamonds. Tin is dredged up off Thailand and Indonesia, for example, and the trail for gold is leading to areas offshore of Alaska. But it is the diamond mining operations off south-west Africa which have so far attracted popular attention. The first prospecting for the marine gems began in the early 1960s, and the initial finds were so promising that by 1964 the Marine Diamond Corporation, which had secured concessions in this area, estimated the potential yield at 13 million carats of diamonds worth well over $480 million. And this estimate did not include possible deposits outside the three-mile limit or the surf zone above the low-water mark. Nevertheless, subsequent operations have not always been as successful as anticipated and the corporation was far from flourishing three years later when de Beers, the South African diamond company which already had an interest in the venture, took control. Since then, the sea-diamond operation has picked up considerably and become profitable once again.

On the whole, the materials taken from the sea floor are far more mundane than diamonds or gold. They are more commonly associated with building sites than jewellers' shops – sand, gravel, shells and limestone are all dredged

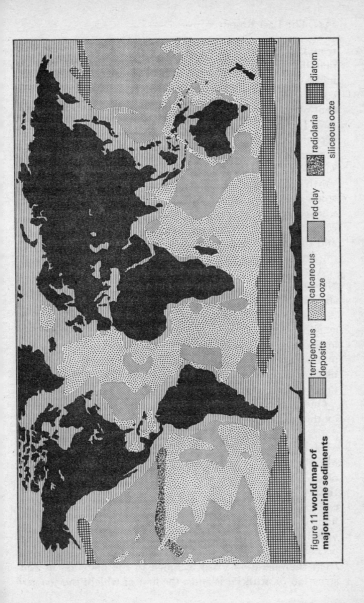

figure 11 **world map of major marine sediments**

terrigenous deposits
calcareous ooze
red clay
radiolaria
diatom
siliceous ooze

from the sea in shallow coastal regions. In the United Kingdom, for example, the gravel companies are turning increasingly to coastal marine deposits as those on the land become depleted or too expensive to work. By 1980 25 per cent of this country's gravel could be coming from the sea-bed. In the United States the value of gravel and sand accounts for 20 per cent or more of the total value of all non-metallic minerals, other than fuels. And of course some sands and gravels also contain other constituents which are worth extracting. The Japanese have been obtaining iron from gravel dredged up from the sea for many years; the iron can be separated magnetically, thus lending to the economy of the process. However, the low grade of the ore and the interference with the fisheries caused by the dredging are reducing the size of this industry.

Attention has now been turned to the 'black sands' of New Zealand, which stretch for hundreds of miles along the shores of North Island. Two million tons of iron-rich sand, worth $20 million will be shipped every year for ten years starting in 1972. The first sand from a site near Waverly was loaded aboard a bulk carrier in the summer of 1971. It is pumped aboard from a stockpile on the land as a thick black slurry via a 12-inch diameter steel pipe. The water is decanted off as the slurry builds up in the holds.

One of the largest underwater mining ventures could be in the Bahamas where one of the richest and purest deposits of aragonite – a calcium carbonate sand – was found over twenty years ago by scientists from the American Museum of Natural History. The deposits, with a potential of 50,000 million tons, were first exploited on a small scale in 1964, yielding only 159,000 tons. The present venture being carried out by Ocean Industries, a subsidiary of the Dillingham Corporation, aims to reach a rate of 12 million tons a year by 1973. By that time, the Bahamian Government expects to be earning more than $500,000 annually in royalties from the operation. Also included in the plans is the construction of artificial islands, the first of which, the 200-acre

Ocean Cay, was completed by May 1972. Title to the islands rests with the Bahamians although they will be leased to Ocean Industries as a base for mining, stockpiling and shipping operations. At the end of the programme, however, a valuable piece of real-estate will be available for development. Although the scheme has met some opposition from conservationist groups concerned about the health and vitality of the country's reefs, experience so far seems to support the conclusions of scientific surveys that 'there is no valid biological objection' to the project. According to reports, the removal of the aragonite sands and exposure of the rocky bottom has stimulated marine life in the Bimini area which has already yielded 2·5 million tons of aragonite.

Apart from their direct use in the construction industry, sand and gravel taken from the sea also play a part in land reclamation. Masters of this art are, of course, the Dutch who have devised several systems for raising sand and gravel by continuous dredging – either conventionally or by suction – and transporting it to the site selected for the new land. The important thing is to devise a system by which they can deposit material faster than the sea currents can sweep it away. Certainly the success of the Dutch in winning back a considerable area of land from the sea must have been at least partly responsible for the British decision to build a third airport on land reclaimed from the shallow Maplin sands at the mouth of the Thames. Dock facilities are also being considered in the scheme. Land reclamation often has the added benefits of deep-water channels created by the dredging operations; the new port of Rotterdam, Europoort, is a typical example.

The British Government announced the choice of Foulness as the site for the controversial third airport on 26 April 1971. The first runway is expected to be operational by 1980. Two large consortia have been formed to exploit the new development: the Thames Airport Group (TAG) and the Thames Estuary Development Company (Tedco). TAG is made up of 15 large operating companies, all of them engaged in design, development and civil engineering construction. It is also backed by the Netherlands organizations that masterminded the rebuilding of Rotterdam and the construction of Europoort. The rival consortium, Tedco, has been formed by John Howard, Mowlem, the Port of London Authority, Shell, RTZ and the Southend Corporation. With the aid of large hydraulic models covering the general area of the Maplin Sands, Tedco has studied the flow of water in the area and has investigated the relationship between the dredging needed for navigation channels and the infill needed to reclaim the land. Preliminary investigations indicate that the 75-foot depth needed for the approach channels would provide dredging spoil sufficient for at least a two-runway airport. The final plans for Foulness, however, envisage four runways so that other dredging will be needed. In its plans TAG proposes to provide a port with 2,000 hectares of water and 5,520 hectares of land. Both schemes which include a complex of airport, deep-water port, oil terminal and refinery, and industrial area present by far the largest dredging and land reclamation project ever considered in the United Kingdom. And, along with the necessary development of communications between London and this isolated part of the Thames Estuary, the Foulness proposal represents a major national scheme.

As in so many marine operations the decisive factor in dredging is the depth of the deposit. Extensive experience in depths that are shallow by sea standards has already been acquired among inland operations but, beyond this, knowledge is scanty and machinery for the deepest operations is still little more than an idea on the designer's drawing-board. In the shallowest workings a dredge armed with a continuous belt carrying scoops is quite adequate. These ladder-bucket dredges are, however, limited in the distance to which the ladder can extend and still scrape up and raise material. Beyond this, the hydraulic dredges come into their own; experience with suction dredges in inland waters suggests that they should be able to pump up loose gravel and sand from depths up to 200 feet. A third type of dredge – the air-lift dredge – has been used in the diamond operations off the west coast of Africa. This creates the necessary lift by feeding in compressed air about half-way up the tube which collects the gravel. The air froths up the contents of the tube making them less dense and causing them to rise to the surface and, providing the upper end of the tube is not too high above the surface, to flow out. The loss is made good by water and material rushing in at the bottom. Surprisingly enough, this system gives quite a substantial flow rate. Then, there is the wire-line dredge which consists essentially of a grab or dredge on the end of a stout wire line. It can be manipulated at any depth and, together with corers, is an essential part of the equipment used to collect samples of really deep sediments. However, the rate at which material can be gathered is obviously fairly limited since – unlike ladder, suction and air-lift dredges – the process is not continuous.

Finally, we move to those unborn monsters of the deep which will wrest the mineral deposits from the deepest oceans. Dr Mero has proposed that the equivalent of giant vacuum cleaners should work over the bottom. These deep-sea hydraulic dredges would remove a thin layer of material from the sea floor while disturbing the floor itself as little as possible. They would be operated remotely from the surface and, to help in this their path would be scanned by underwater television cameras. According to Dr Mero, this type of dredge could recover as much as 10,000 tons of nodules a day and would be able to operate in about 13,000 feet of water – the average depth of the nodules in the Pacific. For shallow depths, less than 4,000 feet, a deep sea wire-line dredge, based on the type used by oceanographers, might be economic. At present both approaches are being investigated in Japan and the United States. The most promising technique so far, however, seems to be the air-lift system being pioneered by Deepsea Ventures, a subsidiary of Tenneco Inc. The first experiments with what could be the scaled-down version of a deep-ocean dredge were carried out in July 1970, over Blake Plateau off the east coast of the United States. According to the company, the air-lift operated satisfactorily at a depth of 3,000 feet using a dredge head 16 foot square and a 'string' of 9-inch diameter piping connecting it to the surface ship.

The dissolved minerals

Only three chemicals are extracted from sea-water on a commercial scale: salt, bromine and magnesium. The history of taking salt from sea-water may go back as far as the Minoan culture, some 5,000 years ago. Many early civilizations – for example in India, the Middle East and South America – probably owed their existence and survival to an access to supplies of salt either in deposits of rock salt or in the sea. Today as much as a third of the world's production of salt still comes from the sea, the heat of the sun being used to evaporate the water just as was done thousands of years ago. The production of salt in this way also led to the extraction of magnesium from the sea in the 1930s, and today most of this metal comes from sea-water or brines. Magnesium is needed in a variety of industries including pharmaceutical, fertilizer and man-made fibre production, and it is also used in most light alloys used by the aerospace and other industries. Bromine too is becoming increasingly important in the photographic and pharmaceutical industries. But its greatest value for most of us is its use with the anti-knock compound, tetraethyl lead, in gas; without a bromide additive, which forms a volatile compound with lead, the motor car engine would become fouled up with inorganic deposits from the leaded fuel.

The influence of salt in social and marine affairs has been

felt since early times. It was a source of trade which sent merchant vessels across the oceans; it was a prize which brought Norse and Arab invaders to centres of its production in Western Europe; and it was an essential ingredient of a fish industry which contributed to the wealth of British and other European traders. According to the Domesday Book, the county of Essex was operating hundreds of salt pans, and the excavation of peat for salt production in eastern England left shallow pits which became flooded and today, as 'the Broads', are centres for sailing and other water sports. In early times the loss of salt-making capacity could bring repercussions in commerce throughout the continent, but today, with the working of rock salt and other deposits as well as extraction from sea-water, such shortages are unknown. Nevertheless, some disparity of supply still exists. For example, in the United States the per capita consumption of salt is 280 grams per day or about four times the world average, whereas the average consumption per person in Bengal is a mere five grams. In other words, some people can still be vulnerable to shortages of salt, particularly if they do not receive enough of it from other sources such as fresh meat.

In the previous chapter it was seen how the Japanese, lacking salt deposits of their own, turned to desalting sea-water. Normally, feats of chemical process engineering are not associated with the provision of salt, but they are definitely needed to extract both bromine and magnesium from the sea. Apart from anything else, these two chemicals are far less abundant than salt in the marine chemical 'soup'; sea-water contains 3.5 per cent salt, but only 0.13 per cent magnesium and even less, 0.0067 per cent, bromine. Because they are such 'lean ores' vast volumes of sea-water must pass through extraction plant to separate meaningful quantities of either chemical – and, weight for weight, bromine requires the processing of some twenty times as much water as magnesium. Figures like a million gallons of sea-water an hour for magnesium and more than twice this for bromine are typical quantities handled by extraction plants.

Prominent in the commercial exploitation of the oceans' bromine and magnesium is the Dow Chemical Company of the United States. Dr Herbert H. Dow, founder of the company, made possible the economic extraction of bromine from sea-water, and today the Ethyl-Dow Chemical Company at Freeport, Texas, has the largest bromine-extraction plant in the world. Other companies in the United Kingdom and France use the Dow process under licence. The process is essentially simple and consists of freeing the bromine from the sea-water by acidifying it with sulphuric acid and then chlorinating it. Sea-water treated this way is passed down a tower against a current of air which blows out the bromine. The bromine and water-vapour mixture is reacted with sulphur dioxide to yield hydrobromic and sulphuric acids. The mixture is then treated with chlorine and steam. The free bromine from this is collected and condensed while the recovered sulphuric acid and hydrochloric acid from the steam and chlorine treatment are used to process more incoming sea-water. In the case of the Dow process the bromine is purified and reacted with the organic compound ethylene to give ethylene dibromide (see figure 12).

The Dow plant for the extraction of magnesium, also set up at Freeport, starts from two raw materials – sea-water and oyster shells mined from the floor of the Gulf of Mexico. The shells are burnt to produce lime which is added to the sea-water in giant settling tanks where a deposit of insoluble magnesium hydroxide slowly collects. Hydrochloric acid is added to this slurry to produce magnesium chloride, which is extracted and dried. The magnesium is finally separated from the chlorine by electrical means and is made up into ingots, while the chlorine is converted to hydrochloric acid and returned once more to the start of the cycle (see figure 13). In other systems of

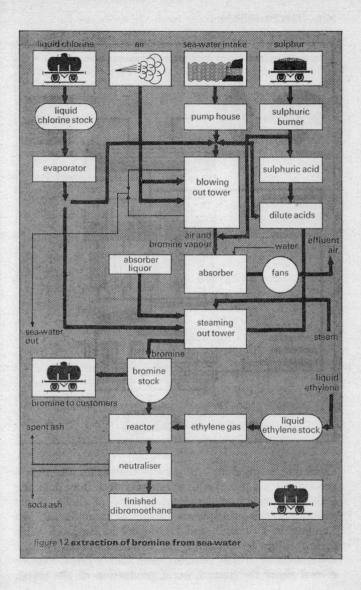

figure 12 **extraction of bromine from sea-water**

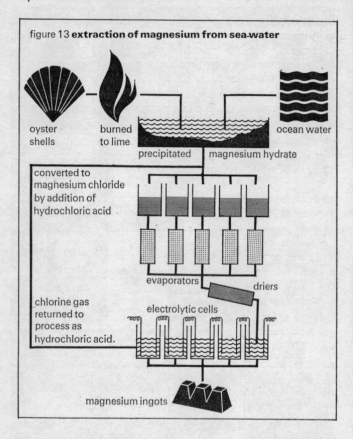

figure 13 **extraction of magnesium from sea-water**

oyster shells — burned to lime

ocean water

precipitated   magnesium hydrate

converted to magnesium chloride by addition of hydrochloric acid

evaporators

driers

chlorine gas returned to process as hydrochloric acid.

electrolytic cells

magnesium ingots

extracting magnesium – usually as the oxide, magnesia – the sea-water is mixed with a lime produced from dolomite (calcium magnesium carbonate) instead of shells. Plants working on this principle are found, for example, at Moss Landing in California and Hartlepool in England. With these facilities for extracting magnesium from sea-water, a cubic mile of which contains over four million tons or several times the annual world production of the metal, future supplies are assured and there seems no need to look for further sources on the land.

So much for the chemicals already taken in large quantities from sea-water; are there any others that might be extracted in the future? As mentioned at the beginning of this chapter, the Germans did at one time consider removing gold from sea-water. In fact the brilliant German chemist and Nobel laureate Dr Fritz Haber devoted some ten years to the problem. He finally concluded that the amounts of the metal dissolved in sea-water – a millionth of a gram per cubic metre – were generally well below previous estimates and the project was abandoned. In fact 0·09 milligrams of gold, obtained by Dow by processing about 15 tons of sea-water, probably represents the bulk of the metal taken from the ocean. With a value counted in millionths of dollars, it is unlikely that the process will be promoted! However, another metal – uranium – found in traces, albeit a thousand times greater than gold, may be worth extracting in the more distant future. Everything depends on how the price of uranium moves; at present it would cost more to extract it from sea-water than to use as yet unexploited low-grade ores on the land. Of course, the process may become competitive with further research, but at the worst according to one British expert, N. J. Keen, the cost of extracting uranium from the sea sets an upper limit to the price that could be demanded for uranium when low-grade resources are exploited.

The British investigations began several years ago when uranium was in great demand. Various chemicals and resins were tested and developed for their ability to absorb the uranium, present as a complex compound in the sea-water. One resin developed at the then National Chemical Laboratory (now part of the National Physical Laboratory) actually achieved an extraction rate of one gram of the uranium salt per gram of dry resin. Unfortunately, the resin's performance fell off rapidly as it became contaminated with other constituents of the sea-water, and ultimately it was discarded in favour of titanium hydroxide – or more correctly hydrous titanium oxide. The discovery that titanium oxide could take up appreciable quantities of the uranium dissolved in sea-water led to prospective studies of how the chemical might be used on a large scale. United Kingdom Atomic Energy scientists devised a scheme involving a tidal lagoon lined with beds of small particles coated with a thin layer of titanium oxide. But before its completion, a world surplus of uranium developed and it was therefore decided to abandon the project.

More recently, it has become evident that the world's supplies of uranium will be under considerable pressure in the 1970s and the British work has been revived. Considerable effort is now being devoted to improving the preparation of the titanium oxide and to devising some kind of inert carrier which will give better absorption with less bulk. Instead of the previous bed concept, the absorbent material is being sandwiched between porous layers. In this way, a compact unit consisting of alternating layers of absorbent and support materials could be built, rather than using trays of absorbent material spread out over the floor of what amounts to virtually the open sea.

One exciting discovery involving dissolved minerals is that in certain places geological processes within the Earth's crust lead to the accumulation of mineral-rich brines. Underwater pools of highly saline water have been found lying in the deeps of the Red Sea. Isotope studies show that the brine, though not the minerals, originates from the Red Sea itself. The largest brine pool, which is 7.5 by 3 miles in size, is thought to lie in the remains of three successive volcanic craters. The theory is that fissures formed in the seabed have provided pathways for the descent of sea-water and then the ascent of hot ore solutions. Although the pools have a temperature of 40°C or more, their density prevents them from rising and mixing with the water above. In this way, each pool provides a discrete body of minerals, including iron, manganese, copper, zinc, silver and gold. The value of the Red Sea finds, which involve an estimated 130 million tons of minerals, has been put at $1·5 billion or more. The problem is that the deposits lie at 6,000-foot depths. Similar hot brines may be found in other areas where recent and active rifts exist.

Finally, no section on the removal of chemicals from sea-water would be complete without mention of the living chemical factories within the marine environment; many marine animals and plants have the ability to concentrate certain elements within their tissues. Many of the chemicals involved – copper, iron and vanadium – play some important role in the life processes of these creatures. For example, the lobster needs copper in its blood just as we need iron in ours. However, the role of some chemicals commonly accumulated is not always so certain, and occasionally chemicals must be collected as a result of the way of life of an animal or plant. This is particularly true of the accumulation of pesticides in shellfish. Although the concentration of various chemicals involved can be remarkably high – some 'sea squirts' (sac-like sedentary animals) can build up stores of vanadium 280,000 times as concentrated as those in the surrounding sea – it is very improbable that such creatures could be used directly as means of collecting minerals from the sea.

However, it is worth remembering that some less extra-ordinary chemicals accumulated by marine animals and plants can prove useful. In the past seaweeds were the major source of iodine, and shell deposits built up by millions upon millions of molluscs are still an important source of calcium carbonate in some areas. Pearls which are produced by layers of mother-of-pearl or nacre coated by some molluscs on irritants inside their shells are another example of commercially important mineral processing by marine animals. Originally pearls resulted from the accidental introduction of sand or similar particles into the fleshy mantle of oysters and other shellfish, but now most pearls are artificially cultivated. A small bead of nacre is surgically introduced into the mantle of the pearl oyster along with a small square of nacre-secreting membrane. At present Japan and Australia are the major producers of such cultured pearls, which take anything from seven to ten years to develop. However, Ceylon may be an important newcomer. According to experts, the pearls found in the Gulf of Mannar are among the best in the world. What is more, the conditions are such that a commercial-sized cultured pearl would take only two or three years to develop.

Minerals in perspective

In 1965 the Shell Oil Company held a day-long conference in London on the rapidly expanding search for oil and natural gas in the British sector of the North Sea continental shelf. In the press kit supplied for the occasion were two small slips of paper containing some very significant information. One sheet, headed 'Hard Facts for Winners', explained that the discovery of oil or natural gas was only the beginning; to develop an oil field can take seven years and cost up to £35 million or £13,700 per day on top of the original outlay. The other sheet, entitled 'Hard Facts for Losers', pointed out that a company can spend from £3 million to £30 million on geological and geophysical surveys and drilling test-wells without deriving any income from the work. Even so, few companies opt out of the marine oil search so that new areas must be explored. A preliminary survey alone might cost some £3 million.

Three years after that conference, journalists were starting to report on the winners. In March 1968 a consortium of companies headed by Phillips Petroleum of the United States made the first commercial agreement with the British Gas Council on the price to be paid for natural gas from a North Sea field – at Hewett Bank, twenty miles off the east coast of England. Accompanied by a storm of protest from other consortia operating in the North Sea, the Phillips group agreed to accept 2·87 old pence per therm (the amount of heat generated by 100 cubic feet of North Sea gas) – a price some 18 per cent lower than that advocated by the other oil groups. In spite of the low price, Phillips, with an estimated outlay of about £25 million to develop the field, can probably expect an income of about £259 million over twenty-five years from 1969.

In the spring of 1970 the North Sea situation took a new twist when Phillips Petroleum discovered 'a giant oil field' in the Ekofisk structure in the Norwegian sector close by its boundary with the British one. The pay structure according to Phillips is approximately 700 feet and seismic information suggested a reservoir of about 40 square kilometres. This was the first commercial oil find in the North Sea although traces of oil had already been found elsewhere. Phillips' success caused a great deal of excitement among companies operating in the area and immediately sparked off a debate as to how the oil might be brought to the land and to which country: Ekofisk is approximately 185 miles from Norway to the north-east, 200 miles from Scotland to the west and 230 miles from Germany to the east. While this debate was still continuing, another factor entered into the situation: the discovery of an even larger field by British Petroleum in the British sector less than six months later. BP's find was followed in April 1971, by the discovery, this time by Shell–Esso, of yet another substantial commercial oil field in the UK sector about 60 miles off the Scottish coast.

In June 1972 an executive of BP, Mr M. M. Pennell, predicted that the North Sea could ultimately yield 20,000 million barrels of oil. The fields already discovered by this time could, he thought, produce about 4,000 million barrels. By the mid-1970s, crude oil production could reach 1·4 million barrels a day, with just over half coming from the UK sector. From the number of structures detected in seismic studies a production of up to 2 million barrels a day might be achieved by 1980. By this time North Sea oil would probably satisfy about 50 per cent of UK demand and some 15 per cent of the total needs of Western Europe as a whole. His forecasts were made the more interesting because a week earlier BP had announced the negotiation of a £360 million loan to finance the development of its Forties Field. Repayment of the money is to be spread over five years from the start of commercial production of oil, scheduled for the mid-1970s.

In the United States the petroleum industry has an investment of over $10,000 million in the exploitation of offshore oil and gas fields and a recent annual sales rate of over $700 million. On a world basis the takings from offshore drillings are probably more than four times this figure. In all, something like a hundred or more companies in sixty countries are involved in the search. This state of affairs results partly from a natural evolution of the exploitation of reserves in swampy coastal regions but mainly because the companies must tap every possible economic source of oil and natural gas to survive and to help satisfy the ever increasing world demand for energy. It is an industry where the profits can be big, but where the risks are correspondingly high. However, the cost of exploiting offshore oil and gas fields is probably modest in comparison with that anticipated for the development of deep-sea dredging. The collector itself, a bottom-crawling tractor capable of dredging a path twenty feet or so wide at a modest speed of two miles per hour, would cost some $600,000, while the 'vacuum cleaner' type of buoyant dredger might cost two or three times this. Then the nodules or other deposit has to be lifted to the surface and a hydraulic or air-lift system to do this might add another $1.9 million. Finally comes the expense of providing the surface terminal, some kind of ocean-going ship. The mining ship would have to be a fairly substantial vessel capable of withstanding heavy storms and seas and would need facilities for controlling and providing power for the dredges and lifting gear as well as some storage and processing plant for the dredged deposits. And yet, on paper at least, it is still possible to show a profit – though whether this will be true in practice remains to be seen.

The first real test of the profitability of deep-sea dredging may well come in the next few years – if Deepsea Ventures meet their objective of mining a million tons of nodules a year by 1974. At the time of writing the company was in the process of constructing a full scale dredging system after successful trials of the smaller scale prototype mentioned earlier. The trials on Blake Plateau cost $10,000 a day and the company has spent in the order of $20 million on manganese-nodule mining over a nine year period. Apart from the problem of raising the nodules from the depths of the ocean, the company has been investigating the best ways of separating out the major constituents – manganese, nickel, cobalt and metallic copper – and other metals such as zinc, cadmium and chromium which are present in much smaller quantities. Deepsea Ventures has built a pilot plant at their Gloucester Point headquarters capable of handling one ton of nodules per day and yielding pure metals of manganese, nickle, copper and cobalt. Using its research ship, it has located several sites in the Pacific suitable for exploitation, which the company's experts believe, would support 'Twenty-year mines'. This is equivalent to relatively level deposits of nodules over an area of about 1,000 square miles each, with concentrations in excess of 2·5 lb. per square foot boasting good nickel/copper assay, and yields in the range of one million pounds of nodules per year at the surface. The company is also confronted in its pioneering effort by questions of the ownership of deep ocean resources as well as the task of organizing an international consortium of companies that would commission and finance their marine mining operations.

According to a report prepared by the Battelle Memorial Institute at Columbus, Ohio, for the US Environmental Science Service (ESSA) in 1966, tentative attempts at commercial mining of phosphorite nodules may take place in perhaps ten years and of manganese nodules in ten to fifteen years. Certainly any temptation to dismiss the retrieval of minerals from the deep ocean floor should be resisted if for no other reason than the meteoric increase in the scale and investment of the oil industry in the marine sphere. After all, few people could have suspected twenty years ago that offshore drilling platforms would have become such a familiar feature in the oil and natural gas industries of the world.

The Battelle researchers point out that all production of minerals from continental shelf regions depends on the services of ESSA (now part of the National Oceanic and Atmospheric Administration): charts; tidal, current and coast pilot information; seismological, geomagnetic, gravity, hydographic, and oceanographic data; weather forecasts and warnings; and so on. They suggest a greatly expanded service is needed even now for the sand and gravel industry. For example, the removal of sand bars or similar natural obstacles to navigation could be accomplished by a co-operative effort between the neighbouring municipality or state, a local sand and gravel producer and the Federal Government. To aid mineral exploration, the report states 'there is a pressing need for charts of mineral showings at regular intervals on the continental shelf ... Once having the location of mineral showings, companies will depend on their own resources for detailed mapping and exploration.'

In the United Kingdom, Dr K. C. Dunham and other experts have reinforced the key role which government-aided exploration can play in encouraging the development of mineral resources. The ideal position would be if any company wishing to consider building up marine mineral operations could consult the results of surveys and geological maps of sea areas which are as detailed as those available for the land masses. The British Institute of Geological Sciences is at present engaged in creating a comprehensive picture of the continental shelf around the United Kingdom. Dr John S. Tooms of London University has made the point that an obvious place to start detailed mapping and surveying is where rich deposits of minerals are known to occur on the adjacent land. But this is only the start, and the plain fact is that more money must be spent on exploratory work if the mineral potential of the seas is to be realized. Of course, both British and American agencies are spending or considering investing large sums of money in marine science, but this expenditure is relatively small when compared with the money being lavished on improving geological knowledge of already well-prospected land areas.

Generally, the principal objection to exploiting seabed resources is that their content of valuable mineral, although enormous on a world scale, is not so great as deposits at present being worked on the land. But the final question must always be 'can a particular mineral be supplied more cheaply by turning to the sea?' And since the final cost depends on many factors other than the richness of the source, some surprising results can occur. The extraction of magnesium from sea-water is a case in point. The concentration of this mineral in sea-water is only 1/300 that of land deposits, but other technical reasons make its removal from sea-water more economic than mining the land deposits: the magnesium content of the sea is extremely uniform; the materials involved – sea-water and magnesium carbonate slurry – can be easily moved; and the process is more or less continuous. These three qualities all help to make the extraction process a candidate for automation – fresh 'lean ore' is brought continuously by tidal currents to the plant, the handling costs are very low and, finally, the end product builds up continuously to make distribution predictable and convenient.

Some scientists have suggested that the development of desalination on a grand scale might be another factor which could tip the scales in favour of extracting other dissolved minerals. They argue that the concentrated brine left after the removal of the fresh water could arrive at possible extraction plants already slightly warm, which might improve reactivity of its chemical content and which at a slight pressure would help in 'pushing' it through the plant. John Mero has worked out the possible yield if, in a few decades' time, there is a coastal population of some 100 million people each consuming 100,000 gallons of water annually for domestic and industrial purposes, all of which comes from the sea via a process about 25 per cent efficient. The volume of sea-water processed each year would contain a total of 6,400,000 million tons of salt, 240 million tons of magnesium, 160 million tons of sulphur, 800,000 tons of boron, 2,000 tons of aluminium and several hundred tons of manganese, copper and uranium. Mero even went on to note that, if the uranium and thorium could be recovered, they could probably provide the fuel for nuclear reactors which would generate the energy required by the conversion plant.

Attractive as this and similar proposals may be, they are still necessarily highly speculative and the techniques needed for extracting and processing so many different materials on such a scale will not be available for many years to come. In fact, disregarding the availability of such a plant, the necessary financial incentives even seriously to consider such grandiose schemes will not become real until the terrestrial resources of many of these materials have become seriously depleted. In the immediate future, we are left with the likelihood of a growing emphasis on resources such as sand, gravel, phosphorite and manganese nodules, and oil and natural gas within the continental shelf areas out to a depth of 200 metres. Nevertheless, those people willing to look beyond into the future and even past their own lifetimes can take some comfort in the vastness of the marine mineral store.

Chapter 5

Restless Energy

Waves, tides and currents more than any other feature have aroused man's curiosity about the oceans, and study of them led directly to the start of oceanography. Matthew Fontaine Maury's book, *The Physical Geography of the Sea,* published in 1855, set the style. The first chapter was devoted to the Gulf Stream. The first plate, a chart, included the results of 1,159,353 separate observations on the force and direction of the wind as well as some 100,000 barometric readings taken at sea. Maury realized that only by such painstaking recording of the physical face of the oceans could man ever hope to move safely over them and place them in his service. The modern oceanographer can call upon sophisticated instruments to provide data, and computers to process this information. Nevertheless, the primary object of his studies has changed little from Maury's day, for the physical influences of the ocean still have by far the greatest impact on life on the Earth.

It is no accident that many countries record their earliest involvement in the study of the oceans with the establishment of hydrographic and meteorological offices usually attached, at least initially, to the navy. These offices were responsible for collecting data on winds, waves and currents as well as charting the seas. It is also no accident that these establishments can frequently trace their origin back to Maury's attempts to organize a universally standard approach to collecting data at sea. In days when computers and automatic data logging were unknown, the only hope of accumulating sufficient detail about conditions over the oceans was to invite the cooperation of ships of all nations.

In return, each country received charts containing thousands of patiently recorded observations.

In the days of sail, a knowledge of likely wind conditions and currents was essential. This does not mean that fundamental studies of winds, waves and currents are any the less important in modern times: the re-routing of tankers and other commercial vessels to avoid adverse conditions out at sea can still save money, time and lives. The difference is that advances in obtaining, transmitting and processing relevant observations promise to replace a passive treatment of information accumulated over long periods. This can be done by active forecasting on a day-to-day basis, with oceanic buoys sending data via satellites and shore stations to meteorological centres.

The influence of the elements is not restricted to the distant oceans; on the shore, energy collected from winds blowing far away is being continually dissipated in surf and breaking waves. Typically, the ocean swell, as it arrives at the shore, releases something like 40 kilowatts of energy (the power of a family car) per yard of coastline. In some parts of the world, the release of energy at the water's edge assumes a much more dramatic and dangerous guise when, from time to time, huge crests of water rise many feet into the air to deliver a destructive force inherited miles away from some violent disruption of the ocean floor. More frequently, the coasts are subject to prolonged and powerful pounding from waves lashed into a fury by gale-force winds. Superimposed upon all this frantic activity comes the more regular pattern of the ebb and flow of the tides. Sometimes waves, wind and tide combine with disastrous results, as in January 1953 when serious flooding in eastern England and the Netherlands caused extensive damage to property and resulted in the death of 2,107 people.

Fortunately, the oceans do not always expend their energy in such aimless and destructive ways. French engineers, for example, have built a tidal power station which diverts some of it to man's use. Every day the tides turn generators set into the dam of the tidal power station, feeding electricity into the national power grid. Sites suitable for tidal power stations exist elsewhere but more immediate attention is likely to be devoted to the disruptive elements of ocean energy than its beneficial ones. In this sense, it may seem something of a 'negative' resource. Nevertheless, intimately involved in all this activity is the important work of distributing the energy arriving from the Sun (as well as heat from the Earth's mantle) and in this way maintaining the largely equable climate of the entire world.

Waves in action

Early on the morning of 28 March 1946, waves over fifty feet high carried out a sudden onslaught on Honolulu, smashing hundreds of buildings and tearing up roads and railway tracks. One hundred and seventy-three people were killed, and about $25 million damage was done. The energy for these monster waves had been generated by an earthquake in the Aleutian Trench and the seismic sea waves, or *tsunami* as they are generally called, had taken a mere 4 hours and 34 minutes to cover more than 2,000 miles of intervening ocean. The report on the tsunami published by F. P. Shepard of the Scripps Institution of Oceanography was to lead to more detailed investigations of this freak phenomenon. Shepard himself had been forced to take refuge in a tree while the tsunami tore into his house.

Three kinds of geological event cause tsunamis: earthquakes where the seabed suddenly slumps or rises; submarine landslides; and finally submarine volcanic eruptions. Of these, earthquakes appear to be the most important. It is no accident, therefore, that tsunamis occur most frequently in the Pacific Ocean since the Pacific is practically encircled by zones of earthquake activity, many of them centred in submarine trenches which gash the deep ocean floor. Tsunamis also occur in the Indian Ocean and to a lesser extent in the Mediterranean. They are practically unknown in the Atlantic Ocean although a large tsunami followed the great Lisbon earthquake of 1755, adding further to the destruction.

The type of disturbance in the ocean floor which creates the tsunami also dictates the final form of the waves; if created by a slumping of the floor, the tsunami starts with a trough whereas a volcanic eruption creates a crest. At first it consists of a few simple waves, but as the tsunami progresses over the ocean its energy is spread over a train of long shallow waves with the highest waves bringing up the rear. When it moves into shallower waters, the reverse process occurs with energy being pushed into a successivly smaller volume of water. By the time it reaches the shoreline the waves extend down to the sea bottom and they can raise themselves to a height of 120 feet or more. The fact that the onslaught may start with a temporary retreat as a trough arrives and that successive waves may well increase in height only adds further to the terror.

Some of the danger can be removed from the situation by adequate warning of a tsunami's approach. When seismic events likely to generate such waves are detected, providing the centre of the disturbance is known, the likely arrival of the resulting tsunami can be calculated and warning broadcasts issued. An early warning system requires networks of seismographs to register the earth tremors and tide gauges to show any abnormal wave activity. After the Hawaiian tsunami of 1946, the United States Coast and Geodetic Survey set up such a system with headquarters appropriately enough in Honolulu. Japan has a local warning system tied in with that of the United States, and the Soviet Union has a local warning system for the Kamchatka Peninsula in Siberia. In addition to local warning systems, an international centre now exists to alert nations situated around the Pacific Basin.

Fortunately, serious tsunamis do not occur frequently and most people are far more familiar with the waves which beat unceasingly against the shore. In fact, the sound of the

surf and the cries of gulls are all most people need to pro-
voke memories of holidays by the sea. Although breaking
waves and surf result from the shallowing of the seabed as
the shoreline approaches, the energy driving them originates many miles away in the open ocean. Here prevailing
winds 'rubbing against the surface of the water' raise
ripples which, under the continuing supply of energy, build
up into waves. How big the waves finally become depends
upon the strength of the wind, the time for which the wind
blows and the extent of water over which the wind blows
without interruption, known as the 'fetch'. Probably one of
the highest waves recorded (112 feet), which struck the
United States Navy tanker *Ramapo* en route from Manila
to San Diego in 1933, occurred in a storm where the wind
had an unobstructed fetch of thousands of miles. However,
as the waves move away from the direct influence of the
winds that raised them, the crests become lower and the
waves more regular, resulting finally in the long low waves
of the oceanic swell. This can travel thousands of miles to
distant shores with very little loss of energy.

Because the swell originates out in the ocean, it is quite
independent of winds occurring in other areas. Nevertheless, local winds do influence the sea and can create wind
waves which help to determine the state of the sea. In 1808
a British admiral, Sir Francis Beaufort, devised a scale of
wind forces and, although he used as his yardstick the area
of sail which a fully rigged frigate of the period could carry,
the Beaufort Scale is still in everyday use. A list of descrip-
tions, approved by the World Meteorological Organization,
has been added so that wind forces can be estimated by
reference to the appearance of the sea:

Beaufort Scale	appearance of the sea	description	wind speed (knots)
0	like a mirror	calm	less than 1
1	ripples with appearance of scales but no foam crests	light air	1–3

Beaufort Scale	appearance of the sea	description	wind speed (knots)
2	small wavelets, short but pronounced; crests have a glassy appearance but do not break	light breeze	4–6
3	larger wavelets, crests begin to break. Foam of glassy appearance. Perhaps scattered white horses	gentle breeze	7–10
4	small waves, becoming larger; fairly frequent white horses	moderate breeze	11–16
5	moderate waves, taking a more pronounced long form; many white horses (chance of some spray)	fresh breeze	17–21
6	large waves; white foam crests are more extensive everywhere (probably some spray)	strong wind	22–27
7	sea heaps up and white foam from breaking waves begins to be blown in streaks along direction of wind	moderate gale	28–33
8	moderately high waves of greater length; edges of crests break into spindrift; the foam is blown in well-marked streaks along direction of wind	fresh gale	34–40
9	high waves; dense streaks of foam along direction of wind, crests of waves begin to topple and roll over; spray may affect visibility	strong gale	41–47
10	very high waves with overhanging crests; resulting foam, in great patches, is blown in dense white streaks along direction of wind; whole surface of sea takes on a white appearance; rolling of sea becomes heavy and shock-like; visibility affected	whole gale	48–56

Beaufort Scale	appearance of the sea	description	wind speed (knots)
11	exceptionally high waves; sea completely covered with long white patches of foam lying in direction of wind; everywhere edges of wave crests blown into froth; visibility affected	storm	57–65
12	air filled with foam and spray; sea white with driving spray; visibility seriously affected	hurricane	more than 65

Away from the direct influence of the wind, the slow undulation of the swell is the nearest that the ocean comes to providing the classic wave forms of physics. The swell advances steadily – at an average speed of 35 m.p.h. in the Pacific and slightly less in the Atlantic – and can cover tremendous distances; California scientists traced a swell arriving on the west coast to a source near New Zealand, more than 8,000 miles or about one third of the Earth's circumference away. Only the shape of the wave travels; the water particles progress very slowly indeed, moving in vertical orbits with diameters corresponding to the wavelength – the distance between successive crests. A cork floating on the water traces out this 'orbit' as it moves up the slope of an approaching wave and round and down its back into the following trough. The movement of the water particles also extends down below the surface although the diameter of the orbits descreases rapidly, halving with each descent of one ninth of the wavelength. At a depth of half a wavelength the displacement of water particles is only 4 per cent that at the surface – a fact which goes some way towards explaining how submarines can escape the most violent seas.

Once the wave train arrives in the shallower coastal areas where the depth of water is less than half the wavelength, the 'drag' of the sea floor starts to have a significant effect on the behaviour of the waves. They slow down and the following crests crowd in behind, pushing more energy into a smaller volume of water just as in the case of the breaking tsunami. The circular orbits of the water particles are squeezed into a tilted ellipse, creating a peak on the wave. This peak, still travelling fast, tends to curve over and finally, unsupported, it crashes down; the wave has broken. As a general rule a wave breaks where the depth of the bottom is 1·3 times its height, but if the waves are already steep on arriving near the shore, they may break fairly soon after 'feeling bottom'. These steeper waves do not plunge over, but spill along their crests, steadily losing height as they come towards the shore. Spilling waves also occur where the bottom slopes gently up towards the shore.

The slightest irregularity in the sea floor influences the path of incoming waves. Occasional identical breaches in breakwaters have been traced back to sea floor structures many miles out to sea, which have focused the energy of a swell coming from an unusual direction on to this part of the breakwater. Knowledge of this process of refraction by which the incoming waves are turned according to the contours of the sea floor is an important factor in both coastal erosion and the transport of material along the shore. During the Second World War the system was used in reverse: by studying aerial photographs of the refraction of waves along enemy coastlines, scientists were able to determine the underwater topography in preparation for amphibious assaults.

The energy brought to bear on the shore by breaking waves is tremendous. At Tillamook Rock, Oregon, which suffers frequent storms, the lighthouse beacon has to be protected by a heavy steel grating from flying rock – and this beacon stands 139 feet above low water! One frequently quoted story about the destructive energy of the sea concerns the breakwater at Wick in Scotland. During storms in December 1872, the designer of the breakwater was amazed to see this massive structure weighing some

1,350 tons moved bodily into the anchorage it was supposed to protect. He rebuilt the breakwater making it twice as heavy, but five years later this improved design suffered a similar fate from waves which must have been exerting a pressure of some 6,340 pounds per square foot! But violent storm waves are not the only ones with influence on the coast. At Covehithe on the east coast of England for example, the land is being eroded slowly but steadily at a rate of about 17 feet a year by wave action.

Many shorelines remain apparently unchanged because equilibrium has been reached between destructive and reconstructive forces. Therefore the removal of, say, gravel or the incorrect siting of a breakwater can have far-reaching consequences. In 1897 in the little Devon village of Hallsands in south-west England, dredging was begun off-shore to provide shingle for harbour works at Plymouth. By 1902, in spite of constant protests, some 650,000 tons had been removed. The removal of this material interfered with the maintenance of the beach, lowering it by 12 feet. Dredging was stopped, but storm waves were already attacking the village. Two years later the beach was 19 feet below its former level of the old sea walls which waves had now destroyed. A dozen houses were lost, but a new sea wall was built. Between 25 and 27 January 1917, north-easterly gales coinciding with spring tides severely damaged 24 of 25 habitable houses remaining in the village.

The discussion so far has been couched solely in terms of simple waves, but while this suffices to explain the basic processes, it is completely inadequate as a description of the state of the sea. There is no such thing as a simple ocean wave: waves are the product of many different interacting forces (see figure 14). To sort out the resulting confusion, the scientist has to fall back on statistical analysis which requires vast amounts of information. Various instruments, such as the ship-borne wave recorder developed at the National Institute of Oceanography, now exist for collecting the necessary data, but even so the complex surface

figure 14 **numerous wave systems add up to produce the surface features of the sea**

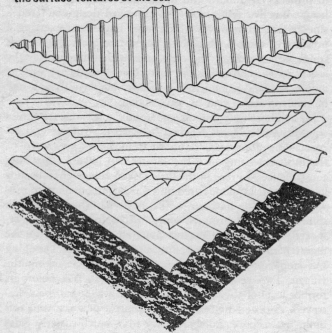

interactions which they record still defy complete explanation. Fortunately enough is known to provide a basis for improvements in ship design (see Chapter 7) and also to help in forecasting oceanic conditions.

Wave prediction based on meteorological forecasts has already yielded some promising results in the North Atlantic and North Pacific Oceans. Forecasts of the likely state of the sea in terms of both weather and waves enable commercial ships to avoid conditions which might cause delay and damage. And as ship operators come to realize the commercial benefits to be derived from these forecasts, forward planning of ship routes is likely to become increasingly important. Some indication of what modern computational and forecasting methods have to offer was demonstrated by the victory of Geoffrey Williams in the 1968 *Observer* single-handed transatlantic boat race. Sailing the yacht *Sir Thomas Lipton*, Williams was guided on his 3,000-mile journey by daily computer forecasts. In one case, at least, the computer correctly sent him in an entirely different direction from the one which he would have taken left to his own devices.

Although Williams found himself becalmed from time to time, there is no record of the *Sir Thomas Lipton* finding itself lying in 'dead water': an effect which gives the sensation of the boat being 'stuck'. It results from the presence of internal waves near the surface, moving in a direction which cancels out the force of any light wind. As yet the generation and distribution of internal waves are only poorly understood. In general, they are found running along the boundary between layers of water with different densities. They progress very slowly and the water particles in the upper layer travel in the opposite direction to those below. In these days of powered craft which can soon shake off the 'grip' of internal waves, surface waves present the major problem. If submarine transport becomes increasingly common, internal waves which can occur at any depth might become more troublesome.

Tides and tidal power

The tides owe their existence to forces generated beyond the Earth – the attraction of the ocean waters by the Sun and the Moon. Of the two, the Moon plays the major part, pulling the nearest water towards it and permitting that farthest away to bulge out from the surface. The result is two bulges of water on opposite sides of the Earth which move round in pursuit of the apparently encircling Moon, causing two tides every lunar day of 24 hours 50 minutes. The Sun also stirs up two tides a day – semi-diurnal tides –

but this time to fit in with the solar day of 24 hours. However, it exerts less than half the tidal force of the Moon. When these two heavenly bodies act together as at new and full moon positions, they cause the greatest tidal range – the spring tide – and when they are at right angles to one another, their forces tend to cancel out giving the smallest tidal range – the neap tides (see figure 15).

Although this movement of the spheres explains the existence of the tides, other factors are also involved. The forces brought into play by the Sun and Moon are extraordinarily slight, and even when acting together would explain tides of only about two feet. In 1774 the French mathematician Pierre Simon Laplace (1749–1827) added to the theory of hydrodynamics – the science of fluids. He

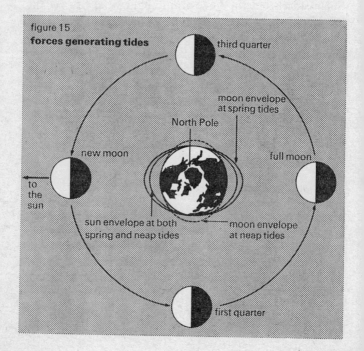

figure 15
forces generating tides

showed that although the Sun and Moon were the driving forces, the behaviour of the liquid masses themselves was also important. The tides could be compared with a child's swing to which the attraction of the Sun and the Moon gives two little pushes every day to maintain its motion. Of course the nature of the 'shove' from outer space varies with the relative positions of the Sun, Moon and Earth.

Superimposed on the basic pattern of the astronomical forces are the complicating factors on the Earth itself. For example, the shape of the ocean basins, the presence of the prevailing winds and the land masses which separate the major oceans all play a part in determining the tide. The tidal range in the open ocean, for example, is only a few feet and in enclosed areas such as the Black Sea it is reduced to nothing more than three to four inches. In contrast to this, the tidal range in the Severn Estuary in western England is more than forty feet because the shape of the estuary funnels the tide into a rapidly decreasing volume. In fact the only escape for the highest spring tide is by pushing up the river – a wall-like front of surf, known as a bore, advances inland as far as Gloucester.

Any mass of water, whether in a bathtub or an ocean basin, has its own 'natural period' at which waves created by some disturbances such as storms will run back and forth; they resonate. The period of the North Sea from the northwest direction, for example, is 35 to 40 hours. The effect is particularly noticeable in lakes – the period of Lake Erie is 14 hours. This kind of fluctuation is called the *seiche* after the French–Swiss name for the rise and fall noticed on the banks of Lake Geneva which has a period of $1\frac{1}{4}$ hours. Seiches have nothing to do with astronomical tides, although occasionally seiches can have a similar period, as in the Bay of Fundy, thus enhancing the tidal range. When such extra-high tides occur, they are known as resonance tides. Therefore seiches can be yet another complication to the study of tides.

Obviously, untangling all the components which make up

the tide as recorded by tidal gauges and similar instruments is not easy. A marigram – the record of the tide – is not a smooth line tracing the rise and fall of the water but has numerous little fluctuations. Working from the observed tide, the scientist can, using a technique called harmonic analysis, separate the various 'simple waves' that have combined to produce this complex recording. With this kind of information and accurate details of planetary movements, a model or analogue machine can be built to compute future tides. In this way the tide tables so essential to shipping and modern ports, as well as seaside holiday resorts, can be worked out a year or so in advance. Clearly, the more tidal components allowed for in the machine, the more accurate the predictions. One tide-predicting machine at the Institute of Coastal Oceanography and Tides, Liverpool, can allow for more than forty different tidal factors. With such machines the tides for the year at any one place can be worked out within hours.

Because the tides are astronomical in origin, and other influences such as the shape of the coast and the depth of the water do not generally change rapidly, the predictions can be very accurate providing no 'unpredictable' forces take a hand. Unfortunately, as any Englishman knows, the weather has that unpredictable quality. When an exceptionally high wind blows consistently over large stretches of shallow sea bordering on an ocean, it causes the water to pile up, producing a storm surge. If this surge coincides with high spring tides, the increase in height can be disastrous with high waves breaching coastal defences. A strong wind has this effect in shallow areas because the seabed prevents the waves from 'escaping' the wind which generates them so that it continues adding energy to the water. In the North Sea, storm surges born in the northern part sweep down in a counter clockwise motion, striking the east coast of England first and then sweeping round to Western Europe and the Netherlands in particular. One of the most notable surges, which led to the disastrous flooding in January 1953,

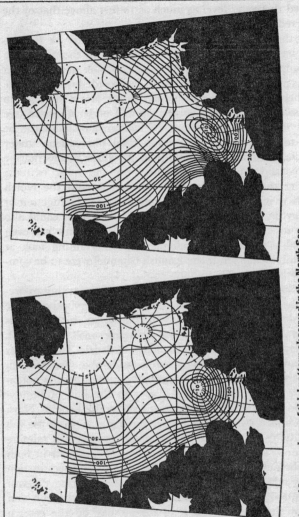

figure 16 comparison of tidal pattern observed in the North Sea with one generated by Dr S. Ishiguro's electronic model

pushed the water level as much as 10 feet above that of the expected tide.

At the National Institute of Oceanography, Dr S. Ishiguro has built a unique electronic model of the North Sea to study these surges. With it he can look at past storm surges and analyses their features or, provided with accurate weather forecasts, he can predict future storm surges – in the 'analogue', a day is covered in well under a second (see figure 16). Equally important, Dr Ishiguro's machine can be used to analyse surges or other tidal phenomena under artificially manipulated conditions. By these means marine and coastal engineers can allow for the most extreme weather that is likely to occur in and around the North Sea. If they intended to make any extensive change out at sea, say, by constructing an artificial island, they could also check for any untoward side-effects. Dr Ishiguro has even been able to take an academic and entertaining look at what might happen if the English Channel were to be completely blocked off!

While scientists like Dr Ishiguro have been trying to prevent the worst effects of tidal and wind energy, others have been devising ways of building 'tidal traps' to make this energy available to man. In February 1968, Dr C. M. Isbister, chairman of the Canadian Atlantic Tidal Power Programming Board, reported 'considerable progress' in engineering and economic feasibility studies on the potential for the capture of tidal power in the Bay of Fundy. The Board established in August 1966 by the Federal, Nova Scotia and New Brunswick governments was given the job of studying the physical and economic prospects of tapping the Fundy's tides to provide electricity for markets in both Canada and the United States. The Canadian investigation is only one in a whole series centred on capturing the vast amounts of energy which run to waste with the ebb and flow of the tides in this long narrow bay on the eastern seaboard of North America. As early as 1920, the US Government considered a plan for a tidal power station at

Passamaquoddy Bay, an offshoot from the Bay of Fundy. The scheme came to nothing, although President Roosevelt revived it at the time of his 'New Deal' policy and the work reached a stage of employing as many as 5,000 men before being abandoned.

1920 seems to have been a good year for tidal power proposals; schemes were suggested almost simultaneously for the Severn Estuary in England, for the fjord of Aber Vrach in France, and, of course, for Passamaquoddy Bay. All these were duly considered by the governments of the day and turned down, although they have been cropping up from time to time ever since. Only the French managed to sustain a proposal for a tidal power station long enough to get it built. As a result, General de Gaulle proudly inaugurated the first tidal power station in the world in November 1966. It had been planned by a French engineer Robert Gibrat in 1942 during the German occupation.

The French power station, which straddles the Rance Estuary in northwest France, providing a direct road link between Dinard and St Malo, is designed to produce 240 megawatts of electricity – enough for a city of about 500,000 people. Receiving the direct force of the great Atlantic tidal wave, this coast enjoys remarkably regular tides. At the same time, the presence of the Contantin peninsula to the north and the funnelling effect of the estuary mouth give a tidal range during spring tides of 42 feet. At the height of the spring tide's flow, water comes rushing into the estuary at a rate of nearly four million gallons per second. Even so, the power station's output is only a small proportion of the 180,000 megawatts of energy thought to flow from the Atlantic into the English Channel and is almost insignificant with that of the world's tides – 1·5 million megawatts. In fact, as a result of this tidal friction, the Earth is gradually being slowed down, thus increasing the day length by a thousandth of a second every hundred years, and the Moon is moving very slowly farther away.

The key to tidal power is the range of the tide, for it is

this which creates the 'head' of water needed to turn the generators. The head can be built up in two ways in a dammed-off estuary or bay: the tide can be held back by the dam until it builds up high above the level inside the dam, or the water can enter freely through to the bay until high tide and then be held back behind the dam wall as the tide outside recedes before being passed through the turbines. With either method, water can be pumped to increase the working head – from behind the dam at low tide in the first method, or into the enclosed water at high tide in the second. In each case, the energy consumed by the pumps in this technical 'sleight of hand' is far less than that subsequently generated; for example water pumped behind the dam at high tide may be raised nine inches, but eventually this same water will fall many feet, generating power on the way.

Ideally both methods of operation should be used, but this would mean double of everything, with some turbines and pumps to handle the incoming tide and others for the outgoing water. The only alternative, using a one-way passage through the generators, is a complicated system of enclosures arranged in such a way that the water passes through the generator coming in, and is then cycled round so that it passes out in the same direction through the generator. Both systems are clearly expensive and even if the motive force – the tides – comes free, cost is still important. The breakthrough came when French engineers devised machines which could pump water either in or out and could generate power by allowing water to pass in either direction through them. Thus these 'bulb sets', as they are called because of their shape, can replace the four different machines needed for continuous operation of tidal power stations.

The Rance station has twenty-four bulb sets let into its dam wall. They allow the power engineers continually to ring the changes during the tidal cycle. It does not matter that because of the 50-minute difference between lunar and solar days the peak generating power of the tides can occur at off-peak times so far as demand for electricity is concerned. The choice of pumping, generating and passive flow can be made to give the best results whatever the state of the tide or the times. The choice is so great that a computer is needed to make the necessary calculations. Although the Rance power station has not been followed up by more ambitious plans, interested parties have visited it from the United Kingdom, the United States, Canada, Russia, Germany and Australia, and several laboratories in the United Kingdom are carrying out experiments on bulb sets for prospective tidal power stations.

Only about two dozen places in the world have the necessary tidal 'head of water' and the type of sites suitable for locating a dam. Of these no more than ten have been seriously considered. Obviously, from what has been said already in this section, the Severn Estuary has been a major contender for some time. It has been estimated that a tidal

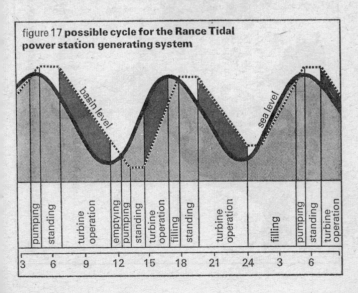

figure 17 **possible cycle for the Rance Tidal power station generating system**

figure 18 areas of the world with sufficient tidal range for power generation

power station set across the estuary from near Cardiff to the north and near Weston-super-Mare to the south could supply perhaps a twelfth of the United Kingdom's power, as well as provide an additional road link between Wales and south-west England.

The Russians will probably be the next to boast a large tidal station. Soviet engineers under Lev Bernstein have their eyes on the potential 16,000 megawatts of tidal energy thought to be available in the White Sea. A series of stations is planned for the Gulf of Mezen north-east of Arkhangelsk. In 1962 the Russians decided to construct a small (800 kilowatt) experimental station at Kislogubsky near Murmansk. The main body of the station was built away from the site and then the 5,400-ton structure was towed into position – a novel solution to the problem of erecting a power station in the harsh conditions of northern Russia. Building the main body of the station near an industrial centre and then floating it into position halved the construction costs. The experimental station was commissioned on New Year's Eve, 1968. Another interesting proposal is that a tidal power station should be built in north-western Australia at Collier Bay. Although the demand for electrical power is not very great in this sparsely populated area, it could provide fresh water by desalination for a very sizeable area of the arid north-western region. And then there is yet another suggestion for a tidal power station at Passamaquoddy.

A global influence

In 1947, the Norwegian scientist, Dr Thor Heyerdahl, set out with five companions from Callao in Peru aboard a raft named after a Polynesian sun god, the *Kon Tiki*. After 110 days of sailing and drifting they arrived at the Tuamotu islands east of Tahiti – a journey of 4,300 miles. The *Kon Tiki* was carried on its way partly by the wind but mainly by ocean currents, first the Peru (or Humboldt) Current running northwards by the west coast of South America and then the South Equatorial Current which sweeps westward across the Pacific Ocean. Unlike the waves in which energy travels the oceans, ocean currents involve the movement of countless millions of gallons of water. They are the circulatory system of the Earth and, like the human circulatory system, one of their most important roles is as a transport system: they carry heat and minerals as well as less desirable contaminants about the Earth.

The reason for Thor Heyerdahl's epic voyage was to show that Polynesia could have been colonized by pre-Inca Peruvians. It is difficult to see how these bold South Americans came to take this presumably 'one-way trip' on these currents, but some more recent navigators were certainly aware of the stronger ocean currents. The writings of Marco Polo include mention of the Agulhas Current off south-east Africa, for example. However, not until the times of Matthew Fontaine Maury was any real effort made to map all the surface currents on the Earth. These currents do not generally extend much more than a few hundred feet beneath the surface. Even the Gulf Stream, described by Maury as the mightiest of the ocean rivers, loses most of its force by about 1,200 feet, although a current of 1·5 knots has been recorded at 1,760 feet over Blake's Plateau on the eastern edge of the United States. Deep-ocean currents do exist but, apart from locally rapid movements, they seem slow and weak compared to their surface counterparts. For instance, water moves along the bottom of the Atlantic Ocean from north to south at an average speed of a thousandth of a knot compared with the Gulf Stream's surface speed of four to five knots.

In general, the surface currents form loops called gyres, each one almost the full width of the ocean. In the Northern Hemisphere there are two – one in the Atlantic and the other in the Pacific – rotating slowly in a clockwise direction. South of the equator there are three counterclockwise gyres – in the Atlantic, Indian and Pacific Oceans

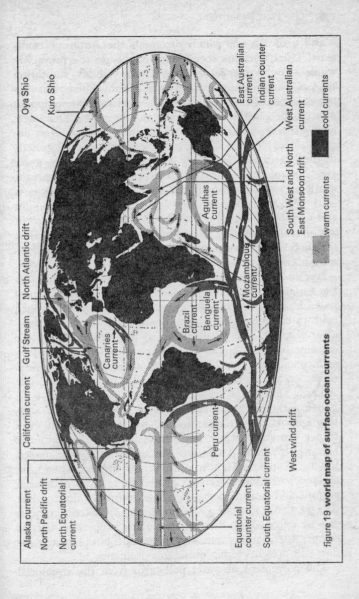

figure 19 **world map of surface ocean currents**

Alaska current
North Pacific drift
North Equatorial current

California current   Gulf Stream   North Atlantic drift

Oya Shio
Kuro Shio

East Australian current
Indian counter current

West Australian current

South West and North East Monsoon drift

cold currents

warm currents

Agulhas current

Brazil current

Benguela current

Mozambique current

Canaries current

Peru current

West wind drift

Equatorial counter current
South Equatorial current

– and a fourth one which surrounds the Antarctic continent. These currents correspond roughly to the prevailing winds – the Westerlies and the Trade Winds – indicating the part these wind systems play in creating them. They do not correspond exactly, because the Earth's rotation applies a force, the Coriolis force, on the moving water. This force, which increases with the distance from the Equator, deflects the currents to the right in the Northern Hemisphere, to the left in the Southern. Northern and southern gyres are separated by an Equatorial counter-current which runs in the opposite direction to the east–west flow of these parts of the gyres. In the equatorial region the winds are so light and variable that it is called the doldrums and the lack of any prevailing driving force permits water 'piled up' against the shores on the western sides of the oceans to flow back as a counter-current.

Not so much is known about the deep-ocean currents as the surface ones. According to one theoretical model, proposed by the American oceanographer Dr Henry Stommel, cold water found in the ocean depths arises from two principal sources – the Weddell Sea in the Antarctic and the extreme North Atlantic. The cold polar waters run, as deep counter-currents for the most part, along the western sides of the oceans, feeding water out eastwards as they go. The Atlantic Ocean has been the most intensely studied. Cold North Atlantic water can be traced as a distinct mass throughout the Atlantic Ocean, but in the south even colder Antarctic water lies beneath it. In the Southern Hemisphere both Arctic and Antarctic waters are topped by the Antarctic Intermediate Water formed when cold surface water meets warmer lighter water from equatorial regions and sinks beneath it. These and other deep waters like the dense salty water flowing out of the Mediterranean can be detected by their characteristic properties such as temperature, salinity and oxygen content; but plotting their flow still presents some formidable problems.

The movement of water polewards from the equatorial

regions is not a simple convection system with warm water spreading north and south from the equator, sinking at the poles and returning once more to the equator as bottom water. Nevertheless the Sun's heat still plays a prominent part in ocean circulation. Cold currents, such as the Peru, Benguela and West Australian Currents in the south and the Oya Shio, Labrador and East Greenland Currents in the north, move towards the equator to join in the gyres of water warmed by the greater solar heating in the tropics. At the same time warm currents, such as the Gulf Stream and the Kuro Shio in the north and the Agulhas, Brazil and East Australian Currents in the south, move towards the poles. In this way heat received from the Sun as well as that permeating through the ocean floor from inside the Earth is distributed over the planet.

If the Earth lived up to its name and had considerably more land than oceans, it would be an unbearable place with temperatures soaring during the day and dropping rapidly at night. The oceans can act as a global thermostat as a result of the remarkable physical properties of water. Water absorbs heat better than the land because the surface water can mix locally by convection, and it has a remarkable storage capacity packing away large quantities of heat with only slight increase in temperature. Once absorbed, this heat is not lost; the water radiates it slowly out to the atmosphere. One has only to consider the typically cool summers and mild winters of coastal regions to appreciate the moderating influence these properties of water can have on the climate.

The equable climate of Western Europe owes much to the influence of the Atlantic and that well-known ocean current, the Gulf Stream. The Gulf Stream starts in the Straits of Florida between Florida and Cuba and meanders north off the North American coast until it reaches Newfoundland, where it veers off towards Europe. On its transatlantic journey the current splits, sending a streak of warm water north past Scandinavia and other branches south past the Iberian Peninsula and Africa. Eventually currents which head south 'complete the circuit' of the North Atlantic gyre by reuniting with the Stream near the Bahamas. Within this circle lies the Sargasso Sea, an expanse of warm still water. The rapidly moving Gulf Stream forms a boundary which prevents the warm water from spreading over cold water from the north and north-west. The boundary is so abrupt that a ship crossing it may record a 20°F difference between readings at bow and stern. The Gulf Stream itself does not warm Western Europe. In the winter the wind blowing from the south-west passes over the encircled warm water bringing warm air to the European coast. As a result the average January temperature in Norway is 45° higher than the usual January temperature at that latitude. Without the heat stored in the Atlantic waters, Scandinavia might be as bleak and inhospitable as south-eastern Greenland, and Ireland might be like Labrador. They all lie on the same latitude. As a result of the Gulf Stream's branches penetrating north, the Arctic regions boast flowering plants at certain times of the year, whereas the Antarctic has none.

Ocean currents, because they can carry minerals and other nutrients needed by plankton, often have a direct influence on the fertility of the sea. In the Sargasso, which is practically devoid of movement, the surface waters support comparatively little life; they are the marine equivalent of a desert where only specialized animals and plants survive. But, where the sub-surface waters mix with those above, the plankton and the larger animals flourish. The mixing may occur when deep mineral-rich water meets with some sea floor obstruction which causes it to swell up at the surface. However, many important upwellings occur as a result of the interaction between winds and surface waters. As mentioned earlier, in Chapter 1, off the west coast of South America the surface water are pushed offshore by strong winds and cold fertile water rises from below to take its place. This continuous cycling of nutrient-rich water ensures an abundant supply of plankton which provides food for the tremendous shoals of anchovy that abound in the coastal waters.

Ocean currents and their effects are not always beneficial. This same region of South America also suffers because from time to time the wind fails to blow sufficiently to create the upwelling. This failure is often associated with the penetration into the region of a warm current called El Niño (Spanish for *the child*) because it arrives around Christmas time. The warm current, which is short of both nutrients and oxygen, forms a stifling, tepid surface layer causing the cold-water animals and plants to sicken and die on a fantastic scale. Dead and decaying fish litter the beaches. The decay may be so great that the water becomes completely deprived of oxygen and an evil-smelling gas, hydrogen sulphide, accumulates in its place. Traces of hydrogen sulphide present in city air are sufficient to darken lead-based paints and in the quantities found in this stagnant water it soon attacks the paintwork of ships. Sailors call this water the 'Callao painter'. The intrusion of El Niño as might be expected also brings climatic changes. The rainfall in March may be several hundred times that of a normal year, causing floods and serious erosion of the land, a further example of the relationship between currents and climate.

Fortunately, the failure of the Peruvian upwelling does not occur every year, but some currents do present continuous hazards of one kind or another. Typical of these are the Labrador and East Greenland Currents. Known as the ice currents, they sweep down from the Arctic bringing with them pack-ice and icebergs. It was an iceberg swept from the north by the Labrador Current which, on 11 April 1912, led to the loss of the *Titanic* and the death of 1,513 people. Nor is this the only menace, for where the cold waters of the Labrador Current meet the warm waters of the Gulf Stream just southeast of Newfoundland, dense fogs are created. Even with the presence of the twin hazards of fog and icebergs, it required the sinking of the *Titanic* to shock the maritime nations into organizing proper surveillance of the area. As a direct result of the disaster, the International Ice Patrol, based in Newfoundland, was formed to watch out for and report on ice movements, as well as to keep the shipping lanes free of other obstacles which might prove hazardous in fog. The ice generally becomes a serious menace in March, when the Arctic floes begin to break free from the grip of winter. The danger rarely persists beyond June or July.

Towards ocean forecasting

The International Ice Patrol operates its own survey vessels and aircraft as well as receiving reports from other ships of any dangerous ice. At regular intervals, surveys of the ice and its expected movements are given out over the radio. Since icebergs are always on the move – some have been known to travel thirty to forty miles per day – their distribution changes continually. The variability of the ocean currents themselves adds a further complication. In the previous section, they were referred to as distinct masses of water, which is largely true but, with no more than other water for boundaries, it is hardly surprising that numerous eddies break away from the parent current. The Gulf Stream which comes into contact with the 'ice currents' meanders as it progresses across the Atlantic, and from time to time loops become so exaggerated that they break away completely. Patches of cold water trapped in a detached eddy can last as long as six weeks, slowly drifting south. Every spring, therefore, the Ice Patrol has to study anew the detail of currents in the vicinity of Newfoundland, particularly over the shallow ocean area which fishermen know as the Grand Banks.

The area covered by the International Ice Patrol is small compared with the total world ocean, and yet even in this restricted area one sees just how variable apparently distinct phenomena such as currents can be. Plots of their paths on ocean maps generally record the average direction of a flow which may fluctuate appreciably from day to day. This variation over quite short spans of time is shown particularly clearly in records of deep ocean currents. Deep-water movements can be tracked in some detail by the use of underwater floats, sometimes called 'pingers', devised by Dr John Swallow of the British National Institute of Oceanography. The Swallow float can be made to stay at any specified depth, and, as it moves with the current, brief blips of sound emitted from it allow a surface vessel to plot its position – continuously, if necessary. Different flows in terms of both speed and direction have been detected with this technique at the same station within a period of days. Similarly, experiments with anchored instruments indicate that records taken over periods as long as a week can still be at variance with the 'average conditions' subsequently found to exist at their location.

Does this variability of the ocean environment place it beyond any kind of forecasting? Fortunately the answer must be a qualified 'no'. Although the inner world of the ocean fluctuates far more than had been imagined in the past, the face it presents to the atmosphere is far more predictable if still barely better understood. As far as the weather is concerned, the oceans have some advantages over the land. For a start, they are flatter. Secondly, the heat capacity of the water means that the temperature is the same over large areas and, even when it changes, it does so slowly. Such features are highly desirable from the weather forecaster's point of view; an embryo storm born at sea grows to maturity in a fairly predictable way, which in turn makes related forecasts of conditions such as the state of the sea much more acute.

The major obstacle to ocean forecasting is the need for information from an area well beyond the scope of conventional surface vessels. Of course, weather and commercial ships supply considerable detail on marine meteorological conditions. British weather ships, for example, make hourly observations at the surface and slightly less frequent surveys of the upper atmosphere. Their information, coded and radioed direct to the Central Forecasting Office at Bracknell in Berkshire, is used along with that from other sources such as ground-based stations, to construct a weather map of both surface and upper air conditions. On the basis of this synoptic map, weather forecasts are issued to shipping, aviation and, of course, the general public. Within its limits, this system works very well; however, on an international scale large tracts of ocean well away from customary shipping lanes can go unobserved. And the question arises, how can over 70 per cent of the Earth's surface be kept under constant meteorological surveillance?

A few years ago the answer to such a question would have been one of despair. Then, in March 1966, an American weather satellite *Essa 2* went into operation, regularly transmitting pictures of the weather over thousands of square miles, from a height of 750 miles above the Earth's surface, to weather centres. Depending on the orbit, most or all of the Earth's surface can be monitored by a satellite. Using information from *Essa 2*, the British Antarctic Survey route their vessels to avoid southern polar pack ice, for example. However, some of the information essential in the formulation of weather and related forecasts, such as waves and swell, must be collected at ocean level. Such extensive observation of the oceans is probably only feasible using large arrays of automatic buoys. Ocean buoys such as the Long Range Telemetering Buoy, developed by the Convair Division of General Dynamics in the United States, probably indicate the shape of things to come. The discus-shaped buoy, 40 feet in diameter, 7 feet thick and topped by a 40-foot aerial, has the ability to weather 60-foot waves, 10-knot currents and 150-knot winds – all while floating on the surface and anchored in depths exceeding 20,000 feet. The buoy can store a year's data in a special memory unit, but a temporary memory enables the buoy to be interrogated by radio signals from over thousands of miles every few hours.

With satellites and arrays of electronically equipped buoys, it is not difficult to envisage a global coverage of ocean conditions – communication satellites can pick up and re-transmit data from the more remote buoys. However, it would be folly to progress too far in this adventure of the imagination without confessing inadequate understanding of the ocean/air interaction. Certainly, one of the first tasks of the arrays of buoys now being established in various parts of the world is to help in the further investigation of the link between the slowly altering climate of inner space and the sometimes fleeting but nevertheless important changes of weather in the atmosphere above. If marine and meteorological scientists can 'crack the code', it may one day be possible to make long-range weather forecasts by observing the much more sluggish behaviour of the sea. Apart from the value of improved forecasts to man's pursuits on the land, they will improve the exploitation of the ocean resource, assisting with such things as the routing of freighters, the deployment of fishing fleets and the prevention of damage to offshore installations. As it is, the improved coverage of ocean and terrestrial conditions is already helping in shorter-term weather forecasting.

Chapter 6

Entry into Inner Space

To exploit the ocean resources more freely, man must be able to enter the alien world of inner space. It is something of a paradox that such a successful land animal should need to grapple with the problem of returning to what was probably the cradle of life on the Earth. Of course, other mammals, notably the whale, have remade their home in the sea. They have gained their underwater freedom via the long slow process of evolutionary change over countless generations. Man, however, must make his debut leaning heavily on the crutch of technology with advanced diving systems, small submarines and machine proxies. Initially, the goal is to bring the entire continental shelf regions of the world within easy reach. These regions, extending down to a depth of 600 feet, are already subject to some commercial exploitation and therefore the prospective gains are not too difficult to envisage. But the continental shelf accounts for less than 10 per cent of the seabed and ocean floor and, ultimately, man will seek to conquer the entire realm of inner space.

The United Kingdom has on its very doorstep a submerged land mass, the continental shelf, which is equivalent to three times the nation's surface area. The continental shelf of the United States – about one third the present land area – stretches over an area of about 860,000 square miles and already provides significant benefits. In terms of oil alone, offshore operations provide almost 9 per cent of the dollar value of US petroleum production, and federal royalties from the production of oil, gas and sulphur from the outer continental shelf amounted to more than

$700 million in 1967. The British Government has been a little slower in realizing the value of its marine assets, but the discovery of natural gas and oil reserves on the continental shelf beneath the North Sea promises to have a lasting beneficial effect on the country's economy, if not, according to some authorities, its energy policy. According to estimates, the country's balance of payments will benefit, from these indigenous energy stores, by well over £1 million in the mid 1970s.

The offshore search for oil and natural gas and the subsequent exploitation of these important energy sources have provided the greatest incentive for the extension of commercial, as against military, diving. The diver has many tasks to perform to support the seaward drive of the drilling rigs: underwater exploration and surveying of sites for drilling operations; measuring the degree of 'scour' round the rigs and placing protective sandbags around the legs (North Sea divers placed 15,000 sandbags around the legs of one rig); inspecting the underwater sections of the rigs for fatigue fractures; and so on. As drilling rigs have moved to deeper waters, diving techniques have been advanced so that divers can continue to give service. As a result, the time lag between experimental descents to depths beyond normal working dives and the commercial follow-up has been shortened to a few years, and several diving companies can now place working divers at any depth within the 600-foot range of the continental shelf region.

Doubling with the diver on many of these tasks is the manned submersible which has become a prominent feature of underwater technology since the early 1960s. Not all submersibles have been constructed solely with a view to exploiting the oceans: they have been built to exhort the value of structural materials; to carry 'trippers'; and to promote particular industrial companies. Nevertheless, submersibles now play a prominent part in both industrial and oceanographic research. For example, Dr Jacques Piccard, who pioneered the mid-water submersible *Ben Franklin*, once likened the marine biologist with his nets and trawls to a blind man making a butterfly collection, but with the advent of the submersible, marine life can be studied at close quarters. Fisheries' scientists can track and observe the migrations of economically important species such as salmon and tuna or make detailed studies of oceanographic factors affecting these and other marine animals. In fact, some of the earliest applications of research submersibles (converted military submarines) were in the fisheries sphere.

The question of whether man must always descend into the oceans to work or to carry out studies has yet to be resolved. Parallel with advances in diving and manned vehicles have come novel developments in instruments and remote-controlled machines. The underwater camera, equipped with a special wide-angle lens, has already proved a valuable tool in surveys on the sea floor, particularly when used in conjunction with a grab. Underwater television and acoustic 'imaging' are other areas where considerable improvements can be expected. Several remote-controlled machines have now been built for underwater salvage work. However, these and other systems need not come into direct conflict with man's underwater aspirations. On the contrary, they offer the kind of choice which should make possible further exploitation of ocean resources – they even introduce the hazard of over-exploitation.

Towards the limit of diving

At the surface a diver can fill his lungs with about six litres of air, but during a dive the water pressure, which increases by one atmosphere for every 33 feet, gradually compresses the air in his lungs until by about 100 feet its volume is reduced to about one and a half litres. At the surface this is the volume of air remaining in the lungs after breathing out completely. If the diver continues to descend, he risks permanent lung damage and probably death. This simple effect of increasing pressure on the volume of a gas, summarized long ago in Boyle's Law (the volume of a given mass of gas at a constant temperature varies inversely with the pressure exerted upon it), sets a natural limit to un-aided diving. To go deeper the diver must be supplied with air at the same pressure as his surroundings – the ambient sea pressure – thus keeping changes in lung volume the same as on the surface.

An early solution was to provide the diver with a helmet which received air pumped down from the surface by a hand operated compressor, any excess air simply escaping from around the edge of the headgear. An Englishman, John Deane, designed one of the first successful diving suits in the early 1800s. He eventually joined forces with Augustus Siebe, a German engineer who had settled in England, to produce a diving dress complete with a hard hat and a watertight suit for the body. In spite of distinct disadvantages, not least being the cumbersome weights needed to keep the diver firmly on the sea floor, the Siebe diving dress has persisted with few modifications up to modern times.

The self-contained diving apparatus came much later. Its important feature was a flexible bag or counter-lung which received oxygen from a small canister. When used in the water, the pressure on the counter-lung maintained the oxygen at the ambient pressure. Exhaled air passed through a canister of soda lime to remove the carbon dioxide before re-entering the counter-lung for re-cycling. Because there were no telltale bubbles of escaping air, this closed-circuit equipment was used by frogmen in the Second World War, and various more sophisticated forms of closed-circuit apparatus are still very important in modern naval diving.

The type of apparatus developed specifically for military purposes, however, is generally far too complicated for every-day civilian use where a more easily maintained piece of equipment is needed. Therefore the closed-circuit was dispensed with in favour of a much simpler system in which expired air is released into the sea. Commander Y. Le

Prieur had devised such an apparatus operating on compressed air in 1926, but the valve which reduced the pressure of the air coming from the supply cylinder had to be adjusted by hand to compensate for changes in water pressure during a dive. The air flowed continuously so that, apart from the disadvantage of a hand-operated valve, by no means a foolproof device, the diver could spend only a short time underwater. The breakthrough came in the 1940s with the design of a valve which supplied gas automatically at the ambient sea pressure but which also conserved the gas by cutting off the supply during exhalation.

Two men, Jacques-Yves Cousteau and Emile Gagnan, were responsible for developing what is now known as the aqualung. Cousteau, an officer in the French Navy, had already tried most types of apparatus available in the early 1940s, and as a result had a good idea as to a diver's requirements. Gagnan, an engineer specializing in gas control valves, converted these specifications into a practical piece of equipment. The essential part of their diving apparatus was the unit containing an outlet valve placed close to a diaphragm demand valve. When the diver breathes out the exhaled gases open the outlet valve allowing them to escape. The air supply controlled by the diaphragm demand valve is switched off. The diver then starts to breathe in. The outside pressure of the sea closes the outlet valve and pushes the diaphragm in, switching on the air supply. The air continues to flow until the pressure is the same on either side of the diaphragm which then returns to its 'resting' position switching off the air in the process. In this way the diver breathes gas at the ambient pressure.

Unfortunately, there are more limits to diving than Boyle's Law. Probably one of the most surprising discoveries was that oxygen becomes toxic at the comparatively low pressure of two atmospheres or 33 feet down in the sea – a fact which nearly cost Cousteau his life during experiments with the oxygen-fed apparatus. Nor is oxygen the only atmospheric gas to become dangerous: nitrogen induces a form of narcosis not unlike that produced by alcoholic intoxication. At 300 feet the diver can become so drunk that he will gaily tear off his mask to join the fish – with fatal results. Cousteau called this narcotic effect 'rapture of the deep'. To complete the picture, as the pressure increases the gases become so thick and heavy that they are difficult to breathe.

The eminent British scientist, J. B. S. Haldane, discovered many years ago that raising the ambient pressure increases the oxygen-carrying capacity of blood serum as opposed to the haemoglobin in the corpuscles, the normal oxygen carriers. This means that, volume for volume, less oxygen is needed in air breathed under pressure. Nevertheless the toxicity of pure oxygen supplies at pressures as low as two atmospheres has not been completely explained. Since the amounts of oxygen in a breathing mixture can be reduced, this toxic reaction does not present such a serious problem as the ill-effects experienced from nitrogen – normally a physiologically inert gas. After flirtation with the idea that carbon dioxide accumulating in the body under pressure might be the cause, most scientists have come to the view that the nitrogen dissolves in the fatty surface membranes of cells, including nerve cells, thereby slightly changing their properties. Nitrogen is not the only inert gas to do this; it is even possible to determine the likely effects of other gases being considered for diving mixtures by their affinity with 'fatty substances'.

By good fortune one of the safest gases, helium, had already been called into service largely because its lightness makes breathing easier. The helium acts as a passive carrier for oxygen but, although the inert gas does not react with the body's tissues, the pressure still forces it into them. The diver becomes the human equivalent of a soda siphon with helium in place of carbon dioxide. Release the pressure abruptly by rapidly ascending from depth, and the gas bubbles out of solution. Getting these bubbles in the wrong parts of a diver's body leads to decompression sickness

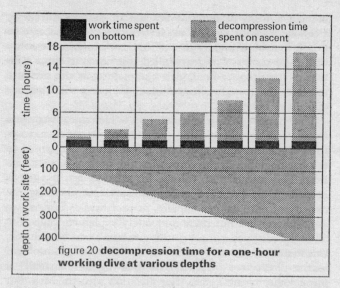

figure 20 **decompression time for a one-hour working dive at various depths**

which, depending on its intensity and where the bubbles appear, has such names as 'chokes', 'staggers' and 'bends'. The only way to treat a 'bent' diver is to recompress him immediately, either by taking him down in the sea again or preferably, and more safely, by placing him in a pressure chamber. Obviously the pressure is best reduced slowly giving the gas time to escape out of the tissues into the circulatory system without forming bubbles. To ensure that this happens, the diver uses a decompression schedule in which he makes a series of stops on the journey to the surface. Usually he ascends fairly rapidly for about two thirds of the way and then pauses after each rise of ten feet, waiting a longer period with succesive halts.

Although decompression schedules provide the peg on which successful diving depends, existing tables are severely limited in reliability. A major difficulty in their preparation is the variability in human response. The Royal Navy tests large numbers of people in its efforts to construct the safest possible route to decompression from deep dives. No more than two cases of bends per hundred entries in the water are considered acceptable in the testing of a schedule, or set of schedules. According to H. V. Hempleman, when some years ago the Navy experts tested its own and other diving schedules, they found that the schedules were inadequate for dives of more than an hour much below 100 feet. Since then the decompression schedules have been modified, but generally speaking they err on the safe side rather than provide the fastest possible decompression. It is quite possible that for general working dives the rate of ascent will never progress much beyond an average of one foot every ten minutes. At this rate a prolonged dive at 1,000 feet requires almost a week of decompression.

Since the ultimate factor governing the speed of ascent is the rate at which the inert gas escapes from the tissues, most efforts to make diving safer and decompression faster depend on manipulation of the way the gas is used during deep dives. According to Professor C. J. Lambertsen of the University of Pennsylvania, the most useful single measure for improving decompression rates will continue to be the use of maximum tolerable oxygen. This limits the uptake of inert gas during descent and at diving depth, increases the outward gradient for the elimination of inert gas during decompression, and finally aids the treatment of bends when or if it occurs.

On theoretical grounds, gas mixtures composed of several inert gases including argon, helium and neon should enable faster decompression. Each gas in the mixture behaves as though it is the only one present, thus giving the effect of a considerable reduction in pressure. Unfortunately, once the smallest bubble forms in the tissues, it grows in response to the total pressure of all the gases as well as of the carbon dioxide, oxygen and the water vapour also present. However, the idea of using several inert gases during a dive has not been entirely discarded; by alternating the gas in the breathing mixture, one inert gas can be eliminated from the tissue while a second one is being taken up. Switching from one mixture to another during descent and ascent has already led to some rapid deep dives.

A further possibility is the use of chemicals which reduce the bends. Dr C. W. Crowdey has shown that the incidence of bends in experimental animals during rapid decompression can be remarkably reduced by treating the animals with the drug PHDA (partially depolymerized hyaluronic acid). The precise action of the drug is unknown, but Dr Crowdey has suggested that PHDA demolishes a coating of fat which covers and strengthens each nitrogen bubble and so speeds up dispersal of the gas.

Ultimately, a limit to the depth of dives can be seen in the purely physical effects of the sea's presure on the breathing mixtures. As the pressure increases, the gases become thicker and more difficult to breathe. Apart from the greater effort needed to move the gases in and out of the lungs, the reduction in ventilation of the lungs may allow carbon dioxide to accumulate, particularly during heavy work. Normally the level of carbon dioxide in the lungs, and therefore in the arteries, remains nearly constant, but once it begins to build up, the situation deteriorates rapidly because the concentration of carbon dioxide in the blood acts as a 'trigger' for respiration. Apart from the danger in an unsuccessful stimulation of the already overloaded respiratory system, the carbon dioxide enhances the narcotic effects of the inert gases.

In order to investigate the limit of oxygen/helium breathing mixtures, Professor Lambersten has used a heavy inert gas, neon, to simulate their densities at various depths. In August 1971, four subjects were kept in an experimental chamber at a pressure equivalent to a depth of 1,200 feet. Although the chamber had an oxygen/helium atmosphere, neon mixtures were breathed for short, repeated periods through face masks. No serious limitations were noticed at rest or during light work when the neon mixtures were used to simulate helium densities down to a depth of 5,000 feet in the sea. The trouble came when the subjects had to carry out heavy work. At the equivalent of 5,000 feet they experienced difficulty in moving the dense gas in and out of their lungs and they could not complete their tasks. Thus the depth limit, at least as far as oxygen/helium mixtures are concerned lies at less than 5,000 feet from purely physical reasons. Experimental dives have already been pushed beyond 1,000 feet. In February 1969, three Swiss divers descended to a simulated depth of 1,150 feet in the RN's Deep Trials Unit at Alverstoke. They spent nearly three days at 980 feet making three excursions to the maximum depth. In all, the divers spent five hours at 1,150 feet. Then just over a year later, two Royal Navy scientists pushed the depth for simulated dives even further when they stayed at 1,500 feet for 10 hours and spent 5½ days at a depth of over 1,000 feet. In 1972, two French divers remained for 100 hours at a simulated depth of 1,640 feet. The men experienced the high pressure syndrome (muscular tremors and spasms, a decrease in awareness and a certain loss of coordination) observed in other deep dives. After the dive, Dr X. Fructus felt that 'in the 1,700-feet zone we are approaching the limit within which divers will be able to live and work in total physiological security'.

Since a diver can take six hours or more to decompress after a dive of five minutes at 600 feet, the volumes of breathing mixture involved in such experimental dives go beyond the kind of supply which can be carried on the back sensibly. Add to this the complexity of maintaining safe ratios of oxygen to helium (which change with depth) and one begins to appreciate that the deep diver needs some form of technical support. The Royal Navy technique is to descend as rapidly as possible in a submersible diving chamber which also carries the necessary gas supplies. For safety's sake each diver also carries an emergency supply of breathing mixture, but if all goes well his supply comes via an 'umbilical' from the gas cylinders on board the chamber even while he is working out in the sea. To return to the surface, the diver re-enters the chamber which now becomes a submersible decompression chamber (SDC). Once at the surface the SDC still under pressure is locked on to a deck decompression chamber (DDC), which is much larger and more comfortable. The divers transfer to the DDC to complete their lengthy decompression. This transfer involves little effort; in earlier systems the divers had to open and close doors and operate pressure locks, but the whole system was automated when navy doctors found that this activity during decompression could cause gas bubbles to form in the tissues and hence bring on decompression sickness.

The Cachalot system of the Westinghouse Underseas Division works on very similar principles (see figure 21). First used in 1965 for work in fresh water at Smith Mountain Dam in Virginia, it enables divers to work at depths of 600 feet or more. In a typical assignment, four divers enter the DDC to begin a week's work under pressure. They work

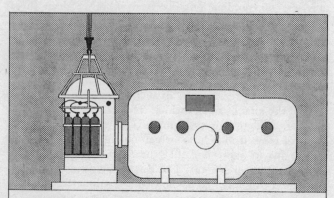

figure 21 **Cachalot diving system showing the submersible decompression and diving chamber 'mated' to the deck decompression chamber**

alternate two-man shifts and are carried to and from their underwater location in the SDC, which serves as both an underwater elevator and a haven. An umbilical line from the chamber supplies the divers with breathing mixture, warm water to heat specially designed diving suits, and communications. Generally they work from two to six hours before clambering back into the SDC, which is usually kept less than 50 feet from the work area, for the return journey to the surface chamber.

When divers are kept under pressure for longer than 24 hours as in the Westinghouse system, their blood and body tissues become saturated with inert gas. But this is no problem; the time taken to decompress is based on the degree of saturation of the tissues and once they are completely saturated there is no further penalty in terms of time. Yet saturation diving greatly increases the ratio of useful working time to decompression time and is one of the main justifications for various current attempts to live for extended periods in bases established deep in the sea.

Living in the sea

The first human experiments in living under the sea took place in September 1962. Early that month a Belgian diver, Robert Stenuit, took part in a series of experiments conducted by Dr Link. Stenuit descended in a chamber designed by Link to a depth of 200 feet where he stayed for 26 hours, eight of which he spent in the sea outside his temporary underwater home. For the experiment a gas mixture of 3 per cent oxygen and 97 per cent helium was used, and Stenuit clocked up a total exposure, including decompression, of 88 hours – at that time a record stay at a record depth. But these were not the only experiments taking place that month; within a week two French divers, Albert Falco and Claude Wesley, swam down to a 'giant can' set on its side and anchored with 34 tons of pig iron to the seabed at a depth of 36 feet. The two divers who were taking part in

Jacques-Yves Cousteau's first Conshelf experiment stayed in the sea for a week using the metal cylinder, named *Diogène*, as a home base for excursions and work in the surrounding sea. Because of the comparatively shallow depth no decompression was necessary, and the divers used air supplies.

This early work by the two groups was in many ways complementary. Stenuit's dive helped to confirm ideas formulated by scientists such as US Navy Captain Dr George Bond, who in 1957 carried out a series of simulated dives to 200 feet in a compression chamber at the Naval Medical Research Laboratory, New London, Connecticut. Subjects for these experiments in 'saturation diving', as Bond called it, were small animals and some monkeys. Later human volunteers followed, showing among other things that it was feasible to breathe oxygen/helium mixtures for long periods without any detectable ill effects. The French divers for their part showed conclusively that men could live and work under the sea without any signs of physical or psychological discomfort, although some medical problems such as gastric troubles did arise. Nevertheless, Cousteau's observations of the two men during their life away from the natural environment of the land led him to comment, 'I had the impression that I belonged no more to the same team; they had taken on another mentality; they were at home there; they were actually doing their work with no reference to the surface. They could stay and I had to go back. This was not my business any longer.'

Since 1962 prolonged stays underwater have remained almost entirely the prerogative of American and French groups. The following year Cousteau's group set up a more complex underwater habitat 36 feet below the surface at the remote Sha'ab Rumi Reef in the Red Sea. The dominating structure of this Conshelf 2 project was a starfish-like house which provided a home for five men for a month. The five men breathed air, but for a week two companions living in a deeper base at 96 feet used a mixture consisting of oxygen, nitrogen and helium. In 1964 Stenuit, now with a companion Jon Lindbergh, lived for just over two days at a depth of 432 feet using a rubber dwelling inflated with a breathing mixture of 4 per cent oxygen and 96 per cent helium as a base. Shortly afterwards the US Navy group made its first entry into the field with Sealab 1. Located at a depth of 192 feeet off the Bermudan coast, four men used a cigar-shaped cylinder, 35 feet long and 12 feet in diameter, as their home for ten days. The men were supplied with a gas mixture of 16 per cent nitrogen, 4 per cent oxygen and 80 per cent helium. Although Soviet experimenters had also become interested in experiments in underwater living by this time, the three groups of Link, who joined up with Ocean Systems, Cousteau, and the US Navy were to spearhead the invasion of the sea in the 1960s.

As data and experience accumulate, the projects become increasingly ambitious. Selab 2 in 1965 was placed at a depth of 205 feet and three teams of ten men, each of which spent fifteen days underwater, took part in the experiment. The popular imagination was captured by the part played in this venture by former astronaut Scott Carpenter who, apart from staying down for 30 consecutive days, brought about a link between the American efforts in both outer and inner space. Even while the Sealab 2 experiment was in progress, Conshelf 3 began. Breaking with the traditional 'underwater cans', Cousteau had devised an 18-foot diameter sphere with two storeys, the lower one for diving and sleeping and the upper one for eating and scientific work. The new style underwater habitat, lowered 328 feet into the Mediterranean off Cap Ferrat, became home for six divers (including Cousteau's son, Philippe) during their stay of almost 22 days on the sea bottom. Sealab 3, which was expected to push the depth of underwater real estate even further, to 600 feet, was stopped 48 hours after lowering the habitat in February 1969 following the accidental death of a diver sent to investigate a leak in the chamber. This tragedy brought a temporary lull to the drive deeper into the ocean.

By the end of the sixties, the number of groups involved
in underwater living had increased significantly. By the close
of this eventful decade in oceanology, the Soviet Union had
announced several projects carried out apparently by non-
military groups: in 1967 four aquanauts spent a week 80
feet down in the Black Sea using a twin-sphere habitat
Sadko-2; and in the summer of 1968 an underwater laboratory, *Chernomor*, was anchored at a depth of 45 feet in the
same sea to provide a home for teams of four or five divers
working in relays of up to six days. The following year, on
28 July, a German underwater laboratory, *Helgoland*, was
lowered 75 feet to the seabed off the east coast of Heligo-
land. Three teams of aquanauts occupied the cylindrical
habitat in succession up to 19 August, carrying out research
in the cold waters of the North Sea. Earlier that year, a
group of British divers had had the good sense to go to the
warmer waters of the Mediterranean off Malta, to experiment with cheap inflatable habitats. Unfortunately, the
experiments had to be abandoned because of violent storms.

Another interesting feature of man's entry into 'inner
space' at this time was the start of the Tektite programmes,
using a habitat built and serviced by the General Electric
Company of America. Although the US Navy is involved in
this programme, it is presented as a cooperative effort between federal agencies, private industry, and the universi-
ties. The aim of Tektite is to determine the capability of a
small group of men to perform scientific research while living on the ocean floor under saturated diving conditions for
a long period of time. During Tektite I, in 1969, four diver-
scientists spend a record-breaking two months working 50
feet down on the floor of Great Lameshur Bay, St John
Island, in the Virgin Islands National Park. Because of the
shallow location they were able to breath mixtures of
nitrogen and oxygen, rather than the more expensive and
exotic mixtures of helium and oxygen used for deep dives.
In April 1970, Tektite II began at the same site, but this time
on a much grander scale, with an eight-month programme

with teams drawn from sixty scientist-aquanauts, engineers and doctors. In all, ten scientific missions were accomplished, involving 2,407 hours of diving, before the programme ended in early November.

Long stays deep underwater soon revealed the serious nature of problems which had been side-stepped to some extent in the course of shorter, conventional dives. Not least among these are the side effects produced by the large percentage of helium contained in the breathing gas: it's lightness changes normal speech into a Donald Duck-like gabble; and its ability to conduct heat almost six times faster than nitrogen causes a rapid loss of body heat.

Not all languages are apparently distorted by helium to the same extent. Dr Pierre Cabarrou, who had already spent some time studying recordings of the Conshelf diver André Laban, found that he quickly became accustomed to the German spoken by Dr Horst Hartmann during a dry dive to a simulated depth of 800 feet. The Conshelf divers, themselves, claimed that after a few days they could understand each other's oxyhelium voices. Certainly, it seems possible to reduce the confusion of the strange sound by more controlled breathing and slower speech. Nevertheless, considerable effort is going into developing unscrambling devices to improve communication both between divers and between them and people on the surface. It has even been suggested that some kind of artificial larynx – voice box – might be used. Diving has always been hindered by difficulties in communication but, if life and work underwater are to be bearable let alone manageable, some kind of solution other than the hand signals and tugs on lines used in shallow dives must be implemented.

To help overcome the problem of heat loss, divers are almost 'cooked' within the underwater habitat. Outside in the water is it quite another matter – one cannot heat the entire ocean. Electricity and hot water circulation have been used to heat the diving suits. The Cachalot system used hot water, for example, and the Sealab 2 divers experimented with electrically heated suits. Radio-isotopes, such as plutonium-238, offer a further alternative source of energy for a compact heating unit. The problem is aggravated by the loss of insulation suffered by contemporary diving suits at depths much below 200 feet. Above this depth the porous structure of the foam material traps air to form a spongy insulator, but below 200 feet the pressure of the water soon presses the suit flat. One solution used by Conshelf 3 divers was to wear a vest made of an incompressible material incorporating thousands of glass 'micro-balloons' filled with carbon dioxide to provide the insulation. At that time the material could not be used to protect the whole body beneath the diving suit because the material was sufficiently rigid to interfere with the diver's freedom of movement. But even the best insulation will be insufficient protection for long stays in the cold deep water and the diver will need some form of auxiliary heating if he is to work efficiently.

Breathing gas mixtures poses many problems other than those created directly by the use of helium. Supplies of gases are limited and, to remain operational, fresh stocks must be sent from the surface or the original supply must be conserved until the end of the stay by 'scrubbing' the gas clean of impurities and re-using it. Obviously many of the advantages of living underwater will be wiped out if a surface support team must dance attendance all the time, and the direction of experiments has been towards complete independence from the surface. Conshelf 3, for example, was a self-contained pressure vessel, although it still relied largely on power supplied from the surface via an umbilical cable which also carried television and radio links. To conserve supplies of the breathing mixture, it had complex monitoring systems and a cryogenic plant which, among other things, froze the exhaled carbon dioxide into a solid block and eliminated it. The ratio of gases in the atmosphere is absolutely critical to safety and survival and all the underwater houses have boasted a formidable array of sensors and controls. Typical of these is the system devised by the American scientist, Alan Krasberg, for controlling oxygen. The Krasberg control embodies a sensor which reacts to the number of oxygen molecules in a gas sample by changes in electrical current – the higher the oxygen content, the greater the voltage. The current opens and closes a supply valve according to whether the oxygen is too low or too high, thus ensuring a constant level of oxygen in the breathing mixture.

The biggest problem of all remains that of decompression and the time it takes to remove the inert gases which have infiltrated the body tissue so successfully. While prolonged stays underwater improve the ratio of time spent in decompression to time spent usefully in the water, the diver cannot move from one depth to another without keeping a watchful eye on decompression procedures. In addition to such restraints, the need to breathe gases fixes the final limit to which dives might one day be made to a few thousand feet, simply because of the physical properties of the gases under the pressure existing at these depths. Therefore, argued Cousteau, man must be prepared to dispense with his reliance on breathing gas mixtures. His suggestion that an underwater man, *Homo aquaticus*, could be created, who would be able to descend deep into the ocean and return to the surface without decompressing, caused a sensation. The Frenchman based this prediction on medical and space research into life-support units which can be connected direct to the human circulatory system. Cousteau envisaged a unit small enough to be strapped on to the body. All that would be needed to create this new race of man, would be for surgeons to plug it into the circulatory system and to fill any air spaces in the body, such as the lungs and sinuses, with an inert incompressible fluid. Drastic though this surgical evolution might seem, Cousteau thought that volunteers for it would come from the ranks of those unfortunate victims of lung cancer.

Even as Cousteau was making this fantastic prophecy, experiments were in hand at the University of Leyden which might make underwater man possible. In a typical experiment, Dr Johannes A. Kylstra would place a mouse through an air-lock into a pressure chamber filled with a liquid with a salt composition similar to that of blood plasma and charged with the same concentration of dissolved oxygen as in the air around us. At first the animal would try to escape out of the liquid, but a grid set below the water level prevented it from reaching the surface. After this initial agitation the animal would then settle down, taking slow deep breaths of the liquid. Breathing like this, it could survive for many hours in the liquid, responding to taps on the walls of the chamber, and moving about from time to time, before finally losing consciousness. Curiously enough, the animals do not die because of a lack of oxygen, but as a result of the accumulation of carbon dioxide. The mouse that survived the longest – eighteen hours – was aided by the addition of a chemical which helps to suppress the untoward effects of high levels of carbon dioxide in animals.

From mice, Dr Kylstra and his colleagues moved on to dogs which, because of their size, made the measurement of oxygen uptake and carbon dioxide retention possible. The experiments were carried out in a large pressure chamber with the air at a pressure of five atmospheres. The dog was placed in a tub of saline charged with oxygen but, before being totally submerged, it was anaesthetized and cooled to about $32\,°C$ (to reduce its need for oxygen). Once submerged, the dog would make vigorous efforts to breathe, blowing out jets of water from its lungs. At the end of the experiment, the dog was taken out of the tub and its lungs were emptied of the liquid and inflated with oxygen. Out of six dogs used in this series of experiments, only one survived. It had breathed the saline fluid for 24 minutes. Appropriately, this sole survivor was adopted by the Royal Netherlands Navy submarine rescue vessel Cerberus as its mascot.

In 1963 Dr Kylstra moved to the United States to continue his research. There he carried out more sophisticated experiments aimed at measuring the precise events occurring in the lungs of animals breathing liquids. Using animals which were anaesthetized, but kept at ordinary temperatures, he and his colleagues were able to show that, when oxygen-enriched liquid was pumped in accurately metered quantities, a dog would extract the same amount of oxygen from it as from air during normal respiration. Once again the carbon dioxide built up, and theoretical models based on these and other results suggest that retention of this gas may be inevitable in view of the basic structure of the gas exchange system in the lung. Other American scientists, Leland C. Clark, Jr, and Frank Gollan, have attempted to solve the problem by using certain silicone oils and fluoro-carbon liquids in which oxygen and carbon dioxide are very soluble. Experimenting with mice, they have found that, providing the animals are cooled, they can survive many hours in a fluoro-carbon liquid with oxygen at atmospheric pressure, The main difficulties appear to be the slow rate of respiration of the viscous liquid and the risk of reaction by the delicate lung tissue to the chemical.

In spite of such drawbacks, the experiments in water breathing continued to progress, and in the August of 1968 issue of the magazine, *Scientific American*, Dr Kylstra reported on an experiment with a human volunteer:

At the Duke Medical Center we use a new method of treating certain lung disorders that is called lung lavage. The method consists of washing the lungs one at a time with a saline solution to remove pathological secretions from the air sacs and bronchi. While one lung is being rinsed, the other breathes gaseous oxygen. The fact that this operation can be conducted successfully encouraged us to try an experiment for which a courageous deep-sea diver, Francis J. Falejczyk, volunteered. His windpipe was anaesthetized and a double-tubed catheter was inserted through it, one tube going to each lung. The air in one lung was replaced by a 0·9 per cent saline solution at normal body temperature. A 'breathing' process consisting of adding more saline solution to the lung and draining an equal amount was then repeated seven times with 500 milliliters of solution used for each breath. Falejczyk, who remained fully conscious during the procedure, told us afterward that the liquid-filled lung had not felt noticeably different from the gas-filled one, and that he had had no unpleasant sensations from the flow of liquid into and out of it. Of course this test was very different from trying to breathe water with both lungs, but it did show at least that filling the human lung with a saline solution will not seriously damage the tissues or produce unacceptably disagreeable sensations, if it is done properly.

The prospects of breathing liquids for deep diving have been followed closely by Captain Bond, Director of the US Navy's Man in the Sea programme (which includes the Sealab series of experiments). At the seventeenth Annual Conference of the American Association of Medical Clinicians, he explained how a hole could be cut in the windpipe – a tracheotomy – and the lungs filled with a special solution into which highly compressed oxygen has been injected. After filling other body cavities, a diver treated in this way would be able to descend to 12,000 feet and perform two hours of useful work there. The lungs would absorb the oxygen while the carbon dioxide would be converted into harmless bicarbonate. After carrying out his deep-sea task, the diver would return to the surface without decompression. Later that year, during a conference at Brighton in England, Captain Bond elaborated further on the process by suggesting that even longer stays would be possible if a pump supplied the solution which would be kept charged with the appropriate level of oxygen from a cylinder – by controlling the rate of pumping, the oxygen supply could be regulated.

And what will life be like for the new underwater man? Continuing in his prophetic vein at the Brighton conference, Cousteau suggested that *Homo aquaticus* will be able to resist pressures down to 1,500 metres or 2,000 metres and move from this great depth mechanically or freely at any speed. (In experiments at Kylstra's laboratory, a liquid-breathing mouse has been brought from a pressure of 30 atmospheres to normal atmospheric pressure within three seconds without any untoward effects.) This new man will probably be born in the deep sea, he will have surgery at his birth in underwater hospitals filled with water and there will be underwater cities and perhaps new nations. Certainly, if *Homo aquaticus* ever comes into being, we will witness the start of a completely new attitude to the sea and, more important in the case of this book, a completely new approach to exploiting the ocean resources.

Underwater vehicles

Penetration of the ocean deeps need involve neither sacrifice nor surgery; men have descended to depths far beyond those anticipated by divers, by surrounding themselves with a protective capsule containing air at normal atmospheric pressure. As early as 1934, the Americans, William Beebe and Otis Barton, descended to a depth of 3,028 feet in the Pacific and became the first men to witness 'the living constellations of the deep ocean'. Admittedly, as a means of exploration their *Bathysphere*, which was lowered at the end of a cable, had strict limitations, but in 1947 a free-moving craft, the bathyscaphe, was unveiled. The Swiss scientist, Auguste Piccard, borrowing from his experience with hot air balloons, suspended a strong pressure-resisting chamber, not unlike Beebe's, beneath a large metal float filled with petrol – a liquid lighter than sea-water. To descend, the underwater balloon was loaded with ballast which was jettisoned for the return ascent. Vents in the float permitted sea-water to enter beneath the petrol and so equalize the pressures inside and outside its thin walls.

The bathysphere concept placed the entire ocean within reach, and bathyscaphes operated by the French and US Navies made successively deeper and deeper dives. Finally in 1960, Piccard's son, Jacques, and Lieutenant Don Walsh, USN, descended in the *Trieste II* to 35,800 feet in the Marianas Trench in the Pacific – the deepest known place in the world. As underwater elevators, these vehicles are unsurpassed, but for extensive underwater exploration and, more particularly, work they leave much to be desired. A mere handful of bathyscaphes, such as the French *Archimède II*, the American *Trieste II*, and the Soviet *North II*, exist at present, and of these *Archimède* is probably the only one which makes regular dives to the greatest depths. Nevertheless, the bathyscaphe led directly to many of the manned submersibles which have become such a prominent feature of underwater activites. Of the forty-plus submersibles operating around the world, only a few show any great affinity with the conventional submarine.

The precise genealogy of the manned submersible, few of which existed before 1960, is difficult to trace largely because several manufacturers have produced their own individual models within a short space of time without any obvious reference to one another. In general, a submersible is comparable in density to water and needs little variable buoyance. Many submersibles have a spherical pressure chamber akin to that of the bathyscaphes, but they dispense with the need for a large float by reducing the diving range of the vehicle to rather lesser depths. The *Aluminaut*, which can descend to 15,000 feet, is essentially an aluminium submarine and few other submersibles can operate as far down as 6,000 feet. Much of their equipment, including batteries, is placed outside the main pressure chamber in a free-flooding 'super-structure'. This metal or fibreglass shell may be strengthened and be given additional buoyancy by a packing of syntatic foam – a composite material consisting of glass 'micro-balloons' bonded together with epoxy resin.

An early submersible which fits neatly into this description in the *Alvin*, built in the United States by the Applied Sciences Division of Litton Industries in 1965. *Alvin*, with a depth range of 6,000 feet, was designed specifically for oceanographic research – in fact the submersible is named

after oceanographer Allyn Vine, who was deeply involved
in its development. Weighing 26,000 pounds, *Alvin* is 22 feet
long with an 8-foot beam. It has a top speed of 4 knots, a
cruising speed of 2 knots and a range when submerged of 15
to 20 miles. The 7-foot-diameter pressure sphere is made of
high-strength steel (HY-100) 1.33 inches thick. Inside there
is room for a pilot and one or two observers, together with
instruments and life-support equipment sufficient for 24
hours or more. Four viewing ports enable the pilot and
observer to see ahead of and beneath the vehicle. A mechanical arm can be used to take samples from the seabed,
although naturally the equipment which the submersible
carries varies from dive to dive, according to its mission.

To compensate for differences in weight of personnel and
instruments, as well as for changes in the density of sea-
water, *Alvin* has a variable ballast system in the free-flooding outer casing. The system consists of aluminium spheres
filled with oil and connected to collapsible rubber bags.
When oil is pumped from the spheres into the rubber bags,
the amount of sea-water displaced by the vehicle is increased (thus increasing the buoyancy), while the weight of
the vehicle remains the same. The overall effect is to make
the vessel 'lighter'. And obviously pumping oil from the
bags into the pressure spheres has the reverse effect. In this
way the density of the submersible can be adjusted to make
it neutrally buoyant – neither sinking nor rising. Major
components such as batteries and the motors which drive
the craft's three propellers, one on each side and one at the
stern, are all mounted outside the pressure vessel. Because
they displace water, they do not 'weigh' as much as in air
and they are completely compensated for by a syntatic
foam packing which also contains a number of aluminium
buoyancy spheres.

Alvin dives by flooding its main ballast tanks while two
trim tanks, one near the bow and the other in the stern, set
the craft at a nose-down angle of up to about 30° to assist
the dive. The trim tanks, filled half with mercury and half

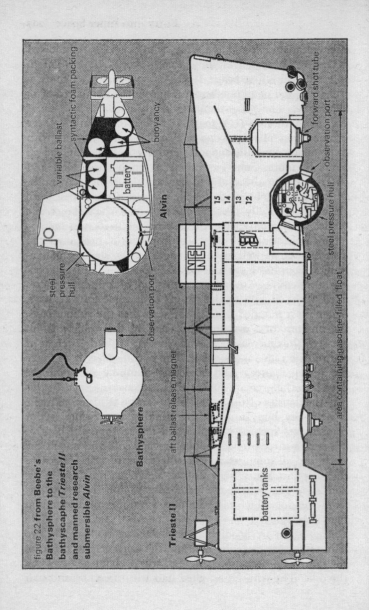

figure 22 from Beebe's Bathysphere to the bathyscaphe *Trieste II* and manned research submersible *Alvin*

Alvin

variable ballast

syntactic foam packing

buoyancy

battery

steel pressure hull

observation port

Bathysphere

observation port

aft ballast release magnet

Trieste II

battery tanks

NEL

15
14
13
12

forward shot tube

observation port

steel pressure hull

area containing gasoline-filled float

with oil, are connected so that oil pumped from the top of one tank to the top of the other forces the heavy mercury from the bottom of that tank back into the first one. The two side propellers may also be used to speed up the dive. When the mission is completed the submersible returns towards the surface, using either or both the oil-filled bags for additional buoyancy as well as the side-propellers. To complete its ascent, the main ballast tanks are 'blown'.

In comparison with conventional submarines, all research submersibles (except converted submarines such as the Soviet *Severyanka*) are exceedingly small. Since buoyancy is determined by the ratio of volume to weight, this smallness inevitably brings with it restrictions and compromises. The deeper a submersible goes – and many of them go deeper than conventional submarines – the stronger the hull must be to resist the increased external pressures. If the same materials are used in its construction, the thickness of the hull and consequently its weight will increase with every extension of the operating depth. Considerable research has therefore gone into ways of improving the pressure hull. The results account for the widespread use of spherical chambers, a shape which offers the greatest known resistance to pressure, and the use of materials with a high strength-to-weight ratio such as titanium, fibre-reinforced plastics, cast glass and super-strength steels in their construction.

A further requirement of modern submersibles is a compact power pack. Most submersibles are electrically propelled and the limited supply of power which they can carry is generally reflected in their slow underwater speed; very few submersibles cruise underwater for very long at speeds much above two knots. To double their speed would take about eight times more power, which is not possible with present batteries. Probably one of the best sources of power for these low horsepower units is the silver-zinc battery with its high energy-to-weight ratio. Unfortunately, this type of battery is both very expensive and sensitive to rough usage: most submersibles manage with lead-acid batteries which have the advantage of being more reliable and sufficiently cheap to use as throw-away ballast if need be. Any dramatic improvement in performance would certainly mean considerable increases in size, and hence displacement, to provide the buoyancy and sufficient space for chemically fuelled or even nuclear systems. In July 1967 the US Navy received Congressional approval for the construction of the world's first nuclear-powered underwater research and ocean engineering submersible, *NR-1*. At that time, construction costs were estimated at $58.3 million, almost double the sum proposed for an earlier version, and by the time *NR-1* was finally launched on 29 January 1969, the costs had escalated even further to $67.5 million. Special equipment, including gear for oceanographic work, it was then estimated, would add about $20 million to the bill. Obviously such a vessel is well beyond normal commercial, non-military investment and most operators have decided in favour of small, lower-powered submersibles brought to the operations site by a 'parent' vessel on the surface.

Of course, one way around the problem is to have an umbilical connection to surface supplies of electricity just as in the early underwater houses. The Japanese submersible *Kuroshio II*, which operates down to depths of 650 feet, trails an umbilical cable 1,900 feet long bringing power from a surface tender. But, on the whole, tethered vehicles belong to an entirely different class of submersible – the unmanned telechiric. Telechiric is derived from the Greek words for 'distant hand' and is an apt description of these underwater vehicles which are controlled by human operators at the surface. The cable connection allows the operator to receive pictures relayed from the vehicle's television 'eyes' and carries his control signals as well as the power needed for the machine to expedite them. In other words, the telechiric is a machine proxy for man, allowing him to carry out work in an alien world without any hazard to himself.

The earliest telechiric machines were found in another alien environment – the radioactive areas of nuclear research laboratories. They were a logical extension of the master/slave devices that scientists and engineers use from behind heavily leaded glass windows to manipulate objects in the radioactive cells. Although some manned vehicles such as the American *Beetle* were built for this duty, the dangers of operating in highly radioactive areas and the sheer weight of the protective shielding needed by its crew members led to a preference for the cheaper and expendable remote-controlled machines. Some, for example the *Minotaur*, hang above the test beds of nuclear and other engines ready to sweep down to carry out the commands of their human master. The *Minotaur* has five articulated limbs protruding from a ball-like body: three of the arms carry television 'eyes', and the other two end in a 'hand'. Other telechirics, such as *Mascot*, look more like science fiction robots. Paired television cameras provide the operator with stereoscopic vision and two arms, controlled by moving an identical master pair, hang from the 'shoulder' of the free-roving machine. Both types of telechiric – the bottom crawler and the kind operating in three dimensions – are represented underwater, although as yet none match the more sophisticated machines which are to be found on the land.

One of the earliest bottom crawlers was the *Rum* (remote underwater manipulator) used for a time by the Scripps Institution at La Jolla, California. It was a converted weapons carrier which had been fitted with television cameras and a mechanical arm. The operator controlled the machine from a shore-based caravan and an umbilical cable, five miles long, carried both the communication signals and the power. The Scripps scientists had hoped that the *Rum* might be used to maintain instrumented automatic stations set up on the sea floor but the machine was defeated by an inability to negotiate minor obstacles, a tendency to become bogged down in soft sea bottoms, and 'bleary vision' caused by the sediment raised by its movement. Not all of these bottom-moving machines have been quite so disappointing, but they have failed to gain the acceptance enjoyed by the 'free swimming' telechirics such as *Téléanaute* which can work away from the sea floor. The *Téléanaute*, used by the Institut Français du Pétrole, can move in all directions at depths down to 3,200 feet, and carries an arm which can handle loads of up to 540 pounds. Behind it the machine trails a neutrally buoyant cable which links up with the control console on the attendant surface vessel.

In 1966, both telechirics and manned submersibles were to be put through a test on which the attention of people all over the world was focused – the retrieval of an H-bomb lost in the sea off the coast of Spain. The story started on 17 January when a B-52 bomber collided with a 'flying tanker' during refuelling. Aircraft debris, including three out of four unarmed dombs carried by the B-52, was showered on and around the coastal village of Palomares, while the fourth deployed a parachute and drifted over and into the sea. Before this bomb was brought to the surface 82 days later, more than 3,000 US Navy personnel, 25 Navy ships, four research ships, four underwater vehicles and many civilian research or contractor personnel had become involved in what amounted to the largest concentrated underwater search in history.

The submersibles *Aluminaut* and *Alvin* and the telechiric *Curv* (cable-controlled underwater recovery vehicle) figured prominently in the recovery of the bomb, which finally came to rest in 2,850 feet of water six miles off the coast of Spain. The operation was not an unqualified success. *Alvin* several times found tracks left by the bomb on the sea floor but was forced to resurface with its batteries exhausted before reaching the bomb. The problem was solved when *Alvin* eventually tracked down the bomb by sending *Aluminaut* to 'baby sit' while the smaller submersibile returned to the surface. During the first attempt to raise the bomb, the line which *Alvin* had managed to attach to it snapped, causing the bomb to be lost for another agonizing nine days. *Curv* finally retrieved the bomb with some difficulty. The telechiric became entangled with the parachute shrouds trailing from the bomb while attaching a third line, forcing an earlier than intended decision to hoist both weapon and machine. The manned submersibles also had their moments: *Alvin* was nearly snagged on the parachute and *Aluminaut* was momentarily seized by the mud. All in all, the 'H-bomb affair' could hardly be called a triumph for underwater vehicles, but it was a difficult mission successfully completed.

Man or machine?

Real competition between man and machine has yet to develop on the underwater scene, but there is no doubt that the hostility of the environment favours the machine. At the first hint of human frailty, the telechiric and manned submersibles are called in. When the oil companies, for example, moved into deeper offshore waters, they found that the divers using compressed air came up from 200 feet feeling extremely 'fuzzy'. Faced with the prospect of curtailing expansion into a lucrative area, they sought an alternative to the diver. Guide wires were used to mount equipment, including the well-head or 'Christmas tree', on the sea floor, and machines capable of completing the structure were developed. One such machine, the *Mobot*, is little more than a 'swimming socket wrench' which, controlled from above, clamps itself on to the underwater well-head and tightens up the bolts. But, even as the oil companies were developing marine telechirics, diving techniques advanced to a point which brought the offshore rigs once more within the diver's range.

It is no accident that a major experiment carried out by Conshelf 3 aquanauts consisted of constructing and servicing a 'Christmas tree' at a depth of 375 feet. In August 1967 two men descended in a diving bell to 635 feet in the

Mexican Gulf and worked on a well-head system as part of a combined experiment by Esso Production Research and Ocean Systems. The British company, Northern Diving Services, has divers operating on a regular basis on drilling rigs in the cold turbulent waters of the North Sea. Several diving groups are busy developing the capability to operate within the entire depth range of the continental shelf. Comex (Compagnie Maritime d'Expertise) of Marseilles has a diving chamber designed to go down to 1,000 feet. The Shell Oil Company has enlisted the aid of Hannes Keller and Professor A. A. Bühlmann, who has cooperated with him, as part of an effort to extend the range of its divers. The British company, Strongwork Diving (International), has developed a new diving system helped by the National Research Development Corporation. There is the *Cachelot* system of Westinghouse; and so the list continues.

Why are commercial groups so keen to push man's underwater range to the limit? The British diver scientist, Dr Flemming, provides some clues: 'Certain attributes of the diver are unique: the sense of touch, dexterity and agility underwater during work, the ability to apply himself to a wide variety of different types of work and to improve with experience, and the ability to adapt methods of work to changing circumstances or information arising during a task, and to take appropriate decisions. When this integration of sense reception, decision making, and action are required on a task, divers are indispensable.' These are certainly valuable attributes. Imagine, for example, a machine trying to feel its way around and repair a faulty piece of equipment with the visibility cut down to zero by disturbed sediment. Yet many of the qualities listed above are those of man rather than the diver alone. Why not let the man stay on the surface and command a telechiric machine?

An engineer-inventor, Hugh Ballinger, at the Atomic Energy Authority's Harwell establishment has countered eulogies on divers by describing the advantages of a multi-purpose marine telechiric system (MTCS):

'*In the explanatory role:* the MTCS can carry out systematic bottom sampling and reduce the lottery aspect of some techniques of underwater rock sampling, for commercial ores. By using the ship to tow the cable of the telechiric and giving via the ship's echosounder a forecast of the bottom level to the MTCS operator, a large search area can be covered.

'*In the inspection role:* the MTCS does not require the "waiting to resurface" delay of other methods, to present a full report of what has been seen and done. The customer's consultant or supervising Engineer can have the satisfaction of seeing the job personally, without hazarding himself.

'*In the work role:* the MTCS has the ability to work around the clock, by using relays of operators. Difficult or important parts of the work progress can be directed with step-by-step decisions from the appropriate expert, seated in the "co-pilot's chair".

'*In the dangerous task role:* the MTCS may be risked in conditions of turbulent water and poor visibility where the hazard to men as divers, or as crew in underwater research vessels, is too high.

'*A final and major advantage* of the MTCS over all other forms of manned diving methods is that: should the ship or diving vehicle get into difficulties, there is the ability to "cut and run" – having buoyed and anchored the cable end! Then, back in the peace and calm of harbour, the next move can be sorted out carefully and advice or assistance obtained.'

At the present time, the diver has two major advantages over the telechiric/man system: 'direct linkage' between the brain and the hand, and the considerable manipulative abilities of the hand. Even the best underwater manipulators end with little more than a pincer in which a simple gripping motion replaces the 22 separate movements of a human hand. Part of the direct linkage of hand and brain includes the information fed back from the sensory receptors in the skin and muscles, but only a few slave arms boast this kind of feedback control, and most marine arms are driven rather like a crane. Provide the diver with powered recoilless tools to compensate for the brute strength and tenacity of the machine, and he becomes an even more potent adversary. Any machine-versus-man match is, therefore, likely to be closely contested.

One important factor holding back underwater machines is the lack of standardization in current industrial effort. Should large-scale exploitation be established, automatic and remote-controlled devices are likely to play an increasing part, parallelling events on the land. In fact, developments in land-based industries might well accelerate the invasion of the sea by the 'robot'. Recent years have witnessed a remarkable success by industrial robots – machines which can perform repetitive or dangerous tasks with unfailing accuracy. But these early models are crude in comparison with what is already possible in terms of control engineering. The design of more sophisticated machines capable of mimicking the very attributes which made the diver so useful could therefore originate and be financed by progress with industrial machines.

For the present, the most numerous underwater vehicles are manned submersibles which are being used increasingly by research scientists from geologists to physical oceanographers. Apart from scientific and military applications, submersibles are employed by industry in a variety of jobs including construction, repair work and salvage. Some submersibles have been designed purely as 'work boats'. The *Deep Diver*, built by Perry Submarine to designs by Dr Link, provides an interesting example of this new class of vehicle. *Deep Diver* combines both diving bell and conventional submersible; it is a 'lock-out' submersible. The 'lock-out' chamber can be pressurized to match the surrounding sea before a diver exits from it. When the diver re-enters, he can use the chamber to decompress or stay under pressure for saturation diving. Meanwhile the pilot and observers in a separate chamber can remain at atmospheric pressure. Both chambers can be 'evened' out so that men can transfer from one chamber to the other. This ability to carry both working divers and non-diving observers enables experts to visit the scene of operations to direct or to advise the men working out in the sea.

Only one British company so far operates an underwater-work boat. The Vickers Shipbuilding Group entered the field in 1966 when it purchased a redundant stern trawler and converted it into a support ship for the *Pisces* submersible which it later acquired. In 1972 Vickers Oceanics Limited was formed to take control of operations. So far most of the charters of the support ship *Vickers Venturer* and its submersible have come from Government bodies and research organizations. On the whole, the submersible has yet to prove itself in the turbulent conditions of the North Sea and certainly early trials by the oil companies were reported to be discouraging. It was at least partly for this reason that the concept of a seabed vehicle was mooted by another shipbuilding company, Cammell Laird, and supported by NRDC. According to its designer, Francis Daniell, the vehicle would be able to traverse steep inclines, to cross gullies and to crouch on the seabed should it encounter strong currents, say, between four and ten knots. Work started on the vehicle, which Cammell Laird named the *Sealbeaver*, in 1969, but unfortunately the company fell upon hard times and the project was abandoned. The only journey that the partially-built vehicle made was across the Cammell Laird Wet Basin at Birkenhead in the autumn of 1970. As a result, there is still no underwater vehicle capable of heavy work duty in the United Kingdom – and probably, for that matter, in the world. The diver still reigns supreme in the shallow seas of the continental shelf.

Chapter 7

Wars and Wayfaring

The military and commercial value of the oceans as highways will be influential in determining any future exploitation. In the First World War, the Royal Navy imposed an effective, if somewhat distant, blockade on merchant shipping destined for Germany, to prevent supplies reaching the enemy by sea. The German Navy, for its part, pointed the way to submarine warfare. Since those times, the world has witnessed a build-up of submarine fleets and the emergence of nuclear-powered submarines armed with ballistic missiles providing the ultimate deterrent to world-wide conflict. Meanwhile, on the surface, massive oil tankers have been built to sail round the Cape, bringing oil to thirsty industries in Western Europe. In addition to bulk cargoes, a revolution in handling general cargo is taking place: major ports have been modified to reduce the time cargo ships lie idle in them – particularly by encouraging the use of large containers. With world trade in the 1960s increasing annually by about 7 per cent and with general freight charges by sea nearly 40 times cheaper than by air, the merchant marine continues to exert a major influence on commerce throughout the world.

The last traditional British sea battle, with big ships lined up exchanging shots until one side was destroyed or forced to retire, occurred in 1941. In May, the heavily armoured German battleship *Bismarck* broke out into the Atlantic accompanied by the battlecruiser *Prinz Eugen*. On the first contact with the British home fleet, *Bismarck* damaged the battleship *Prince of Wales* and sank the battlecruiser *Hood* before escaping from the British forces converging on her.

On 25 May aircraft from the carrier *Ark Royal* spotted the German battleship and attacked it with torpedoes. The following day the British ships caught up with the damaged ship, and *Bismarck* was finally sunk. Without the aircraft from *Ark Royal*, this successful conclusion might never have been achieved and since then the advent of the submarine, aircraft and the guided missile have combined to make obsolete the 'line of battle' – a formation dating from the times of Henry VIII.

With the demise of the battleship, aircraft carriers became the 'capital ships' of the fleet. In 1961 the floating air bases reached a new peak when *Enterprise*, the US Navy's nuclear-powered aircraft carrier, went into service. A modern giant, *Enterprise* carries 100 aircraft and a crew of 4,500. In contrast, the Royal Navy is finishing with large aircraft carriers such as *Ark Royal* and *Eagle* in the 1970s. The British decision to 'run down' its carrier force has been precipitated largely by a contraction of territorial responsibilities, but it also indicates the country's changing needs in an age when submarines, ship-borne guided missiles and 'restricted warfare' present the major threats to peace. For such contingencies, the Royal Navy favours high-speed patrol craft, mobile assault forces, frigates armed with guided missiles and helicopter carriers (helicopters have a variety of roles from supporting amphibious operations to anti-submarine warfare). The Soviet Navy, which has never had a large carrier fleet, has a similar but much larger force with helicopter carriers such as *Moscow* and *Leningrad*, fast inshore craft – some armed with Styx missiles of the type which sank the Israeli-destroyer *Eilat*, assault craft and missile-launching ships of the Kresta class.

Apart from the more familiar trappings of military might, people have become aware of a different type of fighting ship: the 'spy ships' used in the continuous battle for military intelligence. Instead of big guns or missiles, they are festooned with a bewildering array of aerials and are loaded with electronic gadgetry. Taking advantage of the international freedom of the high seas, they hover around strategic areas detecting the movements of shipping, submarines and aircraft and monitoring military communications. Few NATO exercises manage to avoid an uninvited escort of Soviet 'trawlers' carrying electronic rather than fishing gear. Occasionally someone's nerve apparently snaps and an 'electronic counter-measure' ship leaps into the headlines. On 23 January 1968, the North Koreans arrested the United States' ship, *Pueblo*, which they claimed had intruded into their territorial waters to spy. Fortunately, such international incidents are uncommon and most countries protect their military secrets by keeping one step ahead with 'electronic counter-counter-measures' such as jamming devices which flood the spy ship's receivers with meaningless noise.

So long as military minds grapple in the mysterious shadows of this electronic warfare, the world is probably safe, but as an incubator of wide-spread conflict, the open sea is difficult to beat. Patrolling submarines equipped with missiles are just one more uncertainty to add to the balance of ignorance about what is happening within the seas, and this ignorance permits a fantasia of threats to be conjured up. Could secret missile silos be established? Is it possible to build a submarine which could lie hidden on the ocean floor? Perhaps a mobile ocean-bottom system which creeps along very slowly might be better? Men can already live for weeks on the continental shelf. Why not establish hidden bases close to an enemy coastline? Such thoughts spur on the military investigation of the oceans. If some of the more devious schemes were ever to become realities, then the world would once again face the prospects of a confrontation more frightening than the Cuba crisis of 1962.

While submarines prowl beneath the surface of the oceans, the naval fleets above are easily outnumbered by the merchant marine which is responsible for maintaining most of the world's trade. Even landlocked nations depend on the marine transport system, relying on the good services of their neighbours for outlets to the sea, and many a dispute between nations has resolved into a struggle for access to the oceans. But although the merchant marine sustains so much of the world's commercial activities, its ships have not remained immune to competition between companies and seafaring nations. Just as on the land, one of the basic ways of cutting costs has been to start automating the work of the crew. Such savings in expensive manpower are seen in ships ranging from trawlers to the largest tankers afloat. There are now systems, for example, which provide direct control of the ship's engines from the bridge. In a conventional ship, an order such as 'full' or 'half ahead' is given on the engine telegraph on the bridge and the engineer on watch, after acknowledging the signal, sets the engine speed as instructed. In an automated ship, the engine room can be left unmanned for most of the voyage: instructions from the bridge control go to a computer which controls the engines and ensures that they perform as directed. No doubt automation of all manner of jobs will continue unabated during years to come, held back only by the need to design the ships for its most advanced forms. But this is not the only revolution occurring in marine transport.

Cargo revolution

Since 1960, the world's sea-borne trade has been dominated by the bulk transport of oil. The oil tankers are the technological giants of the oceans – the *Idemitsu Maru* is 1,101 feet long and has a deadweight of 209,000 tons (the longest passenger ship afloat, the *France*, is 66 feet shorter). Modern 'supertankers' carry anything from 150,000 to considerably more than 300,000 tons of crude oil, which they can load and unload at impressive rates; a cargo of 165,000 tons of crude oil can be dealt with in 17 hours – a rate of just less than 10,000 tons per hour. These tankers contrast sharply with the first recorded long sea transport of oil in 1881, when the brig *Elizabeth Watts* brought a cargo of 224 tons of oil from Philadelphia to London. Modern 'jumbo' tankers, like the 312,000-ton *Universe Ireland,* are iron and steel testimonies to the fact that the bigger the ship, the lower the cost of transporting the oil.

Bulk cargoes, by virtue of their amorphous nature, lend themselves to rapid mechanical handling, usually at specially built docks. An automatic bulk-loading installation for potash and phosphate at the Israeli port of Ashdod can handle 800 tons an hour. It is the general cargoes that cause the trouble. Manufactured goods, because of their variety, frequently have to be treated as separate units and, as such, need extra handling at warehouses and the quayside. Obviously, the more such goods have to be handled and moved, the more costly their transport, and hence total cost, becomes. In an American study, 54 per cent of the cost of a shipment was taken by port expenses. This is a cause for concern to most countries, because in terms of value rather than 'ton miles', general cargo is far more important than bulk commodities such as oil, iron ore, grain and coal.

An ideal answer to the question of how to move general cargo about the world is to use internationally standard containers. These boxes, which have a cross section eight feet square, may be 10, 20, 30 or 40 feet long and hold up to 20 tons of freight. Some space may be wasted if the container is not full, but this is more than compensated for by the reduced handling costs. Goods can be packed in containers at factories remote from the port and then carried by rail or truck to the docks; and, although formalities such as customs clearance can still cause delays, ultimately transport from remote terminals to a position on the cargo ship should be a continuous process. And, because the containers are made to international standards, they can be loaded and unloaded at any port equipped for container transport. However, at this stage not all ports have the necessary equipment, and some ships such as the American

Seatainer Service ship, *Santa Eliana*, avoid delays resulting from conventional handling by having their own deck cranes.

Some container ships have more in common with aircraft carriers than the conventional general cargo ship. Gone are the holds filled through overhead hatches, and in their place are tiers of decking reached by entrances at the stern or sides of the ship. The super-structure and machinery are packed away at the stern or displaced to one side to give uninterrupted expanses of storage space. Since most of the load is carried above the waterline, containers as well as other cargo such as smaller loads piled up on pallets can be shipped with the minimum amount of manoeuvering. To counteract this high-sitting load, large permanent ballast is placed in the bowels of the ship.

First of the thirty leading United States ports to be equipped for container traffic was Elizabeth, New Jersey, but one of the most highly developed ports is Rotterdam with its Europoort complex. Having lost the income and resources of its colonies, the Netherlands has set itself the task of becoming the gateway to industrial Western Europe. In the United Kingdom, too, preparations are well in hand for the expected increase in container traffic. The first site for container berths was Tilbury, a mere 26 miles from London. At the Tilbury terminal, Overseas Containers Limited can take a ship with a cargo of 1,300 containers and, aided by a central computer, can turn it round with another load of containers within 48 hours. There are other important terminals at Harwich and Felixstowe. All these container ports are linked by the British Freightlines service, which provides a direct rail connection with industrial areas as far away as Scotland.

The trend towards the direct loading of large packages of general cargo helps to remove the most serious weakness in marine freight operations – the time that ships waste lying idle in port. The loss of working time starts from the moment that a ship slows down to take on the pilot and culminates in the docking procedures – up to 30 per cent of the time a ship spends in port may be accounted for by berthing manoeuvers. The port costs for a general cargo can equal the total running costs and, with larger ships coming along, the situation can only deteriorate further if new schemes such as containerization are not adopted.

Research by the Port of London suggests that, for the sea routes serving the United Kingdom, container shipping costs (including ports costs) should be some 40 per cent below those of conventional ships. The savings are not restricted to large cargo carriers; on short coastal and cross-Channel services, British ships can spend more than three quarters of their working lives discharging and loading cargo. Using container ships integrated with rail and road services at either end of the 'sea bridge', small 4,000-ton vessels can make a round trip every 24 hours.

Some experts believe that the whole port procedure needs to be re-thought. Professor Fernando Costa of Lisbon Technical University argues that, with radar and modern communications systems, the pilot should be able to operate from the shore. Working from a central office akin to the control tower of an airport, pilots would 'talk-in' their charges until they were close enough to be taken in tow. The approach up the Thames to the London docks already has the basis for such a system, with its complete radar coverage established in 1968.

Other experts have questioned the need to spend thousands of dollars bringing a large cargo ship into port when all that is required is the cargo. In one experiment at Bridgeport, Connecticut, a Sikorsky 564 helicopter was used to fly containers out to a waiting cargo ship. Lykes Lines has solved the problem by carrying shallow draft barges (lighters) which are lowered down a stern ramp into the sea in the vicinity of the port. One of the best examples of this lighter-aboard-ship (LASH) system is that operated between New Orleans and Rotterdam, by the Central Gulf Steamship Company. A 43,000-ton ship carries 73 lighters loaded with cargo across the Atlantic. At the American end of the journey, the ship puts down lighters carrying general goods from Europe in exchange for lighters loaded with cellulose and paper. At Rotterdam, the lighters from America are exchanged once more for those with general cargo. In this way, with three fleets of lighters, the mother ship need never linger long between its transatlantic journeys. However, in spite of the advent of these kangaroo ships, containerization remains the single most important trend in international transport.

Building better ships

A model boat a few feet long seems far removed from 'jumbo tankers', but it is almost certain that without tests made on scale models such ships would prove difficult, if not impossible, to design. In fact, ship designers have long relied on the use of models to help them devise satisfactory hull shapes. At first, experiments with models had only a qualitative value, and the results could not be scaled up to the full-sized model. Then, about 1870, William Froude, a British engineer, discovered that surface wave patterns created by a ship and by a geometrically similar model are identical at certain speeds, depending on the ship speed and the scale of the model. From this concept, now embodied in the modelling parameter called the Froude Number, he was able to show how the resistance, or hydrodynamic drag, of a ship could be directly deduced from experiments with a model towed at the appropriate speed. Models assumed a much more important role in ship design, and ship model laboratories have progressed from Froude's first laboratory in a field beside his home in Torquay to a stage where few problems of a ship's performance at sea cannot be investigated in them.

The model testing tank built by Froude was a primitive affair little more than 200 feet long, in which wax and wooden hull models and planks could be towed and their resistances measured over a range of controlled speeds. Compare this with the facilities available in modern laboratories such as the Ship Division of the National Physical Laboratory (NPL) at Feltham near London. The largest towing tank of the Ship Division is 1,300 feet long, 48 feet wide and 25 feet deep. Spanning the channel is a carriage which can travel at speeds of up to 50 feet per second, providing an instrument and observation platform from which models over 30 feet long can be towed or propelled, while a wavemaking machine at one end creates realistic sea states. There are also wavemakers along the sides of the large sea-keeping tanks in which stationary or remote-controlled, free-moving models are tested. Apart from such 'indoor oceans', water tunnels, the marine equivalents of wind tunnels, are used to study models, particularly various designs of propellers and stabilizing fins. Finally, the Ship Division has one of the most up-to-date circulating water channels in the world. The channel combines features of both tank and tunnel, by circulating water past a stationary model as in the tunnel, while retaining the free-water surface of the tank. In the NPL circulating channel some one and a half million gallons of water is kept moving in a highly ordered flow. Although officially commissioned only in 1967, the channel has already proved a valuable asset in various ship designs including that of Cunard's *Queen Elizabeth II*.

Many investigations in the laboratory centre on improving the speed of ships by reducing resistance met by hulls moving through water. The two principal causes of this hydrodynamic drag are the frictional resistance resulting from the viscosity of the water, which 'sticks' to the submerged parts of the hull, and the wavemaking (Froude) resistance produced as the bow pushes away the water and creates a surface wave. Both types of resistance are closely related and, until the advent of the circulating channel, very difficult to distinguish in some advanced hull designs. Alec Silverleaf, the Deputy Director of NPL, gives an interesting examples of this, found with the bulbous and ram bows built on many modern cargo ships. The theory behind these projecting bow structures is that the protrusion acts as a 'false' bow to create a wave system which at least in part cancels out that of the 'real' bow. However, the NPL scientists found that the novel bow forms often have a much more significant effect on the viscous drag than on the wave resistance because a well-shaped and suitably placed 'snout' can radically alter and improve the flow of the water around the hull. The practical effect of this finding is that later designs can take advantage of the beneficial effects of large ram and bulbous bows without incurring some of their penalties, particularly the indifferent performance in any but the calmest of seas, by modifying the design.

Thanks to Froude, the findings in the laboratory are generally confirmed in the full-scale ship, but nevertheless actual performance at sea forms an important source of feedback for studies on models. One of the principal activities of the British Ship Research Association (BSRA), since it was formed in 1945, has been to make full-scale tests and trials on ships. And in 1958 agreement was reached between BSRA, the National Institute of Oceanography and NPL to cooperate in a joint programme of research into the sea-going qualities of ships. Naturally enough, trials at sea involve far more unknowns than one would expect in the carefully controlled conditions of the laboratory. In one exercise of collecting and storing data on trials, where information was recorded on punched tape suitable for computer processing, investigators found themselves landed with 54 miles of tape! Instruments have also been installed on drilling rigs to monitor stresses in important structural parts during various drilling operations and in a wide variety of weather and sea states. Altogether, data are being collected on practically every structure which spends most of its time on or in the sea, from the trawler to the most modern offshore rigs.

Building better ships does not end with the kind of work typified by BSRA and the NPL's Ship Division: Japan's global lead in shipbuilding is in part the result of advances in marine engineering. Apart from various welding techniques – including that of putting together two floating halves of a tanker's hull – the Japanese shipbuilders have developed various systems for ship construction. Probably the most important one involves the construction of large 'standard' units which are brought together for assembly in a covered building area, the ship being jacked out stern first on to a slipway as its length increases. The use of 'standard parts' makes for considerable economies in design and production costs. The Japanese shipbuilders have been able to save on material costs. The 205,000-ton *Idemitsu Maru*, which was built in ten months at the Yokohama Yards of Ishikawajima Heavy Industries, contains only 3 per cent more steel than the 132,000-ton tanker *Nissho Maru* built four years earlier in 1962. There is even a 'standard design ship', a bulk carrier of about 65,000 tons deadweight (the maximum size allowed through the Panama Canal). In 1969, Japan launched nearly half the commercial shipping built in the world, accounting for 9.3 of 19.3 million tons. This was the country's tenth successive year of increased production and included 20 per cent of the 42 ships of more than 100,000 gross tons launched in 1969.

The propulsion systems have progressed steadily from the days of sail. Merchant ships being built today are propelled either by diesel or steam turbine plants. Diesel engines are used almost exclusively for small and medium outputs and until recently the steam turbine largely for the much higher powers, but the diesel is now rapidly encroaching on this territory as well. According to W. Kilchenmann, one of the world's foremost marine engineers, neither diesel nor steam turbine will show sensational improvements in its efficiency. Both, he suggests, will retain their leading position in ship propulsion, possibly on a somewhat higher level of development, as long as fuel oil is obtainable for them. However, the gas turbine seems destined to become increasingly important, particularly for what might be termed 'high performance' vessels. The Royal Navy, for example, had a gas turbine-powered patrol boat as early as 1947. The use of gas turbines in major warships followed. The prevailing policy, however, was to limit them to the role of auxiliary boosters for conventional power units. Only in February 1968 was the decision taken to abandon diesel or conventional steam propulsion units in favour of gas turbines in future surface vessels.

Unconventional craft

A tremendous boost for the marine gas turbine will come with the progress of hydrofoils and hovercraft. These 'surface effect' craft are one of the most exciting innovations in marine transport. The idea for the hovercraft was only put forward in 1956 and, in spite of experiments on hydrofoils some seventy years ago, large hydrofoil craft have become feasible only in recent years when large engines with high power-to-weight ratios and high-load carrying, high-efficiency foils have become available. Both types of vehicle have as their aim a reduction in hydrodynamic drag – the hovercraft by moving on a cushion of air and the hydrofoil by 'flying' on foils which act like wings in the water to provide the necessary lift.

Hydrofoils can be divided into three categories according to the types of foil that they use. There are depth-effect foils, surface-piercing foils and fully-submerged foils (see figure 23). The depth effect depends on the breadth of the foil which determines how deep the foil may be below the surface before the 'lift gradient' goes on and the hydrofoil craft loses its stability. In practice, the depth range is sufficiently small to rule out the use of depth-effect hydrofoils in water with high waves. In fact, craft based on this principle can almost be regarded as being built specially for the extensive inland waterways of the Soviet Union where they are said to carry more inter-city passenger traffic than do the roads. More general purpose vessels, typified by the

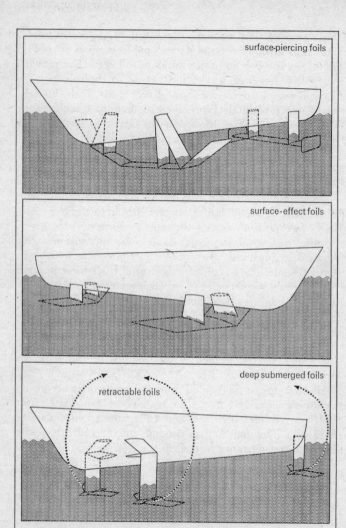

figure 23 **three types of hydrofoil configuration**

Swiss-designed Supramar craft, use surface-piercing foils. They have large vee-section foils fore and aft and ride much higher above the water than depth-effect hydrofoils. The foils are shaped in such a way that waves from any direction tend to increase the area of lifting surface under the water, providing greater stability than depth-effect systems. Unfortunately when the boat catches up with high waves, the upward and downward motion of the water causes violent pitching. This potential hazard limits surface-piercing hydrofoils to fairly sheltered waters such as the Mediterranean and the Adriatic in the summer.

The most sophisticated and seaworthy type of hydrofoil has fully submerged foils. These craft keep their foils constantly underwater, operating exactly like the wings of an aircraft. This similarity is borne out in their control, because to maintain an even depth the angle of the foil beneath the surface has to be continually changing according to the surface of the sea ahead. The craft cuts through small waves with little or no reaction, but it must detect and follow the contours of larger waves which would otherwise smash against the hull. The British hydrofoil expert, Christopher Hook, has devised a bow-sensing foil which moves over the water in front of the boat and adjusts the submerged foils accordingly via a 'dampened' mechanical linkage. A more sophisticated system, developed in the United States, controls the flight of the hydrofoil craft electronically. A sonic beam detects on-coming waves, while gyroscopes sense roll and pitch. The whole system is integrated by a black box which controls the angles of the submerged foils.

While the Soviet Union and the United States concentrated on foil-borne craft, the United Kingdom was busy developing a completely new kind of transport, the hovercraft. Sitting on a cushion of air, the hovercraft escapes almost completely from the viscous drag of the water and, because it rides over, rather than through, the water, experiences very little wavemaking resistance. Christopher

Cockerell, the man who invented this marvellous machine, demonstrated his air-cushion idea to scientists, engineers and government officials in 1956. Within three years the first hovercraft, the *SRN-1*, was on the slipway of the Saunders-Roe Company at Cowes. The *SRN-1*, like Cockerell's earlier saucer-shaped model, was kept hovering above the surface (water or land) by air pumped down and inwards from the outer rim. This peripheral jet raised the 4-ton craft about 10 inches off the ground by means of the ground effect: the annular jet traps a volume of pressurized air which pushes up on the flat underside of the vehicle in an effort to escape.

The 'curtain' of air around the edge also helped to keep the cushion intact and replaced any air which managed to escape, but the limitations of this invisible restraint soon became apparent. Somehow the clearance of the vehicle had to be radically increased for the hovercraft to be anything more than an interesting idea. The solution was a long flexible skirt which formed a soft extension from the base of the craft and trapped a cushion of air several feet thick. The *SRN-1*, for example, was operated successfully with a skirt 4 feet deep. Commercial vehicles now became feasible, and within ten years of Cockerell's initial demonstration, ferry services were operating with the *SRN-5* and the *SRN-6*. (The *SRN-5*, a small 7-ton craft, carries 18 passengers and the *SRN-6*, a larger 10-ton version, can seat 38 passengers.) In the summer of 1968, a 165-ton *SRN-4*, wearing British Rail livery, began a ferry service between Dover and Boulogne. A giant compared with the previous machines, this Mountbatten Class hovercraft, christened the *Princess Margaret*, carries 250 passengers and 30 cars. In spite of her size – 128 feet long, 75 feet wide and nearly 37 feet high – the *Princess Margaret* can travel between England and France in a little over a third of the time taken by the conventional car ferries and takes waves over 6 feet high in its stride.

The *SRN-4*, the *SRN-5* and the *SRN-6* are all built by the British Hovercraft Corporation (BHC) which was formed in 1966 to concentrate the British hovercraft industry's major interests under a single management. BHC combines the hovercraft interests of Westland Aircraft (which took over Saunders-Roe) and the heavy engineering company Vickers. A third partner in the corporation is the state-owned National Research Development Corporation (NRDC) which holds Cockerell's original patents and which, through its subsidiary Hovercraft Development Limited (HDL), grants licences to overseas companies such as Bell Aerosystems in the United States and the Mitsubishi Company in Japan as well as other British companies. Because the Mountbatten Class hovercraft are direct descendants of plans made by Saunders-Roe, but shelved in favour of the smaller *SRN-5* and 6, the large hovercraft have retained their original number. All the later designs have the BH prefix.

The same week that the *Princess Margaret* descended under power down the Cowes slipway (built originally for Princess flying boats and uncomfortably narrow), the first of another line of passenger hovercraft, the *HM 2*, was delivered to the British Rail 'Seaspeed' service. Built by Hovermarine of Southamptom, the *HM 2* has rigid widewalls which sit in the water, so that the only clues to the supporting air cushion are the flexible skirts fore and aft. Manufacturers of side-wall hovercraft have traded the amphibious freedom provided by a continuous skirt for a slower, but, they claim, more easily controlled vehicle, which is cheaper to build, to equip and to maintain than a comparable conventional hovercraft. In place of the fully skirted machine's rather dumpy shape, side-wall hovercraft, because they must contend with the viscous drag of the rigid sides, have boat-like dimensions. The *HM 2* is 51 feet long, 20 feet wide and 12 feet high. When sitting on its air cushion, the draught is 2 feet 3 inches, compared with a draught of 4 feet 10 inches when floating passively. The *HM 2*, which carries 60 passengers, is designed for short-range operation in relatively calm, sheltered waters.

The great attraction of both hovercraft and hydrofoil is the high speeds that these craft can attain. High speed, however, brings its own particular problems. For example, a side-wall hovercraft operating at speeds of about 35 knots can use marine diesels and conventional propellers but above this speed the conventional marine screw starts to become unsatisfactory. Like the air propeller, its thrust stems from pressure forces upon the face of the blades and suction forces on the back. As the thrust increases, the reduced pressures on the back of the blades can become so low that the water there starts to 'boil', forming minute bubbles of vapour. This effect, called cavitation, disrupts the pressure around the blade and, ultimately, reduces the efficiency of the entire propeller. To make matters worse, where the bubbles collapse – generating high transient pressures – the surface of the propellers becomes pitted and eroded. In some experimental craft, erosion has been so severe that propellers have lasted little more than a day of high-speed operation.

To solve the cavitation problem, 'supercavitating' propellers have been designed. These propellers, which operate at the high speeds demanded by hydrofoil and other high-speed craft, encourage rather than discourage the creation of cavitation bubbles. They avoid erosion and loss of power because the bubbles swirl away from the immediate surface and collapse downstream of the blades.

Because of difficulties with cavitation in propellers and transmitting power to them, hydrofoil designers have studied alternative ways of providing the necessary thrust, including air propellers, jet engines and water jets. The most promising of these various systems seems to be the water jet (see figure 24). In one successful craft, the *Tucumcari* designed by Boeing, a 3,200 horsepower gas turbine engine drives a water-jet pump. Water is sucked through

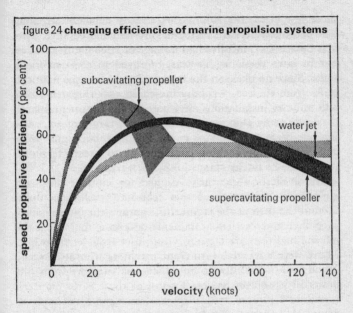

figure 24 **changing efficiencies of marine propulsion systems**

the rear foil struts and up into the pump, which forces jets of water out through nozzles in the hull. At speeds of more than 40 knots, the craft pumps 100 tons of water per minute. A smaller water-jet propulsion unit driven by a diesel engine provides the thrust for hull-borne manoeuvers. Launched in July 1967, the 71-foot craft, designated *PGH-2* (Patrol Gunboat Hydrofoil), is operated by the US Navy.

The submarine deterrent

In keeping with man's aggressive nature, the most startling development in marine vessels began in 1954 with the launching of the *Nautilus*, the United States' first nuclear submarine. It came close to completion on 20 July 1960, with the successful underwater launching of two Polaris missiles by the *George Washington*. Within the space of these few years, the submarine, already a potent weapon, had become a decisive factor in international conflict. The first Polaris (A1) missiles had a range of 1,200 nautical miles but in later versions this was improved to 2,500 nautical miles. Since no place on the land is more than 1,700 nautical miles from the sea, a submarine could now threaten cities and military installations anywhere on the continental land masses. Enemy shipping, the traditional target of the submarine, became secondary to the Polaris submarine's principal goal of approaching close enough to enemy territory to let loose its nuclear-tipped missiles if required.

The earliest submarines designed for military purposes gave little indication of this fearsome evolution. Built around the turn of the eighteenth century, they were hand-propelled and carried armaments so crude that the submarine had to move close to, if not touch, the enemy ship. Many were devised by itinerant inventors who attempted, usually unsuccessfully, to enlist financial support from the powerful European navies. Typical of these early pioneers was Robert Fulton (1765–1815), an American artist and inventor. He spent several years going from one European capital to another trying to sell his idea for a submarine, keeping himself by his painting. Finally in 1800 Fulton persuaded Napoleon Bonaparte to provide the necessary finance and a year later the *Nautilus* took to the water. Although successful in trials against an old schooner moored off Brest, the hand-propelled machine could not approach close enough to the blockading British warships to attach an explosive charge. As a result Bonaparte's interest soon waned and, after trying to interest the British Navy, Fulton returned to his homeland. Undaunted by European 'failures', he prevailed upon the United States Congress to provide for another, more ambitious, submarine powered by a steam engine. Unfortunately, Robert Fulton died before the trials of the submarine were completed, and it was left to rot away at its moorings.

A turning point in the history of the submarine came

when practical, electric-storage batteries became available in the 1880s (partly the result of the impetus for research provided by the rapidly expanding telegraph systems). Experiments with steam power had been only moderately successful and the superiority of electric propulsion was well demonstrated by John P. Holland when he secured a US Navy contract in competition with the Swedish engineer Thorston Nordenfelt who had suggested a steam-powered submarine. In 1895 Holland received an order for a submarine from the Navy but their specifications were such that the boat was never completed. Instead, Holland built his own submarine, the *Holland*, which entered into service with the US Navy in 1900. A year later, the British Government announced an order for 'five submarine vessels of the type invented by Mr Holland'. Germany's first submarine, *Unterseeboot 1*, went into service in 1908. To preserve the life of the batteries, gasoline and then diesel engines were used for surface power.

The first British diesel-electric submarine went into operation in 1908. Even at present the majority of submarines use this type of power plant, which has been superseded only by nuclear propulsion. In a sense the diesel-electric submarine is a surface vessel which submerges for relatively short periods. On active patrol, the early submarines often restricted their speed to a few knots to eke out their battery power. The batteries exhausted, the submarine had to turn to its air breathing diesel engines for propulsion and recharging, which meant returning to the surface. At first surfacing, at night or under the cover of fog, held few terrors but the development of radar in the 1940s put an end to this. The solution was to use a snorkel or snout, an air intake which could be pushed above the surface of the sea. Even this system is not entirely safe; the snorkel, like the periscope, leaves a wake which can be seen from an aircraft or surface ship; the noise of the diesels underwater makes the submarine 'deaf' to other sounds, including those of enemy craft; and, most important of all, up-to-date submarine detection instruments can pin-point submarines lying near to the surface.

The modern nuclear submarine suffers from none of these disabilities. The nuclear power pack enables it to submerge for months and ensures complete independence from the surface by supplying power for desalination and oxygen generation. Apart from satisfying the physical needs of its occupants, the nuclear submarine also caters for relaxation, with film shows, libraries and rest rooms. In fact considerable attention has been given to the best way of keeping the nuclear submariner happy and alert during his sixty- to ninety-day cruise underwater. As a further safeguard, every crew member undergoes special screening and training to ensure that he can comfortably meet the challenge of prolonged underwater missions.

Becoming a complete underwater denizen removes the submarine's navigator from traditional 'signposts' such as stars and sun as well as more modern radio-direction systems. Somehow the navigator has to check the submarine's position without recourse to ground stations, satellites or celestial bodies. The solution is a system developed originally for missiles, called an inertial navigation system. Such a system is entirely independent of any information outside the submarine, other than the natural movement of the earth. Its name comes from the use of gyroscopes which, once set in motion, remain in a fixed plane by their own momentum or inertia. Basically, the ship's inertial navigation system (SINS) uses an accelerometer – a sensitive pendulum – to detect movement, and this is mounted on a stable platform provided by three gyros: one gyro axis is parallel to the axis of the Earth, the longitude gyro; one is parallel to the equatorial plane, the meridian gyro; and the third is horizonal and points east–west. A computer used in conjunction with this mechanical unit presents the navigator with all the information he requires. To ensure the maximum accuracy, the Polaris submarine has three SINS and the 'best' reading is taken after reference to all three sets of readings. In this way, the position of the submarine can be determined within a few hundred feet.

US Navy nuclear submarines have notched up an impressive list of firsts. On 3 August 1958, the *Nautilus* made the first submerged crossing under the North Pole and on 17 March 1959 the *Skate* surfaced there. The twin reactor-powered *Triton* circumnavigated the world in 1960 while submerged. Following the route of Ferdinand Magellan, the *Triton* covered 41,500 miles in 84 days. But the most important first of all was when the *George Washington* fired its first Polaris missiles in 1960.

The ancestry of the guided missile goes back to the German V-2s, but the development programme which led directly to Polaris did not begin until 1956. The previous year the US Navy had set up a Special Projects Office under Rear Admiral William F. Raborn to develop a Navy version of the Jupiter missile planned by the Army. Unfortunately a missile safe enough for a submarine did not fit at all well into the existing design concepts and eventually the Navy decided to develop its own missile which Raborn called the Polaris after the northern star. The programme, which got off to a good start, received additional impetus when on 4 October 1957, the 184-pound *Sputnik* was flung into orbit by a Soviet rocket. This great Russian achievement was capped a month later on 3 November, when a capsule containing a dog was sent aloft. Clearly rockets that could carry these experiments into space were just as capable of delivering less desirable payloads to any foe. Taking heed of a warning given by George Washington in his first annual address to a joint session of Congress in 1790 – 'To be prepared for war is one of the most effectual means of preserving the peace' – the Polaris project was reassessed. By accepting a slight reduction in range from 1,500 to 1,200 nautical miles, it was agreed that the missile could be ready for 1960, and by converting a nuclear submarine already being built to carry and fire them, the first phase of development would be complete. On 15 November 1960, the *George Washington*, equipped with sixteen missiles, put to sea on its first 'peace patrol'. The ultimate deterrent had arrived.

As a result of the Nassau Agreement between President Kennedy and British Premier Harold Macmillan, the United Kingdom took a hand in promoting nuclear stalemate. *Resolution*, the first British Polaris submarine, started her peace-keeping role in June 1968. Other members of the British Polaris fleet are *Repulse, Renown* and *Revenge* – all named after famous battleships and battlecruisers as befits their size and power. Yet, even before they were launched the increasing sophistication of counter-devices began cutting into the effectiveness of their Polaris missiles. For this reason the United States decided to convert many of its Polaris submarines to carry Poseidon missiles, each of which carries ten individually-aimed warheads. The *James Madison* is the first submarine to be converted to carry out these MIRVs (Multiple Independently Targeted Re-entry Vehicles). The British Polaris missiles already have multiple, although not individually targeted, warheads.

For a stalemate to exist, there have to be potential opponents. From the West's point of view, these are taken to be the Soviet bloc and China. The Russians have the largest submarine force in the world, with more than 400 vessels. In 1972 they had 42 Polaris type submarines of which probably over a fifth carry nuclear missiles. This fleet has to be compared with an American force of more than 200 conventional and nuclear submarines including 31 Polaris and 10 Poseidon submarines, and a Royal Navy force with another 4 Polaris submarines. France too is independently building up a nuclear missile fleet and China has the capacity to do so. However the situation improved considerably at a summit meeting in May 1972, when the United States and the Soviet Union agreed to limit their strategic nuclear weapons. The agreement freezes the number of offensive long-range weapons at 1972 levels, but within certain limits it leaves open how they are deployed *vis-à-vis* land and sea.

The Polaris submarines continue to carry more familiar

underwater weapons such as the torpedo. (US Polaris submarines have four bow torpedo tubes with the exception of the *George Washington* which in common with British Polaris submarines has six.) To some, the torpedo may seem a little out of date in a nuclear age, but one should not be misled by the unchanged outward appearance and name of the weapons because they are very different from those of twenty years or so ago. The modern torpedo is as complex as any surface-to-surface or surface-to-air missile. Although perhaps little more than 20 feet long and 21 inches in diameter, it has an electric motor with the power of a modern sports car. It has a wide-angle sonar built into the nose and, on detecting the target, the torpedo can home automatically, or the submarine can control it via a thin connecting wire which relays information about the target and the torpedo's position and speed. Controlled from the submarine, the torpedo can hang threateningly in the water or its mission can be aborted if the danger passes. Should an attack be pressed, the torpedo's own fire-control system can take over while the submarine retreats.

The first torpedoes to strike against enemy shipping revolutionized naval warfare. On 22 September 1914, the German submarine *U-9* sank three British armoured cruisers off the Belgian coast in little over half an hour. A submarine of 450 tons with a crew of 26 had demolished some 36,000 tons of the British war machine and more than 1,200 men were lost. Counter-measures against the roving submarines had been neglected because, until the Germans proved otherwise, the submarine had been reserved for coastal and harbour defence. In fact, in 1915 the German submarine command likened its ocean-going submarines to pike let loose in a well-stocked carp pond. And when the Second World War broke out, the Atlantic became once again a 'carp pond' with U-boats sinking merchant shipping faster than it could be replaced. This carnage was cut short in 1942 when aircraft hunting them were fitted with radar. The development of the snorkel helped to redress the

balance but it required the use of atomic power to put the
submarine back on top: the modern nuclear submarine
holds the key to any future conflict.

Anti-submarine warfare

A Polaris submarine, armed with the A-3 missile, has
8,242,500 square miles of ocean to hide in if covering a target 1,000 miles inland. The nuclear submarine has a range
of more than 100,000 miles without refuelling and can
cruise at speeds in excess of 25 knots, deep under the surface
for months on end. In addition there are hundreds of diesel-
electric submarines, more limited but capable of being very
dangerous, patrolling the oceans nearer to their supply
bases. To keep track of these vessels and to improve techniques of detection and attack are the tasks given to the
Anti-submarine Warfare branches of the navy. And in view
of the difficult nature of this job, particularly since the
advent of the nuclear-powered submarine, it is hardly surprising that ASW research and development accounts for a
large proportion of navy budgets.

Destroying an enemy submarine presents few worries
compared with finding it in the first place. Such weapons as
the 'Limbo' depth-charge mortars of the Royal Navy pose a
serious threat to any submarine that dares to approach too
close. For attacks on submarines at a greater range, modern
homing and wire-controlled torpedoes can be launched
from ships or aircraft (particularly anti-submarine helicopters). The great drawback with torpedoes launched
directly into the sea from a surface ship or submarine is the
time that the weapon takes to reach its target. To reduce
the chances of alerting the enemy, many US ships are now
armed with the ASROC – a rocket which delivers a homing
torpedo in the vicinity of the enemy submarine. There is
also a SUBROC. This weapon is shot out of the water by
the attacking submarine using compressed air. Once clear,

the rocket is boosted to reach the target area within a few minutes where it parachutes a homing acoustic torpedo. The sudden appearance of this weapon severely restricts the freedom of a human operator to take avoiding action. Instead a defence computer takes control and, for example, may launch a noisy decoy which leads the attacking weapon away from the submarine. The decoy is then allowed to be overtaken and destroyed by the attacking torpedo. But, on the whole, the attacker has the advantage when it comes to such contests. This is far from the case when it comes to finding and identifying potential enemy submarines.

Aircraft such as the British Nimrod and the American Orion carry out most submarine 'hunting'. Nimrod, an aircraft based on the Comet 4 airliner, is the first jet to be used for these purposes. It can fly out to mid-Atlantic at 500 miles per hour before settling down to patrol slowly, flying on only two of its four engines. Included in its extensive submarine detection kit is an instrument which 'sniffs' the air for traces of diesel submarine exhaust and another which locates submarine radio or radar signals. A distinguishing feature of the Orion is the sting-like projection from its tail holding the magnetic anomaly detector, an instrument which finds submarines by the disturbance that their hulls create in the Earth's magnetic field. Another device uses a highly sensitive infra-red detector to search for changes in the temperature of the sea-water caused by coolant from the nuclear engines. However, heading the list of submarine sensors used by these aircraft is the air-to-sea search radar developed from the system which was so successful against U-boats during the Second World War.

Surface vessels and submarines generally detect underwater craft acoustically, either by listening with hydrophones for noise, such as caused by machinery and cavitation, or by actively searching the surrounding water with sonar – sound-ranging equipment similar to the fish-detection systems described in Chapter 2. Helicopters also use sonar devices which they dunk in the sea. Fast-moving aircraft have to lay their 'listening posts' (sonobuoys) on the surface of the ocean and then circle above, collecting signals which they relay. A well-laid pattern of sonobuoys gives an Orion a listening rage of about 32,000 square miles, but the reliance of such highly sophisticated 'command posts' upon so tenuous a link is one of the major weaknesses of submarine detection from the air. The DIFAR (DIrection Finding And Ranging) sonobuoy which enables greater accuracy in pin-pointing submarines went into service with Orion aircraft in 1969.

No matter how sonar systems are deployed, by ship or aircraft, the influence of water quality on sound and the general noisiness of the ocean environment curtail their ultimate effectiveness. The speed of sound in water, about 4,980 feet per second, changes as temperature and pressure change, so that sound waves rarely follow straight paths in the sea. Since the pressure increases and the temperature generally decreases with depth, the pattern of refraction, as this bending is known, can be very complex. Changes in temperature have by far the greatest effect on sounds generated near the surface. The decrease in temperature away from the sun-warmed surface bends the sound upwards close to the surface, and alternate refraction upwards and reflection downwards from the surface 'traps' the sound there. Deeper in the ocean where the temperature becomes more uniform, the increasing pressure becomes dominant and causes the sound to bend towards the ocean floor. Between these upward and downward curving zones lies a 'shadow zone' through which no sound passes and where a submarine could stay undetected (see figure 25). One solution to the problem is to lower a variable depth sonar close to the thermocline (the boundary between surface and deeper waters) where the sonar produces a pattern of refracted sound which eliminates the shadow zone.

A considerable problem for sonar operators is the noisi-

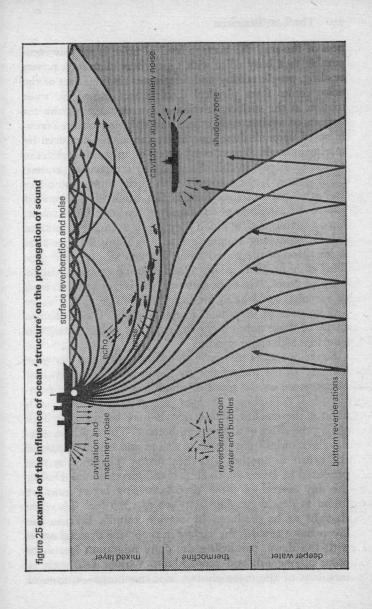

figure 25 example of the influence of ocean 'structure' on the propagation of sound

surface reverberation and noise

cavitation and machinery noise

shadow zone

echo

noise

cavitation and machinery noise

reverberation from water and bubbles

bottom reverberations

mixed layer

thermocline

deeper water

ness of the sea: the average level of noise is roughly comparable to a busy office with typewriters clattering, papers rustling, people talking and telephones ringing. Part of the noise comes from physical disturbances caused by wave motion at the surface; friction of currents against the sea bottom or against each other; and shipping traffic. Superimposed upon all these sources are the sounds produced by marine animals. Almost every group of animal found in the oceans takes part in this chorus. Many crustaceans produce clicking and rasping sounds with their claws, mandibles and other parts of their hard bodies, often when they feed and move. Members of one family of shrimps, for example, have a modified claw which they use as a 'clicker'. Fish and other fast-moving animals create a swishing noise as they swim through the water. Some fish can vibrate their gas-filled swim bladder making a loud drumming sound. Others burp or grunt. Not to be outdone, the larger animals, such as porpoises and whales, produce their own peculiar whistles and squeaks as they 'talk' to one another. Unfortunately, many of these noises occur in frequency ranges which can interfere with sonar signals.

Sonar operators also have to contend with the changing 'climate' of the underwater environment. The influence of temperature on the speed of sound has already been mentioned. Where abrupt changes in temperature occur, such as at a thermocline, sound signals may be reflected back giving the effect of a 'phantom bottom'. The depth of thermoclines varies from season to season and from one part of the ocean to another. Another vexing 'phantom' is that produced by layers which absorb and scatter sound. During the day several of these 'deep scattering layers' may be found at depths ranging from 900 to 1,200 feet. They are thought to be produced by marine animals because the layers move towards the surface at night and descend again with the dawn, paralleling the daily migration known to occur among fish and zooplankton. Various fish (such as members of the myctophidae), siphonophores – a type of jellyfish – and euphausids – prawns related to the krill – have been suggested as the culprits, but no one is really sure about what causes the deep scattering layers.

Navy scientists and engineers have to investigate every possible source of interference. Apart from the ocean's effects on sonar, the noise created by the ship's passage through the water, cavitation noise and that coming from the engines and other machinery present further possible sources of 'contamination'. If left completely unsuppressed, such 'self noise' would obscure any similar types of noise radiated from an enemy submarine as well as give warning of the pursuit ship's approach.

By persistent attacks on the types of disturbance described above, and by improving the detection gear itself, the average range of the first contact with an enemy submarine has increased probably ten-fold or more since the Second World War; some potential aids to sonar such as the existence of deep-sound channels in the ocean are still being explored. These channels can conduct sound over considerable distance with remarkably little loss: one of the longest recorded paths of sound is 12,000 miles – from Bermuda to the Indian Ocean – in experiments by scientists of the Lamont Geological Laboratory. Already underwater 'listening posts' are installed on the seabed off the western and eastern sea-boards of the United States and in other strategic areas. In 1972 the NATO powers and France established an experimental system in the Azores. It consists of three acoustic towers, each 220 feet high, set at 300 to 800 metres depth on the tops of seamounts. Acting as a triangulation device, the aim is to detect and 'fix' submarines at increasing distances. Nevertheless, with all the ocean to play with, the nuclear submarine commander still has the advantage over a surface pursuer, and enjoys the security of a needle in a haystack.

The ocean highways

During the height of the Vietnam war, more than 95 per cent of the US military materials arrived on ships. This reliance of war machines and commercial life on the ocean highways has caused much alarm about the buildup of the Soviet submarine force. Although the prospects of any interference by a military force with the freedom of shipping remains intolerable, as early as 1962 restrictions on the freedom of the choice of shipping routes were being actively suggested. The menace at the time was not the Soviet submarine fleet but ships, too many of them. Each year some 7½ per cent of the world's fleet is estimated to be involved in collisions at sea. The majority of these occur in crowded waters such as the narrow Dover Strait through which some 300,000 ships pass every year. In fact some waters had become so congested that restriction of different streams of shipping traffic to separate lanes seems to be the only sensible solution. Most large tankers, which may take as much as five miles to stop, have already agreed to separate lanes with a suitable safety zone between, and restriction of most classes of vessel is likely as waters become congested or large ships become common.

The pressure on surface space may be relieved to some extent if submarine cargo vessels become a major feature of ocean transport, but they too will have to travel at different depths, rather like altitude-spacing practised in the air lanes on major routes. Commander W. R. Anderson, captain of the *Nautilus* at the time of its journey beneath the Arctic ice, pointed out that nuclear-powered cargo submarines would be able to cut 4,900 miles off the trip between Japan and Europe. The well-known British inventor-scientist, Dr Barnes Wallace, told the annual meeting of the British Association for the Advancement of Science in 1965 that the future strength of the nation on the seas lay in the development of submarine merchant vessels. As Commander Anderson had said, taking the polar route could cut down the length of their journeys, but what is more, these submarine transports would remove any British dependence on the Suez and Panama Canals. Submarine freighters, he argued, might have to be smaller than surface vessels but their greater speed and freedom from weather restrictions could more than compensate for this. Furthermore, fast submarine merchantmen would be less vulnerable to attacks by hostile submarines than the vessels now used for bulk cargoes, particularly the tankers which carry vital supplies of oil and liquid methane.

A switch to carrying cargo underwater would please hovercraft and hydrofoil operators: high-speed craft are the first to suffer from congestion because they lose so much of their economic attraction when they are forced to dawdle. Some indication of the problem is given by the fact that a hovercraft on a typical crossing of the English Channel may expect to meet up to forty ships. Considering that hovercraft (and hydrofoils) travel at speeds of about 70 knots, the prospect of such frequent encounters with other shipping imposes a critical test on their navigational systems – a further test might include a meeting with another hovercraft travelling in the opposite direction, giving a relative approach speed of 140 knots! One solution has been to devise a system, capable of reacting much faster than conventional marine radar, which provides the hovercraft navigator with a continuously computed reference of the vessel's position marked on a roller map. The map also carries the proposed route of the hovercraft so that, by comparing planned and actual positions, the navigator can correct for drift.

Even as new types of transport such as hovercraft ferries became available, the demise of the ocean liner as a means of regular passenger transport began. The sale and retirement of the *Queen Mary* and the *Queen Elizabeth* were signs of this swing away from this form of transoceanic transport. Their successor, the *Queen Elizabeth II*, is a sleeker, smaller vessel designed with both cruise and trans-

atlantic services in mind. The design for cruising, emphasized by the high proportion – more than 75 per cent – of
cabins with an ocean view and the overall high standard of
accommodation, recognizes the continuous rundown of the
transatlantic passenger lists. Just after the Second World
War almost a million passengers made the crossing every
year but, with the arrival of the jet age, these numbers have
been halved. Comparatively few people have the time to
make the leisurely crossing by boat between North
America and Western Europe – and more and more of
those are deciding that a slow comfortable trip can take in
more interesting sights than seemingly endless miles of
ocean.

By the end of the century, the bulk cargo carriers which
so dominate the scene may also be losing ground. We have
already seen the demise of the coal carriers and as oil and
natural gas deposits lose ground to nuclear power perhaps
the giant tankers will no longer be needed. According to
the late J. M. Murray, formerly Chief Ship Surveyor of
Lloyds Register for Shipping, 'In the end it is probable that
bulk cargoes will be piped across oceans instead of being
carried by ships . . . Passengers and light freight will be
carried by hovercraft, but it does not seem possible that the
general cargo carrier in some form or other will ever dis-
appear. That could only happen if, as in the vision of St
John the Divine, there was no more sea.'

Chapter 8

Survival and the Sea

The oceans provide the key to man's survival. At the same time, as the preceding chapters have clearly shown, all Utopian ideas about the ocean resources are best abandoned: the oceans are as vulnerable as the land to abuse and over-exploitation. The very fact that limits to the oceans' bounty do exist, both in terms of food and minerals, has helped to exacerbate a situation where a handful of technologically advanced nations dominate what should be the common heritage of mankind. Add to this the military and strategic value that the oceans hold for the major powers and the situation becomes positively explosive, with nations competing in an inner space race for survival. This escalation of military interest in the ocean promises to aggravate an already delicate balance, making international controls of ocean exploitation difficult and deflecting the path of marine studies away from more humanistic goals.

Before the nuclear submarines existed, the world's navies pioneered the collection of data concerning the ocean environment, but they left a great deal, particularly in deep-sea research and marine biology, to civilian scientists. The arrival of sophisticated submarines changed all this. The oceanographer found himself working in a theatre of war: he became, willingly or not, an important cog in marine warfare and defence. The naval establishments which traditionally maintained a good working relationship with their civilian counterparts tightened their grip. Today there are few established people in oceanography who have not worked, either directly or indirectly, for the navy, and many civilian research centres owe their existence to support, at some time or other, from the navy. The interests of the modern navy are such that little in marine science and technology passes unnoticed or is totally irrelevant to the military purpose. Defence spending remains a dynamic force in deciding the growth and direction of marine studies.

The Soviet Union now keeps more submarines in the world's seas than did the Germans at the height of the U-boat campaign in the Second World War. As the nuclear weapons become more horrific, so the need to detect the vehicles that carry them becomes more desperate. And yet, with every unsung advance in detection comes a counter measure to render it ineffective. As explained in Chapter 7, a favourite trick is to increase the depths at which the submarine can operate: both Russian and American navies seem to be heading hell-bent for the deep ocean. It is a sad comment on the situation that the first man to step out on the deep-ocean floor is unlikely to waddle around in his protective armour proclaiming his steps for peace, but will go secretly about some task of a military nature. In spite of strategic arms-limitation talks and conventions devoted to sea-bed weapons, the deep oceans are destined to become a province for military activity. Unfortunately the knowledge of this casts a dark shadow over operations in much shallower waters where man has much more to gain than some nebulous sense of security.

Twenty years or so ago the question of marine resources was rarely considered as a serious threat to security or world peace. Most coastal states had declared their interest in the shallow continental shelf region. Later, with an international convention for support, the problem seemed practically solved. As we shall see later in this chapter, this early complacency made no allowance for the military encouragement of technology nor, perhaps, the acquisitive nature of major industrial powers. These forces have turned the spotlight on resources remote from existing coastal sites. For example, the Soviet Union has a small coastline, compared with its land mass, but has nevertheless become, along with Japan, a major fishing nation. To stave off the predation by roving fleets from these two countries, coastal nations have pushed out the limits of their fishing zones. The so-called Rhee Line Law proclaimed by South Korea in 1952 was designed primarily to keep out Japanese fishermen. A further source of disagreement among ocean exploiters may arise from the priorities allotted to the various resources. Where no controls exist on exploitation outside of territorial and adjacent fishing zones there is nothing to prevent the exploitation of one resource leading to the dereliction of another.

Clearly, the oceans can provide an unsurpassable array of matters guaranteed to nurture human discontent, and the great naval battles that punctuate history show that in the past nations have not flinched from the use of arms to resolve their differences. The surprising thing is that there have been so few serious disagreements. One reason must be the tendency for great naval powers to arise and to dominate: the British fleet held sway for almost two centuries over vast expanses of the global ocean. In more modern times the nature of warfare and the improvements in the mechanisms for airing, if not resolving, grievances at an international level have mitigated against untoward violence. Dissident factions seek to resolve their differences through the medium of international courts or, in the case of fisheries, through international conventions and commissions. The disputes are legal in nature and even when nations are involved, such as in the Icelandic–British 'Codfish War' or the German appeal against the division of the North Sea continental shelf, the final solutions come via diplomacy. Nevertheless, the need for an adequate framework within which conflicts over ocean resources can be resolved grows daily more urgent and slowly more difficult as a greater number of nations becomes involved in exploitation.

The delay in resolving major international issues concerning the ocean resources encourages the shelving of equally pressing matters which in the long run could have disastrous effects on the marine environment. Pollution is no longer a word that has to be spelled out in most industrial countries, but they continue to pollute the oceans with the unwanted by-products of their industrial metabolism. The oceans have become the sink of the world, the biggest holes in the world, receiving all manner of harmful junk. All that is demanded is that the dumpers stay ahead of the law; which is not very hard to do, as we shall see in the example provided by oil. There was a time when most pollutants entered the ocean via rivers or the air, but now tankers and ships built specially for dumping waste pose a direct threat to the marine environment. Even if such threats were to be removed, growing traffic and increased risk of accidents would help to maintain the danger of a massive release of pollutants into the oceans. In the absence of any satifactory controls, countries, particularly those bordering on overcrowded waterways, will risk international friction by taking unilateral action to safeguard themselves. Already the Canadian government, haunted by fears of accidents to tankers loaded with North Alaskan oil, has proposed new restrictions on navigation through the North-West Passage. The United Kingdom and France are keeping an eye on the Channel after a spate of accidents in the spring of 1971.

At present it is difficult to be anything but pessimistic about the future of the last resource. The reluctance of nations to look beyond the lifetimes of their immediate investments in the oceans bodes ill for attempts at long-term management of marine resources. The situation is not helped either by our comparative lack of knowledge concerning the global ocean. This ignorance is continually being underscored and is particularly alarming when one considers pollution, and undoubtedly this ignorance also encourages a *laissez-faire* attitude among those who would prefer not to see the oceans as a source of conflict. It is appropriate therefore that the remainder of this book, having surveyed the uses of the oceans, be devoted to major issues which will help to determine just how the benefits from this last great resource might be maintained and divided.

Pollution

For years individuals, industrial companies and governments have been paying lip service to the idea of conserving natural resources and of preventing further spoiling of the environment as a result of pollution, over-exploitation or ignorant usage. And yet the prevention of pollution has so far failed to out-pace the deterioration of the environment. It takes a well-publicized catastrophe to have any real influence on either the general public or the politician. The land has had its dust bowls with vast areas laid waste and rivers have become sterile streams made lifeless by excessive industrial waste. In 1967 the sea had its first major case of pollution – oil from the *Torrey Canyon* – the extent of which was apparent to even the most casual observer. When this tanker ran aground off the south-west tip of the British Isles it demonstrated with appalling finality the damage that oil can do. Press and television daily confronted people with news and pictures of dead sea birds, clawless crabs, tar-stained bathers and beaches caked with a dirty brown 'mousse'.

The drama started just before 9 o'clock on the morning of Saturday, 18 March, when the *Torrey Canyon*, loaded with 117,000 tons of Kuwait crude oil, ground to a halt on the Seven Stones Reef fifteen miles west of Land's End. According to reports, six of her tanks were torn open by the impact and they immediately began spilling oil into the surrounding sea. By nightfall a narrow slick, some eight miles long, stretched away southwards from the stranded tanker. The *Torrey Canyon* was finally written off when, as a result of the pounding by rough seas for eight days, her back was broken.

With all hope of salvaging the whole, or even a part, of the ship gone, the British government decided to destroy the remaining cargo by using bombs to open the deck of the tanker over the cargo tanks and then set fire to the oil. The following evening the onslaught began. Buccaneer aircraft of the Royal Navy began a series of strikes using 1,000-lb. high-explosive bombs. They were followed by RAF Hunter jets which dropped tanks of fuel to encourage the fires. In all some 160,000 lb. of high explosive, 10,000 gallons of aviation kerosene, 3,000 gallons of napalm and several rockets were unleashed on the ship. On Thursday, 30 March, it was decided that no significant quantity of oil remained in the wreck and all effort was then centred on the fight to clean over 10 miles of Cornish coastline which had received an estimated 15 per cent of the tanker's cargo.

Within 12 hours of the *Torrey Canyon* foundering, the Royal Navy had deployed two ships to spray detergent on to the growing oil slick to disperse it, and the number of ships increased dramatically over the next few days as oil continued to leak from the stricken tanker. Initially, wind and tide combined to carry the oil away from the English mainland (part of it eventually arrived in Brittany), but the morning tide of Saturday, 25 March, brought the first thick oil to the Cornish coast near St Just. As the oil continued to sweep in on to the beaches, counter-measures, largely spraying with detergent, started in earnest. These cleaning-up operations were spurred on by the fact that the area included holiday resorts anxious to protect their beaches and livelihood. Unfortunately the widespread and sometimes over-enthusiastic application of detergents had a disastrous effect on marine shore-life. Except for an early massacre of sea birds – guillemots and razorbills – the oil apparently did far less damage to wild life than did the detergent.

The rapid decision to spray the oil-slick with detergent was made because the Royal Navy and harbour authorities had regularly used this method to disperse small oil spills. In spite of warnings about the possible effects of the detergent on marine life, the main debate over the decision to use it concerned the cost and effectiveness of spraying. According to one estimate, some 700,000 gallons of detergent dispersed – at a cost of £400,000 – about 15,000 tons of oil which otherwise would have been carried to the neighbouring costline. The French, who tackled the oil much later when the loss of volatile components had thickened it, used a much cheaper material – sawdust mixed with powdered chalk – to sink the oil. According to a Marine Biology Association report, the French estimated that 3,000 tons of the chalk and sawdust mixture could sink up to 20,000 tons of oil. What was not known at that time was that at least some of the sunken oil, made lighter by bacterial action would return. Over a year later came reports of a tarry residue containing 60 per cent water, 30 per cent tar and 3 per cent chalk being washed up on the coast of Finisterre. The French also had time to adapt a ship for pumping the thicker layers of oil from the surface of the sea.

The total bill for the disaster came to an estimated £6 million. However, in November 1969 the British and French Governments settled out of court for only half the amount that they claimed from the tanker's owners, the Liberian-based Barracuda Tanker Corporation, and the charterers of the vessel, the Union Oil Company of California. The acceptance of such a reduced amount of compensation was as much a matter of legal convenience as anything. The UK Attorney-General at that time, Sir Elwyn Jones, explained, 'Having regard to the uncertainties, inevitable delays and expense of litigation, and complex and unique points of law involved in establishing legal liability, and finally the difficulties involved in quantifying and proving damages, this settlement is eminently fair and satisfactory to all parties.' As a result of the *Torrey Canyon* affair, the international oil industry established a voluntary scheme which will provide up to $10 million (£4.2 million) in compensation for any future oil tanker disasters.

Oil pollution is an almost inevitable consequence of the world's dependence on oil-based technology. Nevertheless, much can be done to ameliorate the situation. For example, tighter controls on the exploitation of off-shore resources could protect the oceans from spills such as the disastrous Santa Barbara one which occurred after drilling in an unstable area of the continental shelf. Recently, after a spate of tanker collisions and accidents, the major flag-nation of the tanker world, Liberia, reviewed the qualifications desirable for the officers of such vessels. Even so, oil spills from tankers occur with almost monotonous and certainly alarming regularity. The major accidents, such as the collision between two Standard Oil tankers in 1971 in the San Francisco Bay which released some 840,000 gallons of oil, make the headlines, but these are little more than the tip of the iceberg. For example, it is estimated that of 10,000 pollution incidents ocurring each year in the US, three quarters are caused by oil. The total influx of oil to the ocean through shipping and by accidents in port is estimated to be at least 1 million metric tons per year. This does not include large-scale catastrophes such as 'blow-outs' from rigs or tanker collisions, nor does it include oil pollution coming from sources on the land. In fact, the total influx of hydrocarbons including those from natural sources may be as high as 10 million metric tons per year.

The tragedy of oil pollution is that probably a large part of it could be prevented and that every drop of oil that reaches the sea represents the squandering of a finite resource. The greatest single cause of oil pollution from tankers is the accidental or deliberate discharge of oil ballast and cargo-tank wash water. This release can be prevented by adopting procedures such as 'load-on-top'. After unloading tankers will fill about one third of the cargo tanks with water to preserve stability. Before the new procedure was adopted, most tankers discharged this water ballast along with a hundred or so tons of oil which had stuck originally to the internal steelwork into the sea prior to taking on the next load. However, with the load-on-top system, one tank is used as a 'slop tank', receiving the water and oil washings from the cargo tanks. The oil separates out and floats to the surface so that eventually clean water can be run off from beneath into the sea. The fresh cargo is then loaded on top of the separated oil. This system which is now operated in about 75 per cent of crude-oil shipments prevents the discharge of about 1.5 million tons of crude oil per annum.

At government level the battle against oil pollution has been going on for many years and has led to the International Convention for the Prevention of Pollution of the Sea by Oil. The convention sets out what constitutes an oily mixture and details where such mixtures should not be dumped. The version of the Convention in force at the time of the *Torrey Canyon* incident prohibits the discharge of oil within 100 miles of the world's coastlines with a specially large zone, including the North Sea, which extends out from Northwest Europe into mid-Atlantic. The discharge of oil by new ships of 20,000 tons and over is banned completely. Enforcement of the Convention involves the framing of legislation by nations which are signatories to it and an offending ship can be punished only by the country of registration. Even if all the maritime countries had signed the Convention, which they have not, such laws are difficult to enforce and offenders are rarely reported. As a result, countries in particularly vulnerable areas have enacted laws or are preparing them to enable action to be taken against ships of other nationalities if they present a threat to amenities or fishery resources. In April 1971, the UK government passed an amendment to the Oil in Navigable Waters Act which would enable Britain to act against a foreign ship outside territorial waters. The amendment is based on a new version of the existing convention which at that time still needed the signature of fifteen nations to bring it into effect. The changes were agreed in a meeting at Brussels in 1969 which came as a sequel to the *Torrey*

Canyon accident. The tanker lay outside Britain's three-mile limit, but the government of the time intervened without the owner's consent and bombed the tanker in order to remove the pollution threat.

The volume of oil carried at sea continues to increase: in 1970 tankers transported 950 million metric tons of oil compared with 650 million metric tons in 1967. At the same time, the size of the tankers and their cargo compartments has increased: one wing tank alone on a modern 300,000 ton tanker contains approximately 24,000 tons of oil compared with a total load of 16,000 tons carried by Second World War T-2 tankers. A tanker of half a million tons is on the stocks and even larger ones could be on the way.

Obviously, the time has come for measuring the economic forces that have dictated the construction of the modern tanker against the environmental costs both to man and to marine life when these behemoths are involved in collisions or are grounded and break up. Moves are now afoot to limit the size of cargo tanks and to impose other restrictions on design and operation of these mammoth tankers, but whether these measures will be adopted in times when oil-rich countries are demanding greater and greater royalties from foreign companies operating in them remains to be seen. Powerful industrial lobbies can be expected to resist any further financial burdens such as greater transport costs. However, conservationists may find unexpected allies in the guise of the shipping insurance brokers. Already insurance on tankers accounts for up to 60 per cent of their operational costs and higher rates will be demanded unless they become safer and there are fewer accidents.

Already tarry residues and globules, the end-products of oil pollution, appear to be widespread in the world's oceans. They have been found clogging the fine nets used to investigate the surface plankton far out to sea and in areas remote from commercial shipping lanes. The expeditions of Thor Heyerdahl in 1969 and 1970 produced some surprising evidence of widespread oil pollution in the Atlantic Ocean. Although the voyage of *Ra 1* was intended to show the possible migration of early people on board primitive papyrus boats from North Africa to America, observation of oil pollution became unavoidable. The raft was only a few days out from its starting point, the harbour of Safi in Morocco, when it suddenly came into an area, about 100 miles off the coast of Mauritania, where the sea was so polluted with clots of solidified oil and other oily matter that the clear blue water became opaque. At first they were convinced that they were in a shipping lane around Africa and that the oil spill had happened the day before or the same day. Two days after escaping from this polluted water (the surface current was moving more slowly than the raft), they came into another polluted area, and then yet again when they were in the mid-ocean, halfway between Africa and America. Shortly after abandoning ship, some 600 miles off Barbados, they sailed in polluted water for two full days. Their experience of pollution the following year on *Ra 2*, which finally made the trans-Atlantic journey, was even more alarming. This time one member of the international crew was given the job of watching out for pollution. He found plenty to do: the journey took 57 days and on 43 of these oil pollution was seen. What such evidence means for marine life can only be surmised, but there can be no doubt that oil pollution can do little for the ultimate health of the oceans.

Oil is composed of a wide range of hydrocarbons. The most poisonous ones seem to be the most volatile, but this does not necessarily mean that the heavier fractions are free from blame – at the very least they may become locked away in the bodies of marine organisms, tainting the flesh of fish and shellfish. Less obvious effects of low levels of oil pollution stem from their similarity to natural hydrocarbons which serve as chemical messengers for many marine animals: some predators are attracted to their prey in this way; migratory fish may home on their spawning grounds using chemical signposts; and organic chemicals may also be essential as sex attractants in some species. The pollutants may interfere with these processes either by masking the natural hydrocarbons or by providing false 'signals'. The fact that components of oil may prove attractive to some animals also offers the possibility of larger kills from an oil spill than might be expected. Lobsters, for example, are attracted away from their normal food by kerosene and it may be relevant that after a spill of fuel oil at West Falmouth, Massachusetts, USA, numerous dead lobsters were washed ashore. Oil slicks on the surface of the sea may also help other pollutants, particularly chemicals such as DDT, which have an affinity for oil but are almost insoluble in water, to enter the marine environment.

The marine animals most at risk appear to be those living in the littoral zone where oil may be deposited on a falling tide and where generous applications of oil dispersant often produce further stress. However, the plankton probably also suffers although this is not so easy to detect. Eggs and larvae, in particular, are likely to suffer, but the effects on, say, commercial fisheries would be inseparable from the fluctuations normally found among exploited stocks – unless the damage to eggs and young was very substantial. At the moment, therefore, oil pollution is assumed to be comparatively harmless once the highly toxic components have been dispersed or have evaporated, although this view is disputed by many ecologists, There is general agreement, however, that oil can have a serious indirect effect on marine life because of the large volumes of oxygen used up in its decay and breakdown by bacteria. (One litre of oil, for example, would deplete 400,000 litres of sea-water of its oxygen.) An oil spill, particularly in sheltered or enclosed waters, may rob marine organisms, particularly the larger and more active ones, of their vital oxygen supply. Nevertheless some conservationists would still prefer to take the risk of allowing natural processes of degradation rather than have large volumes of dispersant – even the new so-

called 'safe' detergents – sprayed on the oil thereby aiding
its dispersal into the marine environment.

Although every year thousands of seabirds, some of them
rare, die from the effects of oiled plumage, oil pollution is
generally considered by most people to be much more a
direct menace to the coastal amenities they enjoy than to
marine life. According to Dr M. Bloomer of Woods Hole
Oceanographic Institute in the United States, oil cast up on
holiday beaches, or dispersed on them after spills have been
treated with detergent, may be much more than a threat to
amenities; it could be a direct health hazard. Oil contains
known and suspected carcinogens and studies of marine life
from areas persistently polluted by oil have suggested that
they may suffer cancer-like growths as a result. However,
Dr Bloomer would go much further than this: he suggests
that the presence of oil lumps or finely dispersed oil on
holiday beaches 'may well constitute a severe public health
hazard, through continued skin contact'.

A similar dual threat to amenities and health, but one
that is much more easily proven, comes from untreated
sewage. Apart from the aesthetic insult from odours, filth
and clouding of the water, there is a definite health risk
from pathogenic micro-organisms released along with the
sewage. Fortunately, the sea has a natural cleansing action
which helps to ensure that these micro-organisms are in-
activated, usually within a few hours. But the amount of
sewage the sea can take and still cleanse seems to be
limited. In enclosed and semi-enclosed stretches of water,
ranging in size from tropical lagoons to the Mediterranean
Sea, excessive loads of industrial and domestic waste have
savagely reduced the health of the sea. In Italy, for example, most large cities and all but a fraction of the smaller
ones pump their sewage untreated into the Mediterranean
or the rivers that flow into it. According to reports, 20,000
litres of untreated sewage were spilling out into the Tiber
every second in 1970. Typhoid and infective hepatitis had
become endemic to the area and at least thirty other dis-

agreeable micro-organisms had been identified at the mouth of the river. That summer the Rome health authority was reporting 32 cases of infectious hepatitis per day and the beaches of Ostia – the weekend playground of the Romans – were closed to bathing. In 1971, according to the standards set by the country's Health Ministry, each one of the 6,000 registered beaches in Italy was dangerously polluted.

Even after processing, sewage released into the sea can still create a pollution problem and occasionally a health hazard. Although the pathogens are no longer present, treated sewage still carries a nutrient load which consumes oxygen during its decay and by its fertilizing effects can lead to excessive growths or blooms of plankton. The fertilizer qualities of sewage have been particularly disastrous in tropical and semi-tropical lagoons. Dr R. E. Johannes of the University of Georgia has described the events in Kaneohe Bay, Oahu, Hawaii. Sewage apparently killed the corals in the southern third of this bay, which extends over an area of about 15 square miles, but studies based on conventional water-sampling techniques suggested that the remainder of it was comparatively healthy. The true nature of the situation only became apparent when scuba divers began a detailed study of the area. They were appalled to find large areas in the middle of the bay covered with a billowing mat of green algae – the green bubble alga *Dictyosphaeria cavernosa*. Beneath this cover, which was over a foot thick in places, the divers found dead and dying coral polyps. They also discovered that where the coral was dead the reef was disintegrating far more rapidly than would be expected in such a sheltered area. According to Dr Johannes, the growth of the green bubble algae in the bay has paralleled the increased input of sewage although it may also have been influenced by a number of new construction sites on the coast.

The nutrients contained in sewage, industrial wastes and agricultural run-off from the land strike at the very base of the marine-food web. Normally the nutrients needed by the phytoplankton are supplied largely by geochemical processes such as erosion and the recycling of nutrient-rich sea-water (see Chapter 2), but in estuaries and in coastal waters or semi-enclosed waters, additional amounts introduced by man and his activities can interfere seriously with the natural cycle of plant growth. Chief among the nutrients that dictate the fertility of marine waters are nitrates and phosphates. The phosphate enters the sea via rivers and directly from out-falls via sewage. The nitrate comes via air and rain from the burning of fuels while large amounts reach the sea annually through the use of nitrate fertilizers on the land. Sewage effluents also contain nitrates. Although both chemicals are persistent, neither of them, except in grossly excessive concentrations, are toxic. But they can stimulate excessive growth among members of the phytoplankton. If the injected nutrients are in unnatural ratios, they can encourage the growth of plant species that are not normally abundant leading to toxic blooms in the surface waters. However, the greatest danger from over-fertilization lies in the rapid accumulation of dead and decaying material resulting from the tremendous acceleration in plant production. The water is robbed of its dissolved oxygen and marine life becomes slowly stifled as a result. Finally, all that remains are those bacteria and other organisms that can survive without oxygen in the now evil smelling water.

One of the most dramatic cases of marine pollution – at least for the man in the street – has had nothing to do with either oil or sewage: it concerns the discovery of high levels of methyl mercury in tuna fish and, later, in sword-fish which came about almost by accident. Alarm over mercury pollution in some American lakes and rivers made the analysis of the mercury contents of fresh-water fish a widespread topic for college and university classwork. However, Professor Bruce McDuffie of the State University of New York thought he would bring some light relief from analyses of fish from the Susuchanna River by bringing along a can of tuna from his home. But what started as an amusing experiment took a much more serious turn when he and his students discovered a mercury content of over 0·5 parts per million (ppm) in the sample – a level of contamination above the permissible limit set by the American Federal Drug Administration. Professor McDuffie, therefore, decided to inform the FDA and, as a precaution against inactivity, the press. The FDA and the New York State Health Laboratory investigated the claim, confirmed the professor's results and immediately began screening batches of canned tuna fish from many different sources. As a result, more than a million cans of tuna were eventually recalled.

Concern spread rapidly to other parts of the world, including the United Kingdom, where the Government Chemist was put to work analysing batches of canned tuna. The early results confirmed the American experience that the majority of samples contained less than 0·5 ppm, but a few had levels as high as 0·8 ppm. On the other hand, the British public does not seem to relish tuna like its trans-Atlantic counterpart, eating only one tenth as much of it per head as do Americans. Since medical and scientific opinion was that the total intake of methyl mercury is important and that the amount of mercury in British food is extremely low, withdrawal of canned fish from shops was not considered necessary.

In the meantime, Professor McDuffie and his students turned their analytical attention to other kinds of commercial fish. They were pleased to find comparatively low levels of mercury in flounder, cod fillets and haddock. The real trouble came when they tackled a sword-fish steak. They recorded 1·3 ppm of mercury in it and after further investigations by the FDA, this fish too followed in the path of the ill-fated tuna fish.

As far as is known, not even the most avid eater of canned fish has ever suffered serious mercury poisoning. But despite this fact, the world has already had grim warnings of what mercury contamination of marine fish and shellfish can do. In 1953, a strange disease broke out among the residents of Minamata in Japan. Victims became dizzy, had difficulty focusing their eyes, lost control of their limbs and some eventually went insane and died. According to T. Nitta of the Tokai Regional Fisheries Laboratory, the Minamata disease caused 89 casualties of whom 36 died. When the victims were examined, it was found that more than 100 ppm of mercury had accumulated in their bodies, damaging irreversibly and fatally the brain and central nervous system. This mercury was traced to the effluent running into Minamata Bay from a chemical plant. The mercury, in the deadly methyl mercury form, had accumulated in the flesh of fish and shellfish which had then been consumed by the hapless victims. After the incident, the plant provided facilities for treating wastes to prevent any leak of methyl mercury, but Japan was not finished with Minamata disease. In 1964, the disease broke out again in the basin of the River Agana, resulting in 29 patients and five deaths. The authorities have now banned the release of methyl mercury in industrial effluents and have severely restricted the use of agricultural chemicals containing mercury, but it seems probable that in all nearly 50 people died in Japan from eating marine food contaminated by methyl mercury within the space of a little over ten years.

At the time of the first outbreak of Minamata disease the suspicion arose that inorganic and metallic mercury, themselves poisonous, were being converted into the even more toxic methyl mercury. However, the search for an explanation ended when the chemical factory in question was found to release a small percentage of methyl mercury along with the other forms. The discovery of this further complication to mercury pollution was left to the Swedes who themselves have a mercury problem in fresh-water lakes and rivers. Alarmed by the increasing quantities of the chemical found in wild birds, poultry and fish, the Swedish authorities held a national mercury information conference in Stockholm in 1965. Professor Gunnel West reported that fish and mammals could convert small amounts of inorganic mercury to methyl mercury in their livers. Two other scientists, Dr Alf Johnels and M. Olsson went even further and postulated that inorganic mercury could be converted into the methylated form by micro-organisms living in anaerobic (oxygen-free) conditions. By 1967, Drs Arne Jernelov and Soren Jenson had found evidence in support of this prediction which was confirmed the following year by Dr J. M. Wood and Dr Carl Rosen and co-worker, F. S. Kennedy. In a paper published in *Nature* (October 1968) they described how bacteria (*Methano-bacterium omelanskii*) living in mud converted inorganic and metallic mercury into methyl mercury which then spreads in the environment.

No longer could it be assumed that mercury discharged in industrial effluent would sink and remain inert in the mud at the bottom of lakes, rivers and even the sea. In other words, every source of mercury pollution – and some 4,000 to 5,000 tons are believed to enter the oceans every year from industrial sources alone – can contribute to the build-up of methyl mercury within marine life and ultimately in those who eat it. 'We feel', the three scientists wrote, 'that the example set by these two countries [Japan and Sweden which both restrict the release of mercury to the environment] should be followed elsewhere before concentrations of mercury reach a point where methyl mercury is being titrated [discovered in measurable quantities] in humans as well as fish.'

The accumulation of mercury in marine life underlines an important feature of pollution. Any pollutant that can persist essentially unchanged in the marine environment stands a good chance of becoming concentrated within the food web to a level many times, often thousands of times, that existing in the surrounding sea-water. The half-life of mercury in fish (the time taken for half the mercury in-gested to be lost again) is 200 days. As long as fish feed on contaminated food, they inevitably build up their body content of mercury. The half-life of mercury in people eating these fish is 70 days. Returning now to the complete story, the true nature of the mercury problem can be appreciated. Bacteria convert metallic and inorganic mercury to methyl mercury which in turn finds its way into the cells of the phytoplankton. Since the animals of the plankton need to eat considerable amounts of plant material for energy and growth, the mercury contamination begins to increase dramatically in the zooplankton. These smaller animals are then eaten by larger animals, including fish, producing a further build-up. By the time tuna and sword-fish, which eat other fish, are reached, the mercury contamination can reach serious proportions – particularly as far as their predator, man, is concerned.

Another persistent pollutant which finds its way into the marine-food web is, of course, DDT. In fact, the stability of this and other organo-chlorine chemicals originally commended their use as pesticides. It was some time later, after the application of millions of tons of the stuff, that startling evidence began to accumulate concerning its distribution in the environment and its harmful effects on wild life. A surprising discovery was the presence of DDT and its derivatives in the fatty tissues of Antarctic penguins. It seems likely that some of the insecticide found in them stems from the earliest use of DDT to control mosquitoes and other disease-carrying insects during the latter part of the Second World War. The presence of these pesticides in areas remote from their application is explained by their ability to be drawn up into the atmosphere and transported by the wind. For example, pesticides applied on the African continent have been detected entering the Bay of Bengal and the Caribbean Sea having been carried there by the summer monsoon and the north-east trade winds respectively. Other important routes into the ocean are via run-off from agricultural land and sewage.

World production of chlorinated hydrocarbon insecticides is in the order of 200,000 tons per year. Estimates of the proportion of this amount that reaches the ocean have ranged as high as 90 per cent, but, according to a recent UN report, about 40 per cent is considered more likely. One problem about the continuing build-up of these chemicals, whatever the percentage, is that even when the levels are insufficient to have a direct effect on large marine animals, they can exert subtle but invidious influences on the total ocean ecology. In quite low concentrations, they can reduce the rate of photosynthesis in the plankton and hence restrict the biological productivity of the oceans. At the same time these and other organo-chlorine compounds may present a hazard that becomes apparent only in times of severe stress. Evidence for this was seen in the early autumn of 1969 when thousands of dead seabirds, mainly guillemots, were swept onto the shores of the Irish Sea. The culprits in this seabird wreck were polychlorinated biphenyl compounds, or PCBs, which are products of the plastics industry. The PCBs, which are more persistent but less toxic than DDT, had probably accumulated in the fatty tissues of the birds without any harmful effects. Then for some reason the birds starved and had to draw upon their stores of fat. The PCBs were released into the already weakened body and caused damage to the brain, liver and kidney, so that the worst affected birds died.

The same uncertainties which make the effects of the pollutants mentioned above impossible to forecast cause serious concern over the release of radioactive wastes into the oceans. An illuminating example of what can happen occurred during a visit by US Scientists to the Bikini Atoll, where extensive nuclear tests had been carried out. Navy officers were puzzled to find that levels of radioactivity on the ships' hulls rose at night and decreased during daylight hours. The fluctuations were eventually traced to the daily migration of planktonic animals which had picked up and concentrated radioactive elements in their bodies. More than ten years after the last nuclear test, land-dwelling coconut crabs on the islands were still accumulating such a high concentration of radioactive strontium-90 in their shells that the meat was unsafe to eat, and giant clams living close to the islands had kidneys so radioactive that they sent the survey counters off the scale!

Of course, the Bikini Atoll has been subject to an exceptional radioactive dosage. For a realistic example of pollution by radioactive materials in present times one must look at nuclear power stations, fuel-processing and military establishments. The strontium-90 and caesium-137 released in the effluent from Windscale, Cumberland, where nuclear fuel is processed, is such that a person eating two pounds of fish caught in the fishing grounds nearest to it would not be exposed to more than 0·7 per cent of the permissible daily dose set out by the International Commission on Radiological Protection (ICRP). The ICRP sets limits, considered to err well on the safe side, of the radiation dose to which both individuals and communities may be exposed. Another, much quoted example of the care taken in the UK over this question of radio-active pollution is the control of the waste from the nuclear power station at Winfrith in Dorset: the limit is said to be governed by a local cafe proprietor who eats lobster every day. Even if he continues to indulge in lobsters at this rate throughout his lifetime, his total dose of radiation will not amount to more than 10 per cent of the background radiation. Against these examples there are others which are not so comforting. A worker at the Hanford reactor, which discharges radioactive zinc-65 into the Columbia River in the United States, was found to have taken in an unusual amount of the substance in some way. Finally the source was traced not to industrial carelessness, but to some oysters he had eaten which came from the Pacific Ocean 250 miles away, and which contained 200,000 times as much radioactive zinc as the surrounding sea.

According to the Soviet biologist, G. G. Polikarpov, the authorities responsible for the discharge of radioactive material into the marine environment have consistently underestimated the dangers. He concludes his book, 'Radio-ecology of Aquatic Organisms', with the warning that further radioactive contamination of the seas and oceans is inadmissible because it presents great dangers not only to the marine environment and its inhabitants, but to man himself who consumes some of these creatures. 'It is essential', he claims, 'to end all nuclear-weapon tests and the dumping of liquid and solid radioactive waste into the seas and oceans.' Nevertheless, radioactive material is still disposed of in the oceans, and the concensus appears to be that radioactive waste does not pose any serious threat at present. It probably accounts for less than three per cent of the background radiation emanating from natural sources such as cosmic rays, natural rocks and the body itself. British and European radioactive waste, with low level activity, continues to be released in tremendous dilution along with effluent or is sealed in shielded containers and dumped at depths of over 16,000 feet. Highly active waste is generally stored on the land.

Because the dangers to man of radioactive materials were soon recognized, rapid steps were taken to control its release. As a result, the immediate danger, barring accidents, seems to have been averted. But what will happen in the future as the burden of radioactive waste increases or when the radioactive containers on the seabed begin to break up? The expansion of nuclear power as a source of electricity in Western Europe will inevitably lead to further pressure on already limited facilities for storing high active waste safely away from living things. Unfortunately, radioactive waste cannot be made harmless by treatment with some suitable antidote; it must be left to 'cool off'. The decay in radioactivity can take anything from seconds, hours or days to hundreds of years. The radioactive iodine-131 used in medicine, for example, has a half-life – the time taken to lose half its radioactivity – of approximately eight days and need be stored for only a few weeks or months before its decay is completed, whereas the strontium-90 and caesium-137 produced from reprocessing nuclear fuels need to be kept out of circulation for 600 to 900 years. The containers used for dumping at the present time certainly do not have a life-time measured in hundreds of years. What will happen when they crumble is anybody's guess. In all probability, radioactive material will leak very slowly into the deep-ocean water and, because of the slowness of the deep-ocean currents, it will be many years before any significant increase in radioactive contamination of the oceans is observed. There is a danger that with the levels of contamination still low, this inevitable addition of some radioactive material in the future will be neglected because of the pressure for additional ocean dumping.

A more immediate danger from the growing demand for energy, from both nuclear and conventional sources, is the risk of thermal pollution with warmed cooling water released into coastal and estuarine environments. Although the warm effluent offers the prospects of stepping up the production of protein by farming rapidly growing fish and shellfish, it has also been known to have an adverse effect, killing large numbers of 'cold-water' fish. The release of warmed water could be even more serious in tropical waters where many marine organisms apparently live very close to their upper limit of temperature tolerance. Apart from the ill-effects on marine organisms, the danger of thermal pollution may also spread to human populations. For example, measurements taken in Puget Sound, Washington, indicate that during the summer months a rise in temperature of as little as 1 °F could trigger off a bloom of toxic phytoplankton which could be accumulated by the shellfish eaten by people. Furthermore, how disease-causing bacteria react to thermal pollution is not known. Pathogens sheltering in shellfish and other marine animals or held in estuarine mud might prove a serious source of infection after changes in the environment brought about by thermal pollution.

So far, I have been considering classes of ocean pollutants

rather than activities leading to pollution. Of these, the deliberate dumping of solid wastes – domestic, industrial and military garbage – probably present the most serious challenge. Already many people who have become alive to the threats of pollution are fighting attempts to use the oceans as a repository for all the world's noxious wastes. In 1968 a storm of protest arose after the proposal by Pechiney Aluminium Works in southern France to dump waste slurry in a 6,000-foot deep offshore canyon in the Mediterranean. More recently, there were vigorous protests against the dumping of obsolete and dangerous nerve-gas weapons by the US Army in the Atlantic. Although after some delay the dumping went ahead, it seems unlikely that any more similar exercises will be carried out. In July 1971, public outcry and national protests led to the recall of a Dutch ship *Stella Maris* which was actually on its way to dump 600 tons of chemical waste in the north-east Atlantic. Earlier that year, the *Hudson Stream*, a British ship, had to postpone a proposed voyage to discharge waste at a site in the south-eastern part of the North Sea, about 30 miles from the mouth of the Thames.

Ocean dumping, because of its comparative cheapness, particularly where containerization is not considered necessary, is an attractive escape route for companies that cannot afford to include in their costings the price of recycling or more direct disposal of their chemical wastes. In the United States, for example, ocean dumping has increased almost five-fold in 20 years and in spite of calls for restraint it is expected to increase at a rate of 4.5 per cent annually, or three times the population growth rate. With this spectre looming up, the US Council on Environmental Quality prepared a report to the President in October 1970, recommending that steps should be taken to secure international control of ocean dumping. 'The United States', the report concluded, 'must show its concern by strong domestic action ... But unilateral action alone will not solve a global problem. International controls, supported by global monitoring and coordinated research, will be necessary to deal effectively and comprehensively with pollution caused by ocean dumping.' Even in the absence of such international action, regional action has been taken. In February 1972, the United Kingdom, along with other European countries, attended a Convention for the Prevention of Marine Pollution by Dumping from Ships and Aircraft. The Convention covers the high seas and territorial waters in the North-East Atlantic region, including the North Sea, part of the Arctic Ocean, the Mediterranean and the Baltic. However, steps were taken towards wider controls at the UN Human Environment Conference in June 1972 when it was agreed to hold a meeting in London with a view to establishing an international convention on ocean dumping.

Much of the concern in Western Europe stems from the need to conserve fisheries and the coastal breeding grounds. The bed of the North Sea has become so littered with dumped material that it is no longer an uncommon experience for a trawler to bring up barrels of toxic waste in its net. For example, in April 1971, a Danish trawler brought up 72 barrels of waste that had become ensnared in its nets. According to a study of North Sea pollution published by the International Council on Exploration of the Sea (ICES) in 1968, tremendous volumes of waste were being discharged annually. For example, the Netherlands was discharging 3,600 tons of sulphuric acid per year and 750 tons of sulphur dioxide waste. German industry was discharging up to 600 tons a year of polyethylene and 480 tons of chlorinated hydrocarbons. The signs are that such dumping has increased since that time. One measure of the increasing industrial pollution of the sea and coastal waters is the reduction in biological productivity in some areas.

Theoretically, the amounts of pollutants which find their way into the oceans are miniscule compared with the total volume. In the North Sea, 5,400 tons of any substance dumped in its 1,140 cubic miles of sea-water would lead to an icrease of only one-millionth of a gramme per litre of the substance in the water. Therefore the present rates of discharge coupled with the continuous flushing of the sea by the Atlantic should not lead to anything like toxic levels, but they do. Dr Pieter Korringa, a Dutch fisheries expert, has described the kind of thing that can happen. In March 1965, dead fish were found littering the shore at Noordwijk, north of the Hague. An alert chemist spotted blue copper sulphate crystals on the beach and he analysed the sea-water in the locality: the copper content proved to be 500 times higher than normal. Someone had apparently dumped the copper expecting it to be carried away and harmlessly diluted, but instead a mass of copper-rich water had formed. Two weeks later the toxic water was still around, this time 37 miles further north at the entrance to the Wadden Zee, with its rich mussel beds. Finally, north winds drove the water away from the coast and it presumably dispersed.

Even if dumped material is dispersed, considerable damage may still be inflicted on marine life in the locality. In 1970 after news that large quantities of plastics waste had been dumped, a joint group of Norwegian and Swedish scientists decided to investigate the effects. The first report from the research vessel dispatched to the dumping ground indicated that the substances, chlorinated aliphatic hydrocarbons, were much more dangerous than had originally been assumed. The vessel reported high densities of particles, looking like dead plankton, in the surface waters. In some places, the sea was coloured red-white by them. Subsequent analysis showed that the particles were indeed dead plankton, mainly the crustacean *Calanus finmarchicus* – an important member of the marine-food chain of many commercial pelagic fish. Dead fish larvae, particularly cod, were also found in the dumping zone. The investigations of the Scandinavian scientists also revealed that these substances have a wide distribution in the North Sea and North Atlantic. Even more alarming was the evidence that in

some places they occurred in sufficient quantities to interfere with the rate of photosynthesis in phytoplankton.

The dangers of ocean dumping and marine pollution in
general do not end with incidents of local damage to
marine life. Their impact on the total health of the oceans
has to be considered. As yet man has neither the knowledge
nor the monitoring capacity to do this, but this ignorance
has not prevented further pollution. On the contrary, it is
estimated that pollution will increase seven-fold by the year
2000 unless drastic changes are made in handling waste.
Meanwhile, there is no accurate way of knowing just what
lasting damage has already been inflicted on the oceans. As
a precaution it would be wise to reduce the ecological in-
sults that confront the marine environment. This will involve unprecedented cooperation between the nations of the
world irrespective of whether they themselves think they
have a pollution problem. No one minds very much if
harmless waste – which must be proved to be harmless – is
dumped in a controlled way, taking into account the global
situation, but the unrestricted release of toxic or persistent
pollutants should not now be condoned. If action on this is
not taken very soon, coastal waters and the ocean beyond
could be slowly turned into poisonous slums practically
devoid of life and useless for either recreation or most
forms of exploitation.

International cooperation

With so much discussion on exploitation, it would be easy
to imagine that this was a recent phenomenon, whereas, in
fact, one of the earliest international organizations concerned with the oceans, the International Council for the
Exploitation of the Sea (ICES), arose from the needs of the
West European fisheries. From its office in Copenhagen,
ICES assists member nations with results of 'hydrographic-
biological research' and provides a forum for their fishery

experts. ICES was proposed twenty years before the first purely scientific organization, the International Association of Physical Oceanography, which was founded in 1919. Even today, international organizations devoted to the 'practical uses' of the oceans easily outnumber those concerned with fundamental studies, of which the two most important ones are the Scientific Committee on Oceanic Research (SCOR) established in 1957 by the International Council of Scientific Unions and the Inter-governmental Oceanographic Commission (IOC) set up in 1960 within the framework of Unesco.

The aim of the IOC is to encourage progress in oceanic investigations for the peaceful use of the oceans and their resources, but international participation in these vital areas remains largely divided among inter-governmental organizations both within the family of the United Nations and outside it. Although the major marine programmes of the United Nations are in Unesco and FAO, oceanography is not an important part of the overall effort in either organization. This same fragmentation of effort occurs in bodies concerned with other maritime affairs. Thus the responsibilities of the International Labour Organisation of the United Nations include conditions of work on board ships, and the International Atomic Energy Agency keeps watch on radioactive wastes; but they are both overlapped to some extent by the Inter-governmental Marine Consultative Organization (IMCO) which covers both pollution by some industrial wastes and problems related to marine transportation.

The comparatively recent origin of many international organizations – the Charter of the United Nations was signed on 26 June 1945 – is often revealed in the legislative background to international agreements. An excellent example, relevant to this chapter, is the convention on oil pollution, mentioned in the previous section. Early attempts, first by the United States in 1926 and then by the United Kingdom in 1934, to reach an international agreement on the discharge of oil at sea were complete failures. Further attempts were interrupted by the Second World War. It was not until 1954 that the British government made another approach as a result of recommendations of a committee which had reported on pollution the previous year. At the British government's request, forty nations gathered in London. At the end of the conference they anounced the International Convention for the Prevention of Pollution of the Sea by Oil. The Convention came into force on 26 July 1958, one year after the agreed minimum number of states had established the necessary national legislation. IMCO, the appropriate international organization, did not take charge until 1959 when the British government transferred the Convention to it. In 1962 a further conference was called by IMCO to make amendments designed to strengthen the Convention. The amended Convention did not come into force for five years although it was put in action earlier by the United Kingdom.

The time-lag of five years before the amended Convention came into force indicates the kind of inertia created by conflicting national interests when international agreements are given any real 'bite'. The political ramifications of even the most innocuous suggestions are frequently quite beyond the casual observer and, occasionally, scientific advisors associated with them. This dichotomy between scientists and politicians can lead to very real conflicts of interest. Nowhere is this more apparent than in the operation of various fishery commissions, some of which are composed largely of scientists while others are governed largely by politicians or professional administrators. The failure of the International Whaling Commission to take the advice of its scientific committee is a case in point. The collapse of the whaling industry, described in Chapter 1, could have been prevented if national and commercial interests had not discarded the quotas for catches within the limits suggested by scientific evidence on existing whale populations.

Fortunately, not all international groups prove quite so intractable and agreements reached by them are undoubtedly setting the pattern for future negotiations on other matters such as problems arising from marine mining.

Until very recently, the advanced maritime nations of Western Europe and North America have dominated maritime disputes and agreements, but the developing nations are beginning to redress the balance by taking a more active interest in the oceans. The gulf between the 'haves' and the 'have-nots' remains, but the opportunities to make real contributions to the economy based on even the most modest research efforts are very great. For example, newly trained marine scientists and engineers in developing countries can help improve the exploitation of fish resources in surrounding sea areas. Dr R. Subrahmanyan in a paper published in 1959 provided an illustration of just how ineffective this exploitation can be. He studied phytoplankton production in the Arabian Sea along the 1,200-mile coastline of India and extending offshore for 50 miles. He related this primary production to fish catches in the area and then made a similar comparison of the ratio of phytoplankton to fish caught in the English Channel, an area of intense exploitation. His conclusion was that the potential yield available to Indian fishermen was 1,119,000 tons – an increase in the order of 660,000 tons.

Over the years, developing countries have received considerable aid and technical advice but on the whole this assistance has been on a piecemeal, *ad hoc* basis. While in most cases the results have been beneficial, a more sustained and widespread effort is needed to build up 'centres of excellence' from which further development can be made on a self-help basis. An equally important source of encouragement for scientific and technical improvement is, of course, the international research programme. The useful spin-off from the first major international oceanographic programme, the International Indian Ocean Expedition (1960–65), is still continuing.

The success of the Indian Ocean venture, in which twenty-five nations were involved, must have in part encouraged President Johnson to propose in March 1968 an international decade of ocean exploration for the 1970s. US scientific, business and educational leaders seconded this proposal during the thirty-third American assembly on 'Uses of the Seas' held at Harriman in May 1968. The conference agreed that 'given the expanding prospects at sea it is urgent to take measures to accommodate competing uses, to promote conservation, to refine the laws, to negotiate the appropriate international agreements and to create international machinery to assist in the scientific investigation of the seas and in orderly developments of ocean resources.' According to Robert F. Packard, then director of the US State Department's Office of Space and Environmental Science Affairs, the proposal was developed in the hope that an international programme on such a massive scale would accomplish a task beyond any single nation and would foster relationships between countries which would encourage agreements on the exploitation of the oceans.

Since then it has become accepted by the international community that the 1970s should be the years of the International Decade of Ocean Exploration (IDOE). Progress has been slow in spite of stalwart work by the IOC and UN agencies such as FAO and the World Meteorological Organization (WMO), all of which have vested scientific interests in promoting such a programme, but some advance has been made behind the scenes towards establishing a number of priority areas for the first five years of the programme. The IOC has suggested three areas for 'co-operative exercises': a global investigation of pollution in the marine environment; an intense study of an area of high marine productivity; and a survey of the world's continental margins. These are to be the main ingredients of a Long-term and Expanded Programme of Oceanographic Research (LEPOR) taking in the Decade, which is seen as the accelerating phase of prolonged international activity in the oceans. These choices have an interesting duality of purpose: they are important sites for fundamental research, but they also have considerable value to those whose ultimate goal is the exploitation of ocean resources.

At present, cooperation in research is badly needed. The interest now being shown by developing countries in the oceans does not always produce positive results. Requests from other countries to carry out research in their neighbourhood are often treated with suspicion concerning the real motive, and, increasingly, coastal states want to keep information about their coastal and contiguous areas to themselves. The right to be able to carry out *bona fide* marine research is no longer considered a fundamental ocean freedom and requests to carry out programmes in areas falling within the continental shelf zone or areas claimed for national fisheries are quite likely to meet with a blank refusal. Although no one benefits from this kind of situation, the fact remains that with their restricted ability to invest in ocean development, many developing countries find scientific data of little practical value. In an effort to break this deadlock, the IOC and other inter-governmental agencies are being urged to assist developing nations to apply scientific results to practical ends. Improvement in the presently deteriorating situation therefore depends greatly on successful education and training and the development of national capabilities in marine science and its applications.

The great ocean debate

No greater challenge can exist for international cooperation than that of finding a solution, satisfactory to all nations, on the question of how marine 'spoils' of the kind described in this book should be shared. Such a solution must consider the military as well as the commercial role of the oceans. International accord is difficult enough to achieve in the regulation of fishing, an activity which dates back almost to antiquity, but it is even more illusive when the military interests of the technologically advanced nations are involved or threatened. A mistake made now in these formative years of ocean development could lead one day to open conflict between powerful factions, as well as frustrate the hopes of those who look to the oceans for food, fresh water and national wealth.

The first significant development came in 1945 when the United States made a unilateral proclamation laying claim to the resources on its continental shelf down to the 100-fathom (200-metre) mark. Other countries followed suit with further claims to areas of the sea and ocean floor well beyond their territorial waters. In spite of some protests, it seemed generally agreed that this was entirely reasonable, provided that some kind of uniformity existed over what a country could realistically claim as its own. At the request of the United Nations, an International Commission was set up to study the problem. The findings of this Commission led to the Convention on the Continental Shelf of 29 April 1958 which came into force on 10 June 1964 – thirty days after its ratification by the United Kingdom.

The Convention recognized the right of the coastal state to exercise sovereign rights over the continental shelf defined as 'the seabed and sub-soil adjacent to the coast but outside the area of the territorial sea, to a depth of 200 metres or, beyond that limit, to where the depth of the superjacent waters admits of the exploitation of the natural resources of the said areas'. These rights were to be independent of 'occupation, effective or notional' or of 'any express proclamation'. Thus the Convention placed a seal of approval on most of the underwater territories already acquired unilaterally, but by introducing the ambiguity of depths permitting exploitation it became an 'open-ended' document which placed virtually no restrictions on technologically advanced nations. Indeed, the United States leased tracts of land, situated underwater several hundred fathoms deep, basing this on the assumption that the country's authority 'extends as far seawards as technological ability can cope with the water depth ... in accord with the Convention of the Sea adopted at Geneva'.

Alarmed by the prospects of an underwater land-grab in which the developing nations would inevitably be the losers, Malta decided to raise the issue in the General Assembly of the United Nations. Originally a declaration and treaty were proposed but by the time that the agenda item was assigned to a committee this had been reduced to the 'examination of the question of the reservation exclusively for peaceful purposes of the seabed and the ocean floor, and the sub-soil thereof, underlying the high seas beyond the limits of present national jurisdiction, and the use of their resources in the interests of mankind'. The address given by Malta's representative Arvid Pardo to the committee on 1 November 1967 received widespread press coverage which could not disguise the political interest and the suspicions aroused in the minds of some legislators. One member of the US House of Representatives hinted darkly that the Maltese delegation had been 'put up to make the proposal', perhaps by the British. However, Pardo was content to explain that his country, being situated in the midst of the Mediterranean, could not avoid being vitally interested in the oceans.

The reduction in the forcefulness of the terms of the Maltese proposal indicated the unwillingness of many states to make any definite decision on such an important topic. But although no substantial declaration emerged, the 'defusing' of the proposal shed interesting light upon the views of various groups of states. The developing nations, for example, were either strongly in favour of an international body to regulate exploitation or wanted an immediate declaration of the principles put forward by Malta in a supporting memorandum. The states with the technological capability to move into the oceans, however, were far more cautious and hesitant. The Soviet Union wanted to keep the preparatory work for any decision at a national, rather than international, level. The United States, although apparently more willing to join a cooperative study of the problem, advised that a 'hasty approach would indeed be imprudent'. The fact that the resolution approved by the General Assembly bore little resemblance to the original agenda item probably reflects concessions made to ensure the support of countries including the Soviet Union, the United States, Japan and the United Kingdom who, unlike the developing nations, already have substantial investment in marine and related affairs.

The Malta proposal directed attention to the potential plight of the poorer nations as never before. They responded in a manner which emphasized that the advanced nations would not easily seize this last great world asset. The immediate result was a decision to have an *ad hoc* committee make a general study of the oceans and national and international activities in them. In December 1968, as a result of its report, the General Assembly established a permanent Committee composed of 42 states for the peaceful uses of the seabed and the ocean floor beyond the limits of national jurisdiction; 112 nations voted in favour, there were seven abstentions, but no nations voted against. The Seabed Committee was instructed along four lines: to study the legal principles that would promote international cooperation in the exploration and use of the seabed and sub-soil beyond the limits of national jurisdiction; to study the means of encouraging the use and exploitation of resources in this area in the light of foreseeable technological development and economic implications, 'bearing in mind the fact that such exploitation should benefit mankind as a whole'; to examine the exchange and dissemination of scientific knowledge in these matters; and, finally, to consider how marine pollution resulting from exploitation and exploration might be prevented. A further resolution, instructed it to study the question of reserving the seabed for exclusively peaceful purposes.

The establishment of the Seabed Committee and its subsequent reports provided a catalyst for a whole series of resolutions concerned with the oceans and its resources. The workings of the committee also revealed that, just as in other areas of international activity, the self-interest of states inevitably intruded and prevented any firm decisions. Reflecting the original Malta proposition, the Seabed Committee did suggest that a regime needed to be established concerned with the uses of the resources of the oceans for the benefit of mankind 'irrespective of the geographical location of states and taking into account the special interests and needs of developing countries'. The character and scope of this regime were not, however, defined. By the summer of 1970, the Committee was in a state of deadlock with no effective proposals to place before the General Assembly in the autumn. It might well have ceased to exist but for the decision of the UN General Assembly in December to hold a new Law of the Sea Conference in 1973. As a result, the Seabed Committee was enlarged and given the task of preparing for the great day when the pride and prejudice of the world's states go on show. This new conference presents an opportunity at least to prepare for an ocean regime that recognizes the vulnerability of this last resource to man's activities – a point that only now is being realized and which is not embodied in existing international law.

Any settlement must consider the situation on the continental shelf. It is already too late to change the parcelling up of areas like the North Sea which has been done in accordance with the 1958 Continental Shelf Convention, but some control might be exerted over the gradual extension of claims into much deeper waters. The great problem here is that no convenient physical, economic or political line exists which can be used to separate shallow areas from deeper ones. There is no immutable geophysical law which decrees that the continental shelf and its resources shall stop at the 'magic' depth of 200 metres. In fact, the continuity of exploitable resources from shallow to deeper parts of the sea floor probably accounts for the 'escape clause' inserted in the 1958 Continental Shelf Convention.

Assuming a satisfactory formula could be worked out on control of the sea floor over the entire continental shelf, the fisheries by their very nature would still be sources of disagreement. Unlike minerals, the living resources of the oceans are too mobile to fit into the confines of any particular territory. A state might be given overall jurisdiction of a coastal fishing ground or have 'special rights' to fish there, but the stocks would be free to roam out of the area. The late Dr W. M. Chapman gave a very good illustration of this point by reference to a single region – the territorial seas off Mexico and California. Although most of the sardine and anchovy there are taken reasonably close to the shore, the fish spawn well out to sea and they can also be caught in these international waters. The jack mackerel, also caught mostly near the coast, has a spawning area which stretches at least 1,000 miles out to sea. Another fish commonly caught in these territorial waters, the bluefin tuna, does not even spawn in the eastern Pacific but comes from as far away as ocean areas south of Japan. Marine mammals are just as fickle: the nearest breeding grounds for the fur seals found feeding in the sea off California are the Pribilof Islands in the Bering Sea whilst the grey whales which breed in the lagoons of northern Mexico eventually migrate back across the Pacific to Kamchatka and the western Bering Sea. In spite of such problems some countries can protect important local stocks of fish by extending the national fishing limit, but clearly a different, as yet undecided, regime is needed to protect fish stocks in the high seas from being exploited to the point of exhaustion.

Exhaustion of the resource will not be the main worry where deep-sea minerals are concerned. On the contrary, as explained in Chapter 6, the problem is more likely to become one of preventing overproduction, which could cause a glut of the more common minerals. With the greater part of the oceans to choose from, the question of territorial rights seems far less significant than finding some means of allowing all nations, both rich and poor, to benefit from these remote mineral stores. Unfortunately, these deliberations are made more urgent and difficult because of the military role of the oceans. Neither East nor West will be overly keen to see the other firmly ensconced in a territory marked off for mineral exploitation which, like some 'fishing' activities, might come to be the cover for military operations.

The reluctance of coastal states to relinquish their grip on the seabed is reflected in President Nixon's proposals to internationalize the seabed beyond the depth of 200 metres. This proposal made in April 1970, and later formalized in a draft treaty represents an important concession by a major power in its approach to the allocation of marine resources. The proposal, by accepting the 200-metre mark as the depth limit to national claims on the seabed, helps to plug the most serious gap in the 1958 Geneva Convention. However, even in this proposal, there are strings attached which enable the coastal state to retain at least some control, for commercial and strategic reasons, over the seabed and beyond. According to the American proposal there would be a trusteeship zone beyond the 200-metre mark and down almost to the deep-ocean floor. This zone would be looked after by the coastal state under the supervision of an international authority yet to be established. The trusteeship rights would enable the coastal states to decide whether, how, and to whom licences should be issued for exploration and exploitation. They would also be able to retain a certain amount of the income from activities within the zone, but at least half the income could be made available to the international authority for the benefit of the world community.

In many respects the draft treaty presented by the United States represents something of a breakthrough: it would call a halt to the underwater land grab that is building up at the present time; it recognizes that at least some part of the seabed is the common heritage of mankind; and it includes the land-locked nations which must be feeling a little frustrated at the prospects of being excluded from the benefits accruing from a major part of the Earth's surface. The United Kingdom has followed with a proposal along similar lines, although they do not want necessarily to be restricted to the 200-metre mark as an immutable end to national jurisdiction. A great deal of British concern seems to be focused on finding equitable ways of parcelling up the deep ocean, leaving the rest until the definition of territorial limits has been established and agreed. The Soviet Union is showing its customary aversion to the possible establishment of an international authority which will have supernational powers. In the postures of these and other states can be seen the familiar nervousness that stems from concern over issues of national security and military strategy.

The military shadow continues to lie heavily over much of the current ocean debate. Some hopeful people suggest that the sensible solution to the military 'question' is simply to remove it by reserving the oceans, rather like Antarctica and Outer Space, solely for peaceful purposes. Certainly this is a very tempting proposition but it seems to neglect the current political facts of life. The oceans provide a mantle of secrecy for deep silent-running submarines which carry a second strike force of nuclear-headed missiles. In other words, no matter how much an aggressor might gain the initiative by a surprise attack with land-based missiles, he could expect to suffer drastic retaliation from an ocean fleet of submarines. Remove this force and an important restraint goes with it: far better to preserve the deterrent, at least until a more general disarmament becomes possible.

The presence of large navies and nuclear submarines in the high seas is regarded by some as a block to effective agreements on the use of deep-ocean resources – particularly marine minerals. However, such commercial activity as may occur in this region during the 1970s is not likely to conflict with military interests. In addition, international agreements, which would be more feasible without demilitarization as an essential part of them, might well lay the foundations for later disarmament talks. There are so many other questions involved in developing the ocean resources that to stalemate discussions by bringing in threats to the security of the major states would seem to be madness. Why should we expect to obtain political agreement on the oceans, in many ways an attractive arena for strategic deployment, when they have proved impossible to achieve on the land?

A *laissez-faire* school of thought would go even further and say, 'Why bother with any special agreement on the deep oceans at all?' Broadly speaking, proponents of this line believe that the exploitation of the deep ocean will not be important for decades to come and that present international law is quite up to handling the few incidents which might occur from time to time. Unfortunately, this argument ignores the desires of those nations which do not as yet have the technology even to consider exploiting the oceans. The consequences for the world of allowing a handful of nations to dominate the seabed and the ocean floor would be disastrous: the developing states would not accept peaceably a situation where the strong nations would get stronger, the rich richer and the poor would become little more than their slaves. The tensions between the few nations involved in this conspiracy of marine technology would spiral as their wealth and suspicions of each other grew. The maintenance of any semblance of a balance of power would produce intolerable stress. Finally, the oceans, instead of providing the means for a satisfactory life for the Earth's family of nations, could become the location for the planet's Armageddon.

Glossary

All terms are explained when they are first used in the text but some of the more important or unusual ones are listed here for ready reference. Words in italics are defined separately.

ABYSS: deep ocean floor and all regions deeper than 18,000 feet

ALGAE: one of the four divisions in the plant kingdom. Simpler in structure than garden plants, algae are largely aquatic and range in size from a single cell like the *diatom* to large seaweeds such as the *kelp*

ANODIC EFFECT: influence of direct electric current on fish which tend to move towards the positive pole or anode – see page 38

BEAM TRAWL – see *trawl*

BEAUFORT WIND SCALE: system originally devised by Admiral Beaufort in the nineteenth century which classified wind forces by the amount of sail carried by a ship. It has since been modified and expanded for international meteorological use – see page 157

BENDS – see *decompression*

BENTHOS: the plants and animals attached to the seabed or crawling on it.

BORE: tidal phenomenon which occurs when water is forced by tidal action into large but rapidly narrowing river estuaries. The excess water escapes by moving upstream in a wavelike front over the river water – see page 165

BOUNDARY WAVES – see *interval waves*

BRACKISH WATER: water with a salinity of less than 17,000 parts per million (p.p.m.) and more than 500 p.p.m.

BREATHING MIXTURES – see *nitrogen narcosis*

CAVITATION: formation, growth and rapid collapse of gaseous and vapour bubbles. Cavitation can be a serious source of noise, corrosion and loss of efficiency in marine propellers – see page 234

CONTINENTAL RISE – see *continental shelf*

CONTINENTAL SHELF: extension of continental land mass into the ocean. It slopes gently with a gradient of about 1 in 500 breaking off around the 100-fathom mark into a steeper gradient, 1 in 40, at the start of the continental slope. This leads in turn to the more variable continental rise and, beyond, the abyssal plains of the deep ocean floor – see page 13

CONTINENTAL SLOPE – see *continental shelf*

CORIOLIS FORCE: product of the Earth's rotation. It deflects moving particles to the right in the northern hemisphere and to the left in the southern hemisphere. Together with the prevailing winds and the sun, it is largely responsible for the pattern of ocean circulation – see page 176

DECCA: British navigational system which provides position by comparing continuous synchronized signals from two fixed transmitters

DECOMPRESSION: systematic reduction of pressure during a diver's ascent. It is generally carried out by making stops according to a predetermined schedule. Decompression sickness or bends occurs when the diver ascends too quickly because the rapid release of the pressure allows gases dissolved in the body fluids and tissues to form bubbles before reaching the lungs. The only satisfactory remedy for decompression sickness is to recompress the diver, otherwise bubbles formed in vital tissues will prove fatal – see page 189

DECOMPRESSION SICKNESS – see *decompression*

DEEP SCATTERING LAYER – see *phantom bottom*

DEMERSAL FISH: bottom-living fish as opposed to surface-living or pelagic fish – see page 33

DIATOM: microscopic algae with a shell (frustule) composed of silica. Apart from being important members of the *plankton*, deposits of their shells form vast quantities of ooze on the deep sea floor – see pages 26 and 131

DIVING MIXTURE – see *saturation diving*

ELECTRODIALYSIS: uses selectively permeable membranes to remove salt from sea-water. The driving force is electricity – see page 91

FATHOM: common unit of depth (equivalent to six feet or 1·83 metres)

FETCH: continuous area of water over which the wind blows uninterrupted in the same direction. It is an important factor in the generation of the ocean *swell*

FORAMINIFERA: microscopic animals with chalk shells (test). Like the *diatom* their shells may accumulate in considerable quantities on the sea floor – see page 130

FREEZING PROCESSES (DESALINATION): take advantage of the fact that when sea-water freezes, fresh-water ice forms, leaving the salt in solution. Basically there are two processes, direct freezing where the water is frozen by evaporation in a vacuum chamber and secondary refrigerant freezing which uses the evaporation of a liquefied gas to cool the sea-water to the freezing point – see page 88

GILL NET: fishing net which traps *pelagic* fish when they endeavour to swim through its meshes. Fish which are too large to pass through the mesh become entangled by their gill covers when they try to back out of the net – see page 35

GROUND-EFFECT: principle used by the hovercraft and similar ground-effect machines. If a stream of air is directed through a hole in a flat metal plate down on to a surface, it creates an upward thrust which lifts the plate – see page 231

HARMONIC PREDICTION: method of predicting tides and tidal currents by combining, either mechanically or electronically, constituent wave forms into a single tidal wave – see page 165

HOOKAH: any diving apparatus which receives breathing gas via a hose from a separate independent supply

HYDROFOIL CRAFT: travels on 'wing-like' projections immersed in the water which reduce the area of boat in contact with it. The reduced drag enables hydrofoil craft to attain higher speeds than conventional displacement vessels – see page 229

HYDROGRAPHY: science which deals with the measurement and mapping of the physical features of the seas and oceans

INERTIAL NAVIGATION SYSTEM: once set gives position without any outside reference. It operates by detecting changes in direction and speed by continuous reference to accelero-meters mounted on a stable platform provided by three gyros – see page 238

INTERNAL WAVES: waves created beneath the ocean surface at the boundary between two different water masses. Since the difference in density between the two layers is consider-ably less than that between air and water, internal waves can be much larger than surface waves – see page 163

ISOBATH: depth contour

KELP: a common name for the brown seaweed found fringing most rocky shores. It belongs to a group, the laminariales, which includes the largest known seaweeds

KNOT: unit of speed used in navigation. It is equivalent to one *nautical mile* (1·1508 land miles) per hour.

LATENT HEAT: additional heat required for a change in state, such as from solid to liquid, without an increase in temperature. The fact that the heat of fusion is lower than the heat of evaporation is one of the main reasons for attempts to desalinate water by freezing rather than distillation pro-cesses

LONG-LINE FISHING: use of long weighted line with side branches ending in hooks to catch mainly demersal and mid-water fish

LORAN (LONG RANGE NAVIGATION): American naviga-tional system which fixes ship position by reference to the difference in time of synchronized radio signals from two fixed transmitters

MARIGRAM: the rise and fall of the tide plotted against time

MASCARET – see *bore*

MULTI-STAGE FLASH DISTILLATION (MSF): desalination process in which sea-water is fed into a succession of chambers at progressively lower pressures. Some of the hot water 'flashes' to steam when entering each chamber leaving the salt behind, because the boiling point of water becomes lower as the pressure is reduced – see page 84

NAUTICAL MILE: length of one minute of arc along any great circle on the surface of the Earth. Since this varies with latitude, the nautical mile is agreed internationally to be equal to 1,852 metres (6,076·103 feet or 1·1508 statute miles)

NEAP TIDE – see *tides*

NEKTON: collective name for all animals which swim in the sea

NITROGEN NARCOSIS: effect on a diver's mental processes of excess nitrogen dissolved into his body fluids and tissues. When a *scuba* diver breathing normal air, which contains 80 per cent nitrogen, descends much below 60 feet, the nitrogen begins to impair his performance. The narcotic effects become progressively worse with increasing depth so that by 300 feet even routine tasks become practically impossible. For deep dives, the nitrogen is largely or completely replaced by an inert gas, usually helium. The amount of oxygen in the breathing mixture is also reduced since this gas, normally considered a lifegiver, becomes toxic under pressure if present in the proportions found in air – see page 188

OTTER TRAWL – see *trawl*

PELAGIC FISH: fish found in the surface waters of the sea – see page 33

PELAGIC SEDIMENTS: deposits found on the ocean floor remote from any land. They are generally very fine and range in colour from white to a dark reddish-brown. Pelagic sediments containing less than about 30 per cent of organic remains are called red clay, while those containing more than this are known as oozes – see page 130

PHANTOM BOTTOM: a false bottom indicated by *sonar*. Unlike recordings of echoes from the sea floor, the echoes from this layer are diffuse and ill-defined. When discovered in the early 1940s the source of this sonar disturbance was called the deep scattering layer. Subsequent investigations have revealed the presence of several layers which vary in depth according to the diurnal migrations of marine animals – see page 246

PHOTOSYNTHESIS: the process by which green plants convert solar energy into a form usable by living things. Essentially the process consists of the use of light energy to split water into its constituent hydrogen and oxygen. The hydrogen then takes part in the transformation of carbon dioxide of the air into the carbon-containing organic materials. In the sea, the primary task of photosynthesis is carried out by the phyto-plankton near and at the surface – see page 26

PHYTOPLANKTON – see *plankton*

PLANKTON: the floating, drifting life found in the sea. It is sub-divided into the phytoplankton (plants) and the zooplank-ton (animals). Ultimately all life in the sea relies on the ability of the phytoplankton to carry out *photosynthesis* and because this involves the use of solar energy the small microscopic plants such as *diatoms* are restricted to the sunlit zone of the surface waters. The zooplankton, however, can be found at most depths. Frequently members of the zooplankton migrate upwards during the evening to feed on the phytoplankton, retreating deeper once again with the dawn – see page 26

RAPTURES OF THE DEEP – see *nitrogen narcosis*

RED CLAY – see *pelagic sediments*

RED TIDE: bloom of dinoflagellates (members of the phyto-plankton) in which the plants become so numerous that the surface water becomes coloured red. Where the predominant dinoflagellates are highly toxic, for example *Gonyaulax*, the ensuing red tide may kill many sea birds and fish – see page 30

REFRACTION OF WATER WAVES: the process by which waves moving into shallow coastal water come to conform with the contours of the sea floor. Waves moving in the shallower parts of the sea floor are slowed down compared with those in the deeper water causing the wave 'front' to slew round – see page 160

REVERSE OSMOSIS: fresh water is 'squeezed out' of sea-water by passing it under pressure through a membrane which is impermeable to salt and similar impurities – see page 92

SALINE WATER: water with a salt content of 17,000 parts per million or more.

SATURATION DIVING: the diver remains at or near the work-ing depth after his body tissues have become saturated with the inert gas of his diving mixture. Since *decompression* time is dictated by the degree of saturation, once this point is reached, decompression time remains the same, irrespective of duration at this pressure. The method, therefore, greatly increases the ratio of time spent working to that wasted during decompression – see page 194

SCUBA: stands for self-contained underwater breathing apparatus, of which there are three basic designs: the closed-circuit system – a circulating, inert gas receives fresh oxygen to replace that used; the semi-closed system – a pre-mixed gas is metered out into the breathing circuit so that some is rejected continuously; and the open system – compressed air or gas is supplied from cylinders to a demand regulator and each breath is exhaled to the surrounding water – see page 187

SEICHE: rise and fall of a water mass, whether in a lake or the open sea, which is determined by the structure of the basin. The oscillation of this standing wave may be anything from a few minutes to many hours – see page 165

SEINE NET: a long net which is used to encircle shoals of pelagic fish. When the two ends of the net are brought together, or 'pursed', the net is hauled in with its catch – see page 36

SHADOW ZONE: area of the sea 'unlit' by conventional *sonar* because the sound waves are refracted during their passage through the water – see page 244

SINS: ship's *inertial navigation system*

SONAR: stands for Sound Navigation And Ranging. Although it initially referred to systems using sound to determine the presence, location, or nature of underwater objects, sonar systems are now used much more widely – see page 243

SPRING TIDES – see *tides*

STORM SURGE: exceptionally high water produced by severe storms at sea. Several meteorologic factors may be involved but the most important ones are the low pressure areas in the vicinity of the storm centre and the driving force of the high winds which pile up the water. The profile of the sea floor or the coincidence of spring *tides* can enhance the effect – see page 166

SWELL: a long, relatively symmetrical wave produced by winds and storms occurring in distant parts of the oceans – see page 157

TELECHIRIC: remote control of manipulators and machines. Telechiric machines were originally devised for handling dangerous nuclear materials but they have now found a wide range of applications, including underwater operations – see page 210

TERRIGENOUS DEPOSITS: composed predominantly of

material from the land. These deposits cover practically all of the continental shelf region

THERMOCLINE: region in the sea where the temperature differs markedly from water either above or below it. The existence of a thermocline, either seasonal or permanent, has important implications for biological productivity as well as the use of sonar – see pages 28 and 244

TIDAL WAVE – see *tsunami*

TIDES: product of the astronomical forces of sun and moon acting on the rotating Earth. When the two heavenly bodies pull together or are diametrically opposed the tidal currents show their greatest range – the spring tides. When their forces act at right angles to one another the tidal current has its shortest range – the neap tides. Thus, in every lunar month there are two spring tides and two neap tides with gradations between them according to the phase of the moon – see page 163

TRAWL: a fishing net pulled along through the water. One of the first trawls was the beam trawl, a cumbersome piece of gear which had a heavy cross piece to keep the mouth open. The most important development came with the use of otter boards, 'kite-like' structures placed on either side of the trawl, which sheared away from each other to keep the mouth of the net wide open. Both beam and otter trawl were designed for catching demersal fish: they are dragged over the sea floor. More recently trawls have been designed for fishing in the middle waters of the ocean – see page 36

TSUNAMI: ocean waves produced by a seismic disturbance in the ocean floor. The waves are not usually conspicuous out over the deep ocean but they reveal their tremendous speed and energy by rising tens of feet into the air when they reach the shallows of the shore. Because tsunamis can cause considerable damage, an extensive advanced warning system has been devised in the Pacific areas which suffer most from them – see page 155

TURBIDITY CURRENT: flow of suspended material down a gradient. Turbidity currents are frequently caused by the build up of sediment on the edge of the continental slope

UPWELLING: water rising from deep parts of the sea to the surface. Although underwater banks and shoals can deflect deep water towards the surface, the most prominent upwellings occur where the wind blows parallel to the coastline. The currents generated by the wind cause the surface water to move off-shore, allowing colder water to rise from below. Since deep cold water is generally rich in mineral nutrients, upwellings are usually the sites of important fisheries – see page 28

VAPOUR COMPRESSION (DESALINATION): fresh water vapour driven off salt water is compressed by a fan. The compression and condensation of the vapour provide the heat for further vaporization of sea-water in surrounding heat exchange jackets – see page 86

ZOOPLANKTON – see *plankton*

Bibliography

To assist the non-specialist reader, book titles are shown in capital letters. Those titles marked with an asterisk (*) are written at a popular level.

*THE A-B-SEAS OF DESALTING (United States Department of the Interior, Office of Saline Water, Washington)

Alexandrov, J., 'Underwater with the Russians', *Triton*, June 1968

Bailey, H. S., 'The Voyage of the *Challenger*', *Scientific American*, May 1953

Bainbridge, V., 'Science and the Sea Fisheries', *Advancement of Science*, July 1964

Banks, W., and Sharples, A., 'Studies on Desalination by Reverse Osmosis I', *Journal of Applied Chemistry*, 1966, Vol. 16, January

Banks, W., and Sharples, A., 'Studies on Desalination by Reverse Osmosis II', *Journal of Applied Chemistry*, 1966, Vol. 16, March

Banks, W., and Sharples, A., 'Studies on Desalination by Reverse Osmosis III', *Journal of Applied Chemistry*, 1966, Vol. 16, May

Bannister, J. L., 'Some Developments in Antarctic Whaling 1962–64', *Polar Record*, Vol. 12, No. 77, 1964

Bascom, W., 'Ocean Waves', *Scientific American*, August 1959

*Behrman, Daniel, EXPLORING THE OCEAN (Unesco, Paris, 1970)

Bell, F. H., 'Eastern Pacific Halibut Fishery, 1888–1966', United States Fish and Wildlife Service, Fishery Leaflet 602, August 1968

Bellamy, D. J., Clarke, P. H., John, D. M., Jones, D., Whittick, A., Darke, T., 'Effects of the Pollution from the *Torrey Canyon* on Littoral and Sub-littoral Ecosystems', *Nature*, 9 September 1967

Bennet, P., 'The Narcotic Effects of Air', *Science Journal*, January 1968

Beynon, L. R., 'THE TORREY CANYON INCIDENT: A RE-
VIEW OF EVENTS', The British Petroleum Company Limited,
September 1967

Blumer, M., 'Oil Contamination and the Living Resources of
the Sea', F.A.O. Technical Conference on Marine Pollution
and its Effects on Living Resources and Fishing, December
1970

Bourne, W. R. P., Parrack, J. D., and Potts, G. R., 'Birds Killed
in the *Torrey Canyon* Disaster', *Nature*, 9 September 1967

Bowers, A. B., 'Farming Marine Fish', *Science Journal*, June
1966

*Brandt, A. von, FISH CATCHING METHODS OF THE WORLD
(Fishing News [Books] Limited, London, 1964)

Brown, N., 'Submarine Warfare Today', *New Scientist*, 9 March
1967

Brown, N., 'The Soviet Naval Challenge', *New Scientist*, 24
October 1968

Burgess, G. H. O., DEVELOPMENTS IN HANDLING AND
PROCESSING FISH (Fishing News [Books] Limited, London,
1965)

Burnett, A. M. R., 'Electric Fishing with Pulsatory Direct Current', *New Zealand Journal of Science*, March 1959

Burkholder, P. R., 'Drugs from the Sea', *Armed Forces Chemical
Journal*, March 1963

Butler, P. A., and Johnson, R. F., 'Report on the Bureau of Commercial Fisheries Biological Laboratory, Gulf Breeze, Florida,
fiscal year 1966', Circular 260, United States Fish and Wildlife
Service, June 1967

Carpenter, M. Scott, 'Exploring Space and Sea', Edwin A. Link
Lecture Series, Smithsonian Institution Press, Washington,
D.C., 1967

Clark, L. C., and Gollan, F., 'Survival of Mammals Breathing
Organic Liquids Equilibrated with Oxygen at Atmospheric
Pressure', *Science*, 24 June 1966

Cole, R. C., and Greenwood-Barton, L. H., 'Problems Associated
with the Development of Fisheries in Tropical Countries: II,
the Modernization of Fishing Methods', *Tropical Science*, Vol.
5, No. 4, 1963

Cole, R. C., and Greenwood-Barton, L. H., 'Problems Associated
with the Development of Fisheries in Tropical Countries: III,

the Preservation of the Catch by Simple Processes', *Tropical Science*, Vol. 7, No. 4, 1965

Cousteau, J.-Y., 'Exploring the Sea', *Industrial Research*, March 1966

*Cromie, William J., EXPLORING THE SECRETS OF THE SEA (George Allen and Unwin, London, 1964)

Deacon, G. E. R., *et al.*, AN INTRODUCTION TO OCEANO-GRAPHY (a series of 8 reprints, *New Scientist*, London)

*Deacon, G. E. R., editor, OCEANS (Paul Hamlyn, London, 1962)

*Dickinson, Carola I., BRITISH SEAWEEDS (Eyre and Spottis-woode, London, 1963)

Dietz, R. S., 'The Sea's Deep Scattering Layers', *Scientific American*, August 1962

Dragovich, A., and Kelly, J. A. 'Distribution and Occurrence of *Gymnodium breve* on the West Coast of Florida, 1964–65', United States Fish and Wildlife Service. Fisheries circular number 541, 1966

DuPont, J., *et al.*, 'Power from the Tides', *International Science and Technology*, May 1965

Eaton, B., editor, THE UNDERSEA CHALLENGE (British Sub-Aqua Club, London, 1963)

Endean, R., 'Marine Toxins', *Science Journal*, September 1966

F.A.O., 'The State of Food and Agriculture 1967', F.A.O., Rome, 1967

F.A.O., 'The State of Food and Agriculture 1968', F.A.O., Rome, 1968

F.A.O. Technical Conference on Marine Polution and Its Effects on Living Resources and Fishing, Rome, Italy, 9–18 December 1970

*Friedmann, Wolfgang, THE FUTURE OF THE OCEANS (George Braziller, New York, 1971)

Früngel, F. B. A., HIGH SPEED PULSE TECHNOLOGY, VOLUME I (Academic Press, New York, 1965)

Girelli, A., editor, FRESH WATER FROM THE SEA (Pergamon Press, London, 1965)

Groen, P., THE WATERS OF THE SEA (Van Nostrand, London, 1967)

Gulland, J. A., 'The North Atlantic Cod Fisheries', British Association Annual Meeting, 1963

Gulland, J. A., 'The Collapse of the Whaling Industry', British Association Annual Meeting, 1964

Gulland, J. A., 'The Ocean Reservoir', *Science Journal*, May 1968

*Hardy, Sir Alister, THE OPEN SEA I: THE WORLD OF PLANKTON (Collins, London, 1956)

*Hardy, Sir Alister, THE OPEN SEA II: FISH AND FISHERIES (Collins, London, 1959)

Harvey, H. W., THE CHEMISTRY AND FERTILITY OF SEA-WATERS (Cambridge University Press, Cambridge, 1963)

Hawkins, A. D., *et al.*, 'Spawning of Haddock in Captivity', *Nature*, 26 August 1967

Hawkins, W. W., and Leonard, V. G., 'The Physiological Activity of Laminarin Sulphate', *Canadian Journal of Biochemistry and Physiology*, 1958

Hawkins, W. W., and Leonard, V. G., 'Antipeptic and Antithrombic Properties of Carrageenin', *Journal of Laboratory and Clinical Medicine*, October 1962

Hawkins, W. W., and Leonard, V. G., 'The Antithrombic Activity of Carrageenin in Human Blood', *Canadian Journal of Biochemistry and Physiology*, 1963

Hepple, Peter, editor, POLLUTION PREVENTION (Institute of Petroleum, London, 1968)

*Hinde, P., FORTUNE IN THE NORTH SEA (Foulis, London, 1966)

Holmes, Arthur, PRINCIPLES OF PHYSICAL GEOLOGY (Nelson, London, 1965)

Howe, E. D., 'The Demineralization of Water', *Impact*, Vol. XV, No. 3, 1965

Hutchinson, Sir Kenneth, 'Searching for Gas and Oil under the North Sea', *Journal of the Royal Society of Arts*, October 1965

ICO, 'Undersea Vehicles for Oceanography', ICO pamphlet No. 18, October 1965

Keil, A. A. H., 'The New Challenge of Ocean Engineering', *Technology Review*, March 1967

Keim, S. R., 'The Engineer's Role', Exploitation of the world's oceans, 1967, International Convention of I.E.E.E., New York, March 1967

Khaes, A., 'Living in the Black Sea', *Triton*, August 1967

King, G. A. B., 'Ships of the Future', *Science Journal*, July 1967

Kronberger, H., and Silver, R. S., 'The Role of Desalination in Water Supplies', International Conference on Water for Peace, Washington, 1967

*Kuenen, P. H., REALMS OF WATER (Cleaver-Hume, London, 1955)

Kylstra, J. A., 'Experiments in Water Breathing', *Scientific American*, August 1968

*Loftas, Tony, WEALTH FROM THE OCEANS (Phoenix, London, 1967)

Loftas, Tony, 'Trustees with a Finger in the Pie', *New Scientist*, 13 August 1970

Loftas, Tony, 'Decade for Ocean Escalation', *New Scientist*, 2 July 1970

Loftas, Tony, 'Can Deep-sea Mining Make a Profit?', *New Scientist*, 3 December 1970

Loftas, Tony, 'New Threats to Coral Reefs', *New Scientist*, 24 December 1970

Loftas, Tony, 'Equitable Access to the Ocean's Wealth', *Ceres*, Vol. 3, No. 5, September–October 1970

Loftas, Tony, 'Mediterranean Pollution – Another Year of Neglect', *New Scientist*, 15 July 1971

Long, Capt. E. J., editor, OCEAN SCIENCES (U.S. Naval Institute, Annapolis, Maryland, 1964)

Lucas, J., 'Conserving Whales', *Science Journal*, April 1966

MacFarlane, C., 'A Survey of Certain Seaweeds of Commercial Importance in South-west Nova Scotia', *Canadian Journal of Botany*, January 1952

MacInnis, J. B., 'Living Under the Sea', *Scientific American*, March 1966

MARINE SCIENCE AFFAIRS – A YEAR OF PLANS AND PROGRESS; The second report of the President of the Congress on marine resources and engineering development,

March 1968, US Government Printing Office, Washington D.C.

McVay, S., 'The Last of the Great Whales', *Scientific American*, August 1966

Mero, John L., THE MINERAL RESOURCES OF THE SEA (Elsevier, London, 1965)

Miles, S., 'Man Against the Sea', *Discovery*, October 1963

Miller, D. G. 'Desalting', Special subject No. 1, International Water Supply Association, London, 1967

Miller, D. G., 'Salt Water into Fresh', *Journal of the Royal Society of Arts*, Volume CXII, Number 5095

Mitchell, N. T., 'Radioactivity in Surface and Coastal Waters of the British Isles 1967', Ministry of Agriculture, Fisheries and Food, Fisheries Radiobiological Laboratory, Lowestoft, Technical Report FRL 2

Mookerjea, S., and Hawkins, W. W., 'The Antilipaemic Activity of Laminarin Sulphate', *Canadian Journal of Biochemistry and Physiology*, 1968

National Academy of Science, 'Disposal of Low Level Radioactive Waste into Pacific Coastal Waters', National Research Council, Publication 985

National Academy of Science, 'Oceanography 1966, Achievements and opportunities', Publication 1492, National Research Council, Washington, D.C., 1967

Nitta, T., 'Marine Pollution in Japan', FAO Technical Conference on Marine Pollution and Its Effects on Living Resources and Fishing, December 1970

'OCEAN DUMPING: a National Policy', a report to the President prepared by the Council on Environment Quality, October 1970 (US Government Printing Office, Washington, D.C.)

OECD ENEA, 'Environmental Radioactivity and Waste dispersal problems', OECD ENEA 7th Report, Paris, December 1965

*Ommanney, F. D., A DRAUGHT OF FISHES (Longman, London, 1965)

O.N.O. Technical Advisory Group, United States Navy, 'Aircraft Salvage Operation Mediterranean – Lessons and implications for the Navy', Department of the Navy, Washington, D.C., 1967

Ovington, J. D., editor, THE BETTER USE OF THE WORLD'S FAUNA FOR FOOD (The Institute of Biology, London 1963)

Paakkola, O., and Voipio, A., 'Strontium-90 in the Baltic Sea', *Suomen Kemistilehti*, B 38, 1965

Park, F., 'Deep-sea Vehicles', *International Science and Technology*, March 1965

Parkin, D. W., and Tilles, D., 'Influx Measurements of Extraterrestrial Material', *Science*, Vol. 159

Pearsall, I. S., and Spencer, E. A., 'Cavitation', *Science Journal*, May 1966

Pérès, J. M., 'Exploring by Bathyscaphe', *Science Journal*, April 1967

Phillips, J., 'Tsunamis', *Science Journal*, December 1967

Phillips, Jean, 'North Sea Gas', *Science Journal*, March 1968

*Polmar, Norman, ATOMIC SUBMARINES (Van Nostrand, London, 1963)

PROCEEDINGS OF THE CONFERENCE ON THE TECHNOLOGY OF THE SEA AND THE SEA-BED Volumes I, II and III (H.M.S.O., London, 1967)

Rechnitzer, A. B., 'Underwater Exploration', *Science Journal*, October 1965

Report of the Panel on the World Food Supply, Volume I, United States Government Printing Office, Washington, D.C., 1967

Report on the Soviets and the Seas, 89th Congress, 2nd session, House report No. 1809, 4 August 1966

Research and Development Bulletins, White Fish Authority, London

Revelle, R., 'Ocean, Science and Man', *Impact*, Vol. XIV, No. 3, 1964

Revelle, R., 'Water', *Scientific American*, September 1963

Risebrough, R. W., Menzel, D. B., Martin, D. J., Olcott, H. S., 'DDT Residues in Pacific Sea Birds: a Persistent Insecticide in Marine Food Chains', *Nature*, 11 November 1967

Rounsefell, G. A., and Nelson, W. R., 'Red-tide Research Summarized to 1964', United States Fish and Wildlife Service, 1966, Circular No. 535

Ruivo, M. O., and Ben-Tuvia, A., 'Trends in World High Seas Fisheries and Potential Exploitation of Living Resources of the Sea' in Studies in Tropical Oceanography, No. 5, University of Miami Institute of Marine Science, October 1967

'Saline Water Conversion Research: 1966 Progress Report', University of California sea-water conversion laboratory, 1967

Sealab 1 project group summary report, 'An Experimental Eleven-day Undersea Saturation Dive at 193 Feet', Office of Naval Research, Department of the Navy, Washington, D.C., June 1965

Sears, Mary, editor, PROGRESS IN OCEANOGRAPHY: VOLUME 2 (Pergamon Press, Oxford, 1964)

Sharples, A., 'Reverse Osmosis', Science Journal, August, 1966

Silver, R. S., 'Fresh Water from the Sea' (Institution of Mechanical Engineers, London, 1964)

SIPRI, 'Towards a Better Use of the Oceans' (International Institute for Peace and Conflict Research, Stockholm, 1968)

Smith, J. E., editor, TORREY CANYON POLLUTION AND MARINE LIFE, A REPORT BY THE PLYMOUTH LABORATORY OF THE MARINE BIOLOGICAL ASSOCIATION OF THE UNITED KINGDOM (Cambridge University Press, London, 1968)

Sporn, P., FRESH WATER FROM SALINE WATERS (Pergamon Press, Oxford, 1966)

*Stenuit, R., THE DEEPEST DAYS (Hodder and Stoughton, London, 1966)

Stenuit, R., 'Life and Work Under Pressure,' Discovery, May 1966

Sturmey, S. G., et al., SHIPPING: THE NEXT 100 YEARS (Denholm Limited, January 1967)

Sverdrup, H. U., Johnson, Martin W., Fleming, Richard H., THE OCEANS: THEIR PHYSICS, CHEMISTRY AND GENERAL BIOLOGY (Prentice-Hall Inc., Englewood Cliffs, New Jersey, 1942)

Terrell, M., THE PRINCIPLES OF DIVING (Stanley Paul, London, 1965)

'THE SEA: Prevention and Control of Marine Pollution', Report of the Secretary-General, UN Document E/5003, 7 May 1971

Tinker, John, '1969 Seabird Wreck: PCBs Probably Guilty', *New Scientist*, 8 April 1971

*United Kingdom Atomic Engery Authority, DESALINATION AND ITS ROLE IN WATER SUPPLY (Central Office of Information, London, 1967)

United Nations, 22 UN GAOR, Provisional Verbatim Record of the 1524th Meeting, UN Document No. A/C.1/PV.1524, 1967

United Nations, 22 UN GAOR, Provisional Verbatim Record of the 1525th Meeting, UN Document No. A/C.1/PV.1525, 1967

Wallis, N. D., 'The Strength of England', Address to the Annual Meeting of the British Association for the Advancement of Science, 1965

Water Resources Board Publication, Number 4, 'Morecambe Bay and Solway Barrages', H.M.S.O., 1966

Wheeler, F., 'Uranium: The Next Thirty Years', *New Scientist*, 28 March 1968

*Williams, Frances L., MATTHEW FONTAINE MAURY SCIENTIST OF THE SEA (Rutgers University Press, New Brunswick, New Jersey, 1963)

Williams, H., 'Bikini Nine Years Later'. *Science Journal*, April 1967

Wilson, E. M., 'Energy from the Tides', *Science Journal*, July 1965

*Yonge, C. H., THE SEA SHORE (Collins, London, 1949)

Yonge, C. M., 'Food from the Sea', in Penguin Science Survey, 1963 B (Penguin Books, Harmondsworth, 1963)

Yonge, C. M., 'Farming the Sea', *Discovery*, July 1966

Index

More about Penguins and Pelicans

Penguinews, which appears every month, contains
details of all the new books issued by Penguins as they
are published. From time to time it is supplemented by
Penguins in Print, which is a complete list of all
available books published by Penguins. (There are well
over four thousand of these.)

A specimen copy of *Penguinews* will be sent to you
free on request, and you can become a subscriber for
the price of the postage. For a year's issues (including
the complete lists) please send 30p if you live in the
United Kingdom, or 60p if you live elsewhere. Just
write to Dept EP, Penguin Books Ltd, Harmondsworth,
Middlesex, enclosing a cheque or postal order, and
your name will be added to the mailing list.

Note: *Penguinews* and *Penguins in Print* are not
available in the U.S.A. or Canada

Some Pelicans on the Environment

Polluting Britain: A Survey

Jeremy Bugler

Polluting Britain takes a close, detailed and
representative look at the industrial pollution of
Britain. Jeremy Bugler, the Environmental
Correspondent of the *Observer*, chronicles here just
what is going on; he also answers the crucial question:
'How do the companies get away with it?'

The Environmental Revolution: A Guide for the New Masters of the World

Max Nicholson

'A masterly review of man's changing relation with
nature throughout his history. As a life conservationist
I commend to all those concerned with preserving our
natural heritage and preventing our earthly habitat
from being ruined by our own folly and lack of
forethought' – Sir Julian Huxley

New Lives, New Landscapes

Nan Fairbrother

New Lives, New Landscapes is concerned with the
future of land use in Britain. Making a realistic
assessment of the problems, Nan Fairbrother presents
plans to halt haphazard development and create a
landscape which will preserve rural areas while
accommodating the paraphernalia of an industrial
democracy.

Not for sale in the U.S.A.